Audio IC Op-Amp Applications

Third Edition

WALTER G. JUNG

HOWARD W. SAMS & COMPANY

A Division of Macmillan, Inc.
11711 North College, Suite 141, Carmel, IN 46032 USA

THIRD EDITION
FOURTH PRINTING—1989

International Standard Book Number: 0-672-22452-6
Library of Congress Catalog Card Number: 86-62437

Acquisitions Editor: *Jim Hill*
Editor: *Frank N. Speights*
Designer: *T. R. Emrick*
Illustrator: *Ralph E. Lund, Jr.*
Compositor: *Photo Comp Corporation, Brownsburg, Indiana*
Cover graphic by: *Kathi H. Brethauer/Keller Mier Inc.*

Printed in the United States of America

Contents

Preface

Although there are numerous IC op-amp types available to circuit designers, the incorporation of these devices into higher-performance audio circuits has been relatively slow to develop until recent years. One may note this, for example, when comparing their prolific incorporation into other (nonaudio) types of circuits. The reasons for this are partly device-based, and partly due to the incomplete treatment in technical literature of the problems that beset the audio designer when he/she attempts to utilize op amps in a circuit.

With the advent of the many higher-performance IC op amps, which are tailored more towards audio requirements, very-high-quality circuits are indeed possible today. The potential advantages to be gained from using IC op amps in audio circuits are quite numerous. These include small size, low power consumption, reliable and stable performance at low cost, and a minimum usage of associated circuit components. However, these goals cannot be successfully attained without an overall understanding of the technical barriers to performance, and an intimate knowledge of basic op-amp theory. Of course, a good working knowledge of the characteristics of the various devices available is needed as well. When all of these factors are mastered, IC op amps can be effectively applied to audio use in a wide variety of circuit applications, including circuits with very high levels of quality.

Audio IC Op-Amp Applications, Third Edition describes methods for realizing the full potential of IC op amps for audio use, and it also discusses the various pitfalls that may be encountered. It is assumed that the reader is already familiar with basic op-amp theory; therefore, the organization and style of the book is directed toward both the theoretical and practical applications of audio circuits (as was true in past editions).

The advantages of applying op amps to audio uses have increased markedly in the time span between the first (as well as the second edition) of this book and now. Better devices have appeared, as well as better ways to use them. (This is true as well for the older units.) The currently available audio-IC op amps offer excellent to superlative performance, at attractive prices. Nevertheless, for some not altogether obvious reasons, there may still be some reluctance on the part of some individuals to consider IC op amps for the very-highest-quality audio applications. Typical reasons cited for this are varied: "too noisy," "op amps just don't sound good," and so on. This book provides solutions to these issues by giving many different circuit examples.

This current edition of the book is updated broadly in terms of the latest device information, which includes many significant new devices, such as the very-high-slew-rate and dynamic-range FET-input units. One such important update is within the device audio-characterization section, which includes both the new and older devices. This section contains analytical methods and information that will be of great value in high-performance designs (for all devices).

The applications sections of the book are also updated throughout, with many new circuits added. Many of the circuits retained from the previous editions have been re-optimized, for use with the latest devices. Also, emphasis is given to improved and "sound" circuit techniques throughout, such as the use of DC servo feedback, the use of high-quality passive components for optimum stability and accuracy, and the use of high-quality power supplies. In addition, supporting computer analysis is supplied with the text applications, for those using the latest in computer-aided design technology.

The format of the book is identical to its last edition, and is also similar to the author's related but more general op-amp-based book, the *IC Op-Amp Cookbook, Third Edition*. (The *Cookbook* will be found to be useful by those who are new to op amps.)

WALTER G. JUNG

Acknowledgements

For this third edition of the book, the author would again like to acknowledge the aid of those whose help was instrumental. In the second edition, the assistance of the following was appreciated: Lew Counts and Jeff Riskin of Analog Devices; Don Jones of Harris Semiconductor; Deane Jensen of Jensen Transformers; Bob Dobkin, Bob Pease, and Bill Gross of National Semiconductor Corporation; George Erdi and Don Soderquist of Precision Monolithics; Guy Caputo of Signetics; and Byron Bynum of Texas Instruments Incorporated. In the present edition, thanks again are extended to all of the above. In addition, thanks goes also to Scott Wurcer and Don Travers of Analog Devices, to Bob Cordell of Bell Laboratories, to Neil Albaugh of Burr-Brown, to John Curl of Lineage Inc., to Bill Davis of Motorola Semiconductor Products, to Prasanna Shah and Nick Gray of Signetics, and to Bill Sacks of Straight Wire Audio.

For the use of portions of their technical material, the aid of the following companies is appreciated: Analog Devices, Burr-Brown, Motorola Semiconductor Products, Precision Monolithics, and Signetics. (Note: The complete op-amp manufacturers' addresses and listing of devices that they produce can be found in the Appendix.)

The cooperation and assistance of *The Audio Amateur* magazine in allowing use of copyrighted material is also gratefully acknowledged.

Finally, my sincere thanks go also to Anne, Jeannie, and Mark, for assistance in this edition as meaningful as the times previous.

To Jeannie and Mark

ONE

Introduction

Although the IC op amp is familiar to most, if not all, circuit designers, it is appropriate to reiterate the basic definitions before discussing the devices that are most applicable to audio circuit use—the subject of this book.

The basic theory of op amps is by no means new, and originally came to us from the field of analog computers. The name *operational amplifier* derives from the concept of an extremely high-gain, differential-input dc amplifier, the operating characteristics of which were largely determined by the feedback elements used with it. By changing the types and arrangement of feedback elements, different analog *operations* could be implemented; to a large degree, the overall circuit characteristics were determined *only* by these feedback elements. Thus, the same amplifier, by arrangement of the external input/output connections, was able to perform a variety of functions.

In the past few years, IC op amps have matured to a remarkable degree of sophistication, and specialized types are currently available that are optimized for virtually any aspect of performance. Along with the so-called "general-purpose" types, there are many specialized op amps that are best suited for audio service. These are devices that are optimized in terms of speed, input noise, output power, and other significant audio performance parameters. Understanding the differences between the standard IC op amps and the more specialized devices is a necessary prerequisite to the effective application of audio circuits.

1.1 GENERAL-PURPOSE IC OP AMPS

Before we can begin a detailed discussion of the op amps specialized for audio use, it is appropriate from an overall perspective to briefly review the general-purpose types. In the past, the most popular of these have been the 301A and 741 device families, and the older 709. A general-purpose type is loosely defined as having a unity-gain bandwidth of 1 MHz, operation from power supplies of ± 5 volts to ± 20 volts without serious degradation of performance, and may or may not be internally compensated. The 301A, 709, and 741 types are by far the most popular of the general-purpose units, and many more modern devices are closely related to their basic characteristics.

1.1.1 The 301A Family

Any "301A-type" amplifier can be said to belong to the 301A family. This includes the basic LM301, the LH301, the LM301A, and the LM307. It also includes corresponding devices of all temperature ranges. For example, LM301A op amps are supplied in three basic temperature ranges: (1) –55 °C to + 125 °C (LM100 series), (2) –25 °C to + 85 °C (LM200 series), and (3) 0 °C to + 70 °C (LM300 series). Thus, an LM301A is the 0 °C to + 70 °C temperature-range equivalent to an LM101A. Both are 101-type devices, since they belong to the same family tree. Throughout this book, the numbers used in referring to a device will be the basic commercial part number, e.g., a "301A" amplifier. Thus, to use such an amplifier for 0 °C to + 70 °C operation, an LM301A device would be specified. The reader should be cautioned, however, that there are specification differences between military- and commercial-grade devices, such as reduced supply voltages, lower gain, higher offset, etc. The military-grade devices will almost always have superior ratings and, consequently, higher cost.

1.1.2 The 741 Family

As with the 301 family, any "741-type" amplifier can be said to belong to the 741 family. This includes the basic 741 and the dual versions, such as the 747 and 1458. It also includes the 748, although the 748 may be said to be a "gray-area" device; it comes from the basic 741 design, but has the ac characteristics of a 301A.

1.2 SPECIAL-PURPOSE IC OP AMPS OPTIMUM FOR AUDIO USE

There are a great many audio applications that cannot be met satisfactorily or optimally by general-purpose types. Special situations may demand very high speed (either wide bandwidth or high slew rate), very low input current, high input impedance, very low voltage or current noise, high-voltage or high-current output, or low-distortion operation. This section introduces special-purpose audio types. The array of types presented here is broad, and cost-effective solutions can be found for virtually any audio use. The types are also standard, and are representative of the popular version of a particular device type. Data sheets for selected devices are included in Appendix A.

1.2.1 High-Performance Devices

These types of op amps have one or more of the following features that are significant to audio use.

1. High unity-gain frequency.
2. High gain-bandwidth product, and/or the capability of response optimization.
3. High, symmetrical slew rate, and/or high input dynamic range.
4. Low input noise (voltage and/or current).
5. High input resistance, and/or low input current.
6. High voltage and/or power.
7. Low inherent distortion.

These types are best, in terms of audio performance, at either low or high levels for most general applications. They are single 8-pin devices (except as noted); representative devices are listed in Table 1-1.

The devices listed in Table 1-1 are those that have been found to be most suitable for audio use when applying the stringent performance requirements. They are also the devices that are the most defect free in terms of unspecified modes of operation, and free from certain operating quirks that can be found in most others.

All of these devices are not concurrently excellent in each and every regard—rather, each device has certain notable characteristics that cause it to stand out from all others, and from the others of its class. All of these devices maintain their high performance, for either the inverting or noninverting modes of operation, and, also, when faced with significant output loading.

Table 1-1. High-Performance Audio IC Devices

Device	Comments
OP-27 (OP-227)	Excellent all-around performance; good for low-noise applications; unity-gain stable.
OP-37 (OP-237)	Similar to OP-27 but with greater SR and bandwidth (stable at gains of ≥ 5)
NE5534, NE5533 (dual)	Excellent all-around performance with regard to audio; unity-gain stable with 22 pF capacitor. Has low-noise, high-slew rate, wide bandwidth, higher than normal power output, low distortion. Externally compensated for unity gain; no compensation required for gains of ≥ 3. See also NE5532, a similar-performance, internally compensated, dual device.
NE530 and NE5535	Excellent high-level performance due to high dynamic range and slew rate. Both are unity-gain stable; the 530 is a single unit, the 5535 is a dual unit.
AD711 (AD712)	Excellent performance for medium- to high-level applications; fast settling, unity-gain stable.
OPA606	Excellent performance for all but lowest-level applications; fast settling, unity-gain stable.
MC34080 (series)	Excellent performance for medium- to high-level applications; fast settling, unity-gain stable. An FET-input device; see also the related MC34070 (series), which are bipolar.
TL070 (series)	Good performance for medium- to high-level applications; low cost.

As a group, perhaps the best audio performance, where economy is a big factor, is with the devices represented as second-generation FETs. These include the (early) TL070 series and similar devices (LF351, LF411, μA771, etc.). These devices (in particular, the more recent differential JFET-input-pair types), have generally excellent audio characteristics, with low noise, high slew rate, and medium-to high-bandwidth common traits. Although some of the devices exhibit appreciable (plus) input mode and output loading nonlinearities, these factors can often be circumvented with good overall results, at low system cost. Also notable performers are the high slew and dynamic range bipolars, such as the NE530- and NE5535-type designs.

For further information on any of the devices listed, a list of references is included at the end of the chapter. Individual data sheets are available from the respective manufacturers (see manufacturer's addresses in Appendix B).

Further insight into the relative qualities of performance between the various op-amp types is contained in Chapter 2, in the characterization discussion.

1.3 STANDARD COMPENSATION AND PINOUTS: OFFSET ADJUSTMENT

Although a great many IC op amps are internally compensated, this is not universally true. For audio uses, in particular, it is often advantageous to compensate a device externally to optimize bandwidth and slew rate, and, thus, to ultimately lower distortion. In this section, the standard compensation components (where applicable) for unity gain are shown, along with the pinouts for different devices, and the null techniques. Many pinouts are now standardized; this will be emphasized as appropriate.

In applications that require a high degree of dc accuracy, the residual input offset voltage of the op amp used may be a significant source of error, particularly when operating at high stage gains. These situations may require that the input offset voltage be adjusted to zero (nulled) for best performance. Offset nulling can be accomplished either by using a technique recommended by the manufacturer for the particular device used (termed internal nulling in these discussions), or by using a universally applicable external nulling procedure.

In general, the manufacturer's technique for nulling a particular device is optimum for that device. Unfortunately, the exact method of nulling used varies widely from device to device, and there is no completely standard method of internal offset adjustment (although the 741 technique, to be covered later, enjoys a fair degree of usage). Although most op amps are available in a variety of packages, the most popular are the 8-pin packages—the TO-99 metal can and the 8-pin dual in-line package (MINI-DIP). For dual devices, the 8-pin dual in-line package (MINI-DIP) is the most popular. For quads, the 14-pin DIP is the most popular. Alternate pinout arrangements may be arrived at by consulting the manufacturers' data sheets for the particular device.

The information provided in this section is sufficient to apply any of the devices in their basic circuit arrangements. Offset adjustments, in particular, and, in some cases, compensation components, are not required in all circumstances and may be deleted where not necessary. Power-supply connections are obviously always required and are shown in this section for reference. Throughout the remainder of the book, however, the power connections are not shown as long as they involve standard ± 15-volt supplies. In special circuits or nonstandard power-supply operation, the power connections will be shown in full detail.

1.3.1 Standard Pinouts

Many internally compensated amplifiers have standard pinouts (and offset arrangements) such as are shown in Fig. 1-1A. Offset nulling is accomplished with a single 10-kΩ potentiometer, with the arm returned to the V-supply for single units. This arrangement has the virtue of appearing at a relatively low-impedance point in the circuit, and the null adjustment is not dependent upon the supply voltage. This null technique is not wholly universal, however, so data sheet consultation is recommended.

The standard dual pinout of Fig. 1-1B is functionally equivalent to two amplifiers, but is usually supplied only in a single 8-pin package. This offers the advantage of space economy, but it sacrifices the internal offset null capability. A similar comment applies to quad-pinned devices, such as shown in Fig. 1-1C. All devices listed here are *internally* compensated types.

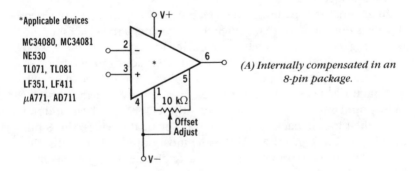

*Applicable devices

MC34080, MC34081
NE530
TL071, TL081
LF351, LF411
µA771, AD711

(A) Internally compensated in an 8-pin package.

Fig. 1-1. Standard

Op amps of the high-performance category are shown in Fig. 1-2. The 5534 device is compensated for unity gain with a single capacitor, connected as shown. Without this capacitor, the device is stable at a minimum gain of 3. Nulling is accomplished in the V + supply line and is independent of the supply voltage. Note that nulling will often *not* be required, only the compensation capacitor, C_1.

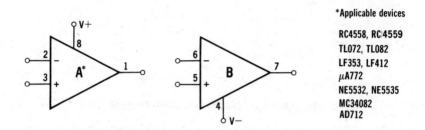

*Applicable devices

RC4558, RC4559
TL072, TL082
LF353, LF412
μA772
NE5532, NE5535
MC34082
AD712

(B) Dual amplifiers in an 8-pin package; internally compensated, no offset null.

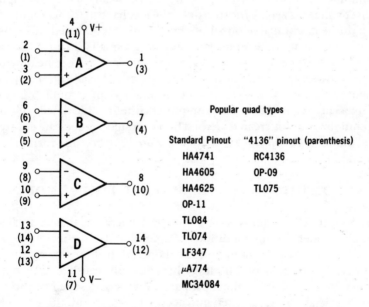

Popular quad types

Standard Pinout	"4136" pinout (parenthesis)
HA4741	RC4136
HA4605	OP-09
HA4625	TL075
OP-11	
TL084	
TL074	
LF347	
μA774	
MC34084	

(C) Quad amplifiers in a 14-pin package; internally compensated, no offset null.

pinout amplifiers.

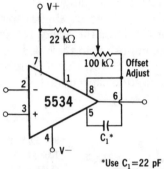

Fig. 1-2. Standard
compensation, pinout, and
offset adjustment for a
high-performance IC op amp.

*Use $C_1 = 22$ pF for
unity-gain compensation.

1.3.2 Universal External Offset-Nulling Techniques

As pointed out earlier in Section 1.3, the optimum method of offset adjustment for a particular op amp is the internal method provided for by the manufacturer. This method results in the condition of minimum input offset-voltage drift, which occurs when the input offset voltage is zero. Unfortunately, the mechanism for accomplishing this is not available on all op amps, and external methods must sometimes be used. By externally summing a small (± 10 mV) variable voltage at the + or – input terminals, any op amp can be nulled. This allows types which do not provide an internal offset adjustment to be used with greater precision. Since offset nulling is not universally required for audio amplifiers, the specific details of this technique are not treated here. The interested reader can consult the author's *IC Op-Amp Cookbook, Third Edition* for further information.

1.4 PROTECTION AGAINST ABUSE AND FAILURE MODES

Monolithic IC op amps have a few idiosyncracies that can cause trouble under certain conditions of operation. Unfortunately, these troubles are not evident by abnormal operation alone; in certain instances, a device may fail altogether, possibly causing damage to other components. For the most part, however, these failure modes are predictable, and, if taken into account beforehand, there should be no problems in applying the devices. In this section, we will discuss such failure conditions and give positive treatment for their prevention.

1.4.1 Input Limitations

Failure in IC op amps can be induced in the input stage in two general ways: (1) by exceeding the differential input rating, or (2) by exceeding the common-mode rating. Of these two, the differential input rating is the parameter that is most susceptible to abuse; therefore, it will be discussed in some detail.

Differential Input Breakdown

One of the easiest methods of inducing failure in an unprotected op-amp input stage in to exceed its differential-input voltage rating. When this happens, one or the other of the differential-input transistors (depending on the relative polarity of the input voltage) will go into emitter-to-base zener breakdown. This is shown in Figs. 1-3A and B.

A pair of npn differential-input transistors is actually equivalent to a pair of back-to-back 7-volt zener diodes, as shown in Fig. 1-3B. The anodes of these two diodes are the (+) and (–) input terminals of the op amp.

Whenever the difference between the input terminals exceeds ± 7 volts, these emitter-base diodes will break down (as will any zener) and will conduct a current which will be limited only by the external source resistance. If the source impedance feeding both inputs is low, the current can rise to destructive levels very quickly. Currents greater than 50 mA will cause permanent failure—usually a junction short. Currents lower than this, while not causing junction damage, are still very undesirable because they can cause permanent changes in such dc input parameters as bias, offset current, and gain.

Obviously, in order to prevent this type of breakdown, we must anticipate it beforehand. However, the possible sources of input breakdown can at times be somewhat subtle, as the following examples illustrate.

If a voltage follower (Fig. 1-3C) is driven with a fast step input of + 10 volts, the op-amp output will be limited to a rate of rise determined by its slewing ability. During the slewing interval, the amplifier is not operating in a normal closed-loop mode where the differential-input voltage is zero; rather, a large differential error voltage exists, as shown by the waveform sketches. These spikes are caused by the fast input rise times which the amplifier cannot follow, so a ± 10-volt peak differential exists during the slewing interval(s). In a voltage follower, both inputs can see low source

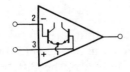

(A) Unprotected differential-input stage.

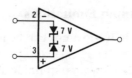

(B) Zener equivalent to differential-input stage.

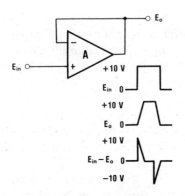

(C) Differential-input voltage in a slew-rate-limited voltage follower.

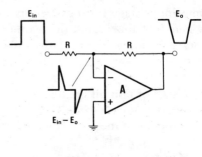

(D) Differential-input voltage in a slew-rate-limited inverter.

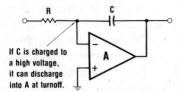

(E) Differential-input voltage in a charged integrator at turn off.

Fig. 1-3. Possible causes of differential-input breakdown in unprotected op amps.

impedance, so this can quickly ruin an input stage due to excessive zener current.

An inverter stage (Fig. 1-3D) can also go into zener breakdown due to slew-rate limiting. Here the problem is not nearly as bad because the resistances limit the zener current during breakdown.

Another problem configuration is the integrator, shown in Fig. 1-3E. In this circuit, input breakdown can result if the supply voltages are turned off while the capacitor is charged to a high potential.

The solution to all of the preceding is quite simple. It involves an input clamping network to limit the differential-input voltage and some series resistance to limit the current during clamping. Two methods of accomplishing overvoltage protection are shown in Figs. 1-4A and B. Either method will suffice, but the reverse-connected parallel diodes (Fig. 1-4A) are less expensive. The resistances used with any op amp may range up to 10 kΩ with little degradation of offset voltage. In an actual working configuration, the input ends of the resistors may be considered the inputs of the op amp and used accordingly. Generally, for best dc accuracy, equal resistance will be desirable in each leg, and, for lowest noise, the resistance should be minimum. However, in many instances, it will be possible to eliminate one or possibly both resistors, as long as input or feedback resistances limit the clamping-diode current. Such an example would be the circuit of Fig. 1-3D, which could be protected just by the addition of the diodes, using the input and feedback resistances as current limiters. The resistance value should be minimized, of course, if low noise is a requirement.

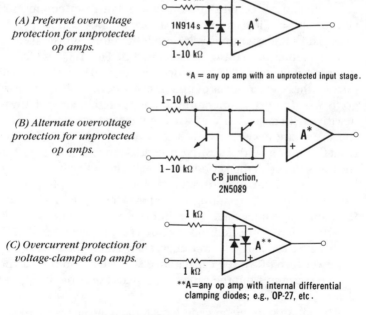

(A) Preferred overvoltage protection for unprotected op amps.

1–10 kΩ

1N914s

A*

1–10 kΩ

*A = any op amp with an unprotected input stage.

(B) Alternate overvoltage protection for unprotected op amps.

1–10 kΩ

1–10 kΩ

A*

C-B junction, 2N5089

(C) Overcurrent protection for voltage-clamped op amps.

1 kΩ

A**

1 kΩ

**A=any op amp with internal differential clamping diodes; e.g., OP-27, etc.

Fig. 1-4. Differential-input overvoltage/overcurrent protection methods.

The reader may wonder if perhaps these points on differential-input protection are not belabored, since many IC op amps of recent design do not have restrictive input-voltage limitations. This is certainly true for some op amps, but it is by no means a universal practice with other designs. It is of prime importance, particularly in high-performance low-noise ac amplifiers, to prevent differential-input breakdown because it can seriously degrade the dc and low-noise properties.

Other amplifiers, such as the 5534 and the OP-27/OP-37 series, have the differential clamping diodes built into the device. In the absence of internal resistance, amplifiers such as these must be used with external resistors to prevent possible excessive current in the diodes. This is illustrated in Fig. 1-4C.

Common-Mode Input Breakdown

Another cause of input-stage failure is a possibly destructive input-current flow due to exceeding the common-mode input voltage range of the device. Although such general-purpose families as the 301A op amp are notably free of differential-input breakdown, they can under many certain circumstances fail from common-mode voltage abuse. Since monolithic types operate similarly in some cases, and some caution is warranted; therefore, it discussed here.

This failure mechanism is illustrated by Fig. 1-5A, which shows the input stage of a 301A-type op amp. In a 301A op amp, both inputs are the base terminals of npn transistors, the collectors of which go to V + . In normal operation, the input terminals will always be negative with respect to V + , so the collector-base junctions of these transistors are never forward biased. If, however, V + is removed from the op amp with a positive potential remaining on pins 2 and 3, the transistors will then conduct through the collector-base junction into V + line. If the source impedance seen at either pin 2 or pin 3 is sufficiently low, the resulting current may be high enough to destroy the input transistors. Such a condition may occur when the input to a system is left connected and the power is removed. Another example is with a capacitive source charged to a high potential at the time of power turn off. If the capacitance is greater than 0.1 μF, the discharged current from the capacitor can also destroy the input transistors.

The solution to the preceding example is also rather simple. It involves the use of series input resistor(s) to limit the worst-case fault current to 10 mA or less (Fig. 1-5B). Since 301A input characteristics

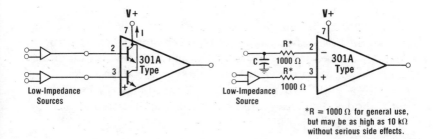

(A) Reason for common-mode
input failure in 301A-type
op amps.

(B) Protection against
common-mode input failure in
301A-type op amps.

*R = 1000 Ω for general use,
but may be as high as 10 kΩ
without serious side effects.

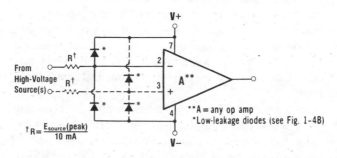

(C) Protection against excessive source-voltage peaks for any op amp.

Fig 1-5. Common-mode input protection methods.

are relatively unaffected by input resistance up to 10 kΩ, the resistors may be this high with no side effects. For general use, however, 1000 ohms per side will be adequate. The resistors need only be connected to those inputs that see potentially low impedances or excessive voltage. If it can be guaranteed that neither of these conditions will occur under any combination of input and power, then the resistors can be deleted.

Before concluding, it should be noted that this type of failure mechanism may not be peculiar to only 301A-type op amps. The *exact* internal circuitry of many IC types will vary from one manufacturer to another. It is best to check the particular devices you intend to use, either with a simple ohmmeter check (pins 2 and 3 to pin 7) or by measuring fault current in a series resistor under the stress conditions. Also, it is wise in general to be wary of possible power-sequencing phenomena in any op-amp circuit, regardless of the device. Finally, when operating from sources of voltage that may have peaks in excess of the op-amp power supplies, the scheme of Fig. 1-5C can be used to protect any op amp. The low-leakage diodes clamp the inputs to a level such that the source-voltage peaks cannot exceed V + and V– by more than the forward-biased voltage drops of the diodes. The series resistor limits the input current.

Latch-up

A phenomenon that sometimes occurs in op amps is called *latch-up*. Latch-up occurs most often in voltage-follower stages where the output swing is equal to the input and the op amp is driven to a high level. If the bias levels of the input stage are not well in excess of the maximum peak-to-peak voltage swing that the input terminals must undergo, the input stage can saturate on the peaks. When saturation occurs, a normally inverting stage no longer inverts; thus, what was negative feedback becomes positive feedback. With positive feedback, the stage will then remain in saturation, and thus it is said to be *latched-up*.

This is illustrated on Fig. 1-6A, an example of an op-amp input stage. To use a specific example, the older 709 device was subject to latch-up since its minimum common-mode range was + 8 V, but its output swing could be as high as + 14 V. If a signal greater than + 8 V were applied to a 709 that is connected as a follower, it was quite possible that it could latch up due to saturation of Q_2. Once latch-up occurs, the positive feedback can usually be broken only by removal of power (for any type).

Aside from the "nuisance" disadvantages of latch-up (the necessity of removing power to restore normal operation), there is a more serious potential hazard with the phenomenon. If the circuit of Fig. 1-6A (an unprotected pair) is driven beyond its common-mode range, it will latch up on the positive peak. If a bipolar input signal from a low-impedance source is assumed, the input signal at pin 3 need go only 7 volts below the saturation level before Q_1 will go into emitter-base zener breakdown. This will almost surely ruin the device because both inputs are connected to low-impedance sources in this stage. Latch-up may not even be triggered by the input signal. Any positive transient on the output line which is fed back to Q_2 can trigger it, and, once in the latch-up condition, the circuit will stay that way until power is removed.

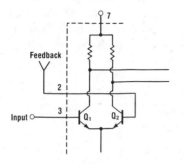

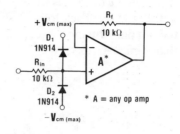

(A) General example illustrating latch-up source in an op-amp input stage.

(B) Elimination of latch-up (any op amp) by input limiting.

Fig. 1-6. Illustration of latch-up in IC op amps, and methods of elimination.

Since latch-up will occur only at the extreme limits of the input common-mode range, any method that reduces the common-mode input swing will eliminate (or lessen) the latch-up problem. Therefore, latch-up in any amplifier prone to it will have little likelihood of occurrence when the amplifier is operated at gains higher than unity or in cases when the input levels are safely less than that voltage which triggers latch-up.

A circuit that takes advantage of this latter point can be used to prevent latch-up with any op amp and is shown in Fig. 1-6B. Since latch-up will occur at only one common-mode limit, only one diode is usually needed. The $V_{cm (max)}$ can be a simple divider across the ± 15-V supply.

In more recent device types, particularly many of the JFET-input units, latch-up can occur as the *negative* common-mode limit is exceeded (that is, more negative than −10 V with a −15-V supply).

1.4.2 Output Short-Circuit Protection

Some early op amps did not incorporate full-time current limiting in the output stage. Although such devices often will survive a short of a few seconds duration, a sustained short to ground, V + , or V− will result in destruction of the device.

Any op amp that does not incorporate current limiting may be protected against short circuits by a low value resistor placed in series with the output as shown in Fig. 1-7. If this resistor is connected within the feedback loop as shown, its presence will have little effect on performance, except for the obvious drop in output voltage that it entails.

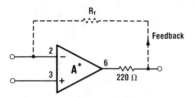

*A = any op amp with an unprotected output stage

In addition to preventing destruction of the amplifier due to shorted loads, the series resistance will enhance stability by isolating capacitive loads.

Fig. 1-7. Output short-circuit protection.

A side benefit of this approach is the extra stability it provides with capacitive loads. For this reason, the series resistor may be helpful even if the amplifier used does have current limiting.

1.4.3 Supply-Voltage Protection

Because of their internal construction, ICs must always be operated with the specified supply-voltage polarity. If the voltages ever become reversed, even momentarily, destructive currents will flow through the normally reverse-biased isolation diodes of the IC chip. This is a point to be wary of in any IC op amp, with no exceptions. Positive protection against this may be provided by connecting a rectifier diode in the negative supply lead as shown in Fig. 1-8A. Protection for a number of amplifiers in a system or on a printed-circuit card may be provided by connecting a single pair of power diodes in reverse across the supply leads as shown in Fig. 1-8B. The diodes used should have a current capacity greater than the fuse or short-circuit current limit of the supplies used. When a supply reversal or transient condition attempts to force opposite polarity voltages on the amplifiers, D_1 and D_2 clamp the supplies into the limit mode (or blow the fuse) and nothing is damaged. This is a good feature to incorporate into any but the very smallest system.

Included in this diagram are supply bypass capacitors of 100 to

1000 μF. These should be low-ESR electrolytic types for low-supply impedance(s) at the card level.

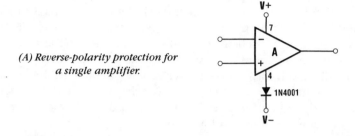

(A) Reverse-polarity protection for a single amplifier.

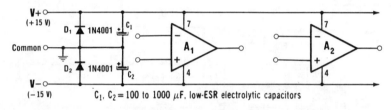

(B) Reverse-polarity protection for a number of amplifiers in a system, with bypassing.

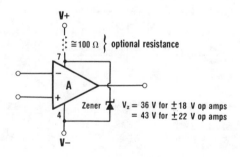

(C) Overvoltage protection.

Fig. 1-8. Supply-voltage protection methods.

Commercial-grade IC op amps are generally specified for a total operating voltage of 36 volts (± 18 V), while full-temperature-range devices can operate up to 44 volts (± 22 V). These limits on supply voltage should not be exceeded even for brief durations. If there is a likelihood that the supply may exceed 36 V (or 44 V), a voltage clamp in the form of a zener diode should be used across the terminals as shown in Fig. 1-8C. This zener will be nonconducting with normal ± 15-V (30-V) potentials. For higher maximum-rated supplies, choose the zener voltage closest to but not more than the total maxiumum—for example, for ± 22 V, use a 43-V zener. Alternately, the reverse clamping scheme of 1-8B can be adapted to use a pair of ± 18-V zeners (or about 3 V greater than the supplies in use).

A medium-current, ± 15-V power-supply circuit suitable for audio IC circuitry is shown in Fig. 1-9. This circuit uses a 36-V center-tapped bridge to derive ± 20-V unregulated dc. A toroidal power transformer is specified, for lowest noise.

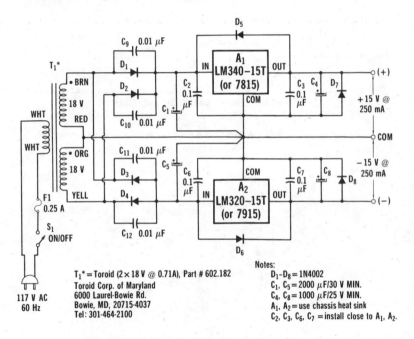

Fig. 1-9. A ± 15-V power supply for audio IC circuits.

Low-ESR capacitor types are recommended for the electrolytics, for best results. While this circuit is general in the sense that it uses standard 15-V regulators, it can easily be adapted to other voltages, such as ± 12 V. For such uses, substitute IC regulators with the lower voltage (i.e., 17812 and 7912, etc.).

1.5 OPTIMUM-STABILITY GROUND RULES

In using IC op amps, there are many operating conditions where ac stability becomes a significant problem. Stabilizing a feedback amplifier is no easy task, and it can turn into an impossible situation if good, basic, high-frequency practices are not followed in the layout and circuit arrangement.

1.5.1 Layout and Bypassing

Of utmost importance to stability is a compact, minimum-lead-length layout. The leads to the input and compensation terminals (if used) of any op amp should be as direct as possible, with a minimum of conductor length and proximity to other signal leads. Ground paths should have low resistance and low inductance. In wideband circuits, it is good practice (if possible) to use a ground plane on printed-circuit cards to obtain a high-quality ground. In audio circuits, the the minimum-lead-length and quality-ground rules usually go hand-in-hand with good practices for low-noise amplifiers as well.

Supply leads to amplifiers should be bypassed at least once for each PC card with low-impedance capacitors. This should include the larger devices used in Fig. 1-8B, and the local low-inductance types used at one or more ICs, as shown in 1-10A. If the amplifiers used have a gain-bandwidth product above 10 MHz, more thorough bypassing will be necessary. For example, OP-37 or 5534 amplifiers require a set of local, rf-quality bypasses for each amplifier.

Low-speed, general-purpose devices with 1-MHz unity-gain frequency are less critical as to bypassing, but cannot be ignored. It is good practice, even with general-purpose devices, to include at least one set of bypasses for every five devices, or at least one set per card, regardless of the number of ICs used.

1.5.2 Input Capacitance Compensation

Stray input capacitance in feedback amplifiers can also lead to stability problems. Fig. 1-10B illustrates the nature of input-related capacitance problems. At the input of an op amp, there will always be a few picofarads of stray capacitance, C_s, which consists of the amplifier input capacitance plus wiring capacitance. From the feedback path through R_f, this capacitance represents a potential phase shift at a corner frequency of

$$f = \frac{1}{2\pi R_f C_s}$$ (Eq. 1-1)

The problem is particularly noticeable if R_f is large, since this moves the R_f-C_s frequency downward into a region where it can add to the amplifier phase shift. The result of these cumulative phase shifts may be enough to cause oscillation.

A simple solution is to keep R_f low, which forces the R_f-C_s frequency upward beyond the amplifier limit. But this is not always practical, since R_f may need to be high for gain or impedance reasons.

A more general solution is to use a compensation capacitor, C_f, across R_f, which in effect makes C_f-R_f and R_{in}-C_s a frequency-compensated divider. It may not be possible to readily determine the exact value of C_f to satisfy this relation, since C_s is not precisely known. Capacitor C_f is best determined by experiment; or, if the amplifier used is compensated for unity gain, C_f may be greater than the formula relation to whatever degree desirable. In practice, values of 3–10 pF are typical with feedback resistors of 10 kΩ.

1.5.3 Output Capacitance Compensation

On many IC op amps, the phase shift caused by stray output load capacitance and the amplifier output resistance can be troublesome if the output capacitance is much more than 100 pF. By adding a series

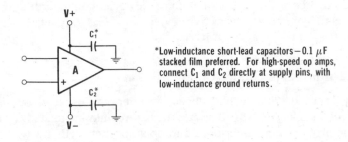

*Low-inductance short-lead capacitors—0.1 μF stacked film preferred. For high-speed op amps, connect C_1 and C_2 directly at supply pins, with low-inductance ground returns.

(A) Power-supply bypassing.

Fig. 1-10. Stability

output resistance, R_o, the load capacitance is isolated from the amplifier (Fig. 1-10C). Feedback is taken after this resistor, thus compensating for its dc loss. The feedback capacitor, C_f, is then added to reduce the gain of the loop at high frequencies. Capacitor C_f is chosen so that its reactance is one tenth (or less) that of R_f at the unity-gain frequency of the amplifier used. The amplifier must be compensated for unity gain, since C_f reduces high-frequency gain to unity. Again, typical values for C_f fall in the 3–10-pF region.

1.5.4 Other Instability Sources

The preceding by no means represents all the sources of possible stability problems in IC op amps—just those that are most likely to occur. Other problem areas are more specific, either in terms of the devices themselves or in terms of circuits in which the devices are used. For example, source resistance may be a problem with some devices. In stubborn cases of instability, when other alternatives have been exhausted, amplifier overcompensation may be the solution. If extra bandwidth or optimum slew rate are not necessary, it is usually wise to overcompensate an op amp. For example, this may be accomplished on such amplifiers as the TL080 by increasing the compensation capacitors by a factor of 10 (or by the ratio necessary to obtain stability).

In general, many of the stability ground rules simply amount to good practices in layout and construction. These rules should obviously be followed for consistently stable results. Always consult the

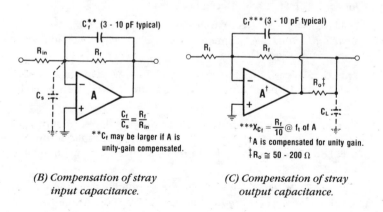

(B) Compensation of stray
input capacitance.

(C) Compensation of stray
output capacitance.

enhancement techniques.

manufacturer's literature for specific recommendations and for more thorough background on specific op amps.

With regard to other sources of instability and/or spurious signals, cross-coupling within the power rails should not be overlooked, when high-performance is required. For example, high-current stages can cause instability by feedback through the power supplies. Such stages should be decoupled to localize their circulating currents. Similarly, ground-return paths for high-level and high-gain stages should be kept separate.

Optimum power-supply decoupling for complex systems can be designed in the system by adding local regulators for indivdual stage(s), fed from a common master regulator (of higher voltage) similar to Fig. 1-9. The local regulators can be designed for high performance; i.e., low broadband output impedance.

1.6 REFERENCES

1. Brokaw, A. P. "Analog Signal Handling for High Speed and Accuracy." *Analog Dialogue,* Vol. 11 #2, 1977.

2. Cave, D. L. and Davis, W. R. "A Quad JFET Wide-Band Op Amp IC Featuring Temperature Compensated Bandwidth." *IEEE JSSC,* Vol. SC-12 #4, August 1977.

3. Davis, S. "IC Op Amp Families." *EDN,* January 20, 1978.

4. Davis, W. F. and Vyne, R. L. "Design Techniques for Improving the HF Response of a Monolithic JFET Operational Amplifier." *ISSC Journal,* Vol. SC-19 #6, December 1984.

5. Dobkin, R. C. "LM118 OP Amp Slews 70 V/µs." *National Semiconductor LB-17,* September 1971, National Semiconductor Corp., Santa Clara, CA.

6. Erdi, G., Schwartz, T., Bernardi, S., and Jung, W. "Op Amps Tackle Noise and for Once, Noise Loses." *Electronic Design,* December 12, 1980.

7. *Fairchild Semiconductor Application Bulletin APP-136,* July 1969. "A Low Drift, Low Noise Monolithic Operational Amplifier for Low Level Signal Processing." Fairchild Semiconductor, Mountain View, CA.

8. Fullagar, D. "A New High Performance Monolithic Operational Amplifier." *Fairchild Application Brief,* May 1968. Fairchild Semiconductor, Mountain View, CA.

9. _____."Better Understanding of FET Operation Yields Viable Monolithic J-FET Op Amp." *Electronics,* November 6, 1972.

10. _____. "The 8007—A High Performance FET-Input Operational Amplifier." *Intersil Application Bulletin A005,* March 1972, Intersil, Inc., Cupertino, CA.

11. Hearn, W. F. "Fast Slewing Monolithic Operational Amplifier." *IEEE JSSC,* SC-6 #1, February 1971.

12. Jung, W. G. "An IC Op Amp Update." *Ham Radio,* March 1978.

13. _____. *IC Op-Amp Cookbook, 3rd Edition,* Howard W. Sams & Co., Indianapolis, IN, 1986.

14. _____. "IC Op Amps for Audio, Parts I, II." *The Audio Amateur,* issues 2/73, 1/74, 2/74.

15. _____. "IC Op Amps Have Evolved." *Electronic Design,* January 4, 1978.

16. _____. "Stable FET-Input Op Amps Achieve Precision Performance." *EDN,* November 10, 1982.

17. _____; Marsh, R. "Picking Capacitors, Parts I & II." *Audio,* February & March, 1980.

18. Metzger, J. "Bipolar and FET Op Amps." *Electronic Products,* June 1977.

19. Morrison, R. *Grounding and Shielding Techniques in Instrumentation, 2nd Edition,* Wiley & Sons, NY, 1977.

20. Motchenbacher, C. D. and Fitchen, F. C. *Low-Noise Electronic Design,* Wiley & Sons, NY, 1973.

21. Och, S. and Flink, J. "LM143 Monolithic High Voltage Op Amp Applications." *National Semiconductor AN-127,* April, 1976, National Semiconductor Corp., Mountain View, CA.

22. Roberge, J. K. *Operational Amplifiers, Theory and Practice.* Wiley & Sons, NY, 1975.

23. Russel, R. W. and Culmer, D. D. "Ion-Implanted JFET-Bipolar Monolithic Analog Circuits." *IEEE ISSCC Digest,* February 1974.

24. Stout, D. F. and Kaufman, M. *Handbook of Operational Amplifier Design.* McGraw Hill, NY, 1976.

25. Solomon, J. E. "The Monolithic Op Amp: A Tutorial Study." *IEEE JSSC,* Vol. SC-9 #6, December 1974.

26. _____, Davis, W. R., and Lee, P. L. "A Self-Compensated Monolithic Operational Amplifier With Low Input Current and High Slew Rate." *ISSCC Digest of Technical Papers,* Vol. 12, February 1969, pp. 14–15.

27. Sulzer, M. P. "A High Quality Power Supply Regulator for Operational Amplifier Preamplifiers." *The Audio Amateur*, issue 2/80.

28. _____. "Regulators Revisited." *The Audio Amateur,* issue 1/1981.

29. Tobey, G. E., Graeme, J. G., and Huelsman, L. P. (Ed). *Operational Amplifiers: Design and Applications.* McGraw Hill, NY, 1971.

30. Widlar, R. J. "A Monolithic Operational Amplifier." *Fairchild Application Bulletin APP-105/2,* July 1965. Fairchild Semiconductor, Mountain View, CA.

31. _____. "A New Monolithic Operational Amplifier Design." *National Semiconductor TP-2,* June 1967. National Semiconductor Corp., Santa Clara, CA.

32. _____. "A Unique Circuit Design for a High Performance Operational Amplifier Especially Suited to Monolithic Construction." *Proceedings of the NEC,* Vol. XXI, October 1965, pp. 85–89. (Also available as *Fairchild TP-32/2,* November 1965; Fairchild Semiconductor, Mountain View, CA.)

33. _____. "IC Op Amp Beats FETs on Input Current." *National Semiconductor Application Note AN-29,* December 1969, National Semiconductor Corp., Santa Clara, CA.

34. _____. "IC Op Amps Close the Performance Gap on Discretes." *National Semiconductor TP-9,* December 1968, National Semiconductor Corp., Santa Clara, CA.

35. _____. "The LM110—An Improved IC Voltage Follower." *National Semiconductor LB-11,* March 1970, National Semiconductor Corp., Santa Clara, CA.

36. Witten, S. "Designing Junction FET Input Op Amps." *Siliconix Application Note AN74-3,* August 1974.

Two

IC Op-Amp Parameters Important in Audio Applications

Some of the most useful IC op-amp applications are in audio-frequency circuits where the inherently high gain and linearity of the device elevates the quality of attainable performance to a new high. Distortion can be reduced to extremely low levels; frequency response can be shaped at will by the proper selection of external passive components; and smaller, simpler, and more economical circuits can be built.

However, these obviously attractive virtues cannot be realized by haphazard selection of op-amp types. Although many IC op amps possess excellent dc characteristics, they are not all equally useful at audio frequencies, particularly when operated at high gains, at high frequencies, and at high-output levels. The successful designer of quality audio circuits must take these factors into account; therefore, in this chapter, the optimization of high-frequency, as well as low-frequency, performance will be stressed, and methods to circumvent the common pitfalls will be illustrated. Since frequency response, low noise, and distortion considerations are basic to all audio-frequency circuits regardless of their configuration, it is appropriate to consider the factors that govern correct IC selection prior to the discussion of specific circuits.

2.1 OPEN-LOOP GAIN

One important dynamic specification of any op amp, including IC op amps, is open-loop gain. Open-loop gain ultimately affects the quality of all closed-loop parameters—distortion, input impedance, output impedance, gain variations, frequency response, and frequency-response variations. The degree of improvement due to feedback is in direct relation to the loop gain—the difference in dB between the open-loop gain and the closed-loop gain in a given circuit configuration. This basic concept is illustrated by the simple inverting amplifier of Fig. 2-1A, which uses a 741[*] op amp. The open-loop frequency response of the 741 is shown in Fig. 2-1B. If we disregard any nonideal op-amp characteristics for the moment and consider the gain of the circuit for any combination of feedback, the gain is simply R_2/R_1, where R_2 and R_1 are the feedback and input resistances, respectively. Any desired value of gain may be obtained simply by plugging in the appropriate values for R_2 and R_1.

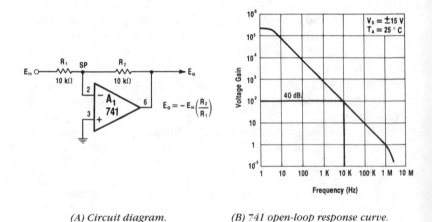

(A) Circuit diagram.   (B) 741 open-loop response curve.

Fig. 2-1. Unity-gain inverter using the 741 general-purpose op amp.

At this point, it is appropriate to reiterate the characteristics of an ideal op amp—infinite gain, infinite bandwidth, infinite input impedance, zero output impedance, and zero output with zero

---

[*]The 741 is used here for the purpose of illustration; the general comments apply also to many other low-gain-bandwidth-product devices as well.

differential-input voltage. Also, the reader is advised to review the inverse relationship between gain and bandwidth—referred to as the gain-bandwidth product (GBP). This will be helpful in understanding the following discussions of gain-bandwidth product as they generally relate to audio circuits.

2.2 GAIN-BANDWIDTH PRODUCT

With reference to Figs. 2-1A and B, and with regard to the effects of a 741 op amp on the simple inverter, it becomes clear that there are definite limitations on the total available open-loop gain. Also, this available gain is reduced as the frequency increases. It is obvious that you can obtain no more gain or bandwidth from a given amplifier than its open-loop response can provide. Inspection of the open-loop response of a 741 (Fig. 2-1B) will show the available gain at a given frequency (heavy vertical line) or, conversely, the available bandwidth for a given closed-loop gain (heavy horizontal line). For example, a gain of 40 dB will yield a maximum frequency response of 10 kHz. This is the absolute best that can be done, and the only way to obtain more bandwidth to reduce the gain. Also, it should be noted that in a 40-dB, 10-kHz-bandwidth amplifier such as this, there is a decreasing feedback characteristic in the region from 10 Hz and above due to the rolloff in open-loop gain. Therefore, the benefits of the very high open-loop gain of the amplifier exist only at 10 Hz and below. In fact, the full dc gain of the amplifier is not realized within the total audio spectrum (approximately 20 Hz to 20 kHz), and the gain decreases at a rate of 6 dB/octave (20 dB/decade) until a point is reached at the upper frequencies (10 kHz in the 40-dB example) where the circuit simply runs out of gain. At this point, the closed-loop gain becomes equal to the open-loop gain. Thus, the 741 would be a poor choice for the 40-dB amplifier of Fig. 2-1, since at the upper frequencies there is no feedback due to the rolloff in loop gain.

For audio-frequency use, the 1-MHz response as typified here is better suited to lower-gain configurations, such as 0 dB or 20 dB, where the op amp still possesses some feedback at the higher frequencies. Even then, the loop gain resulting with a 0-dB (unity gain) 741 amplifier is only 40 dB at 10 kHz, which is far from the loop gain of 100 dB at 10 Hz. Similarly, a 20-dB 741 configuration results in only 20 dB of loop gain at 10 kHz. The reader should note that a

0-dB unity-gain configuration occurs only with the voltage follower, where the feedback attenuation factor (β) is 1, or feedback is 100%. The unity-gain inverter (Fig. 2-1A) has a β of 0.5 due to the noise gain ($1/\beta$) of 2 (6 dB). (The two resistors, R_1 and R_2, reduce the feedback signal by a factor of 2 at the summing point.) Therefore, the loop gain of the inverter will be 6 dB less than that of the follower. From this, we can conclude that the open-loop frequency response of a 1-MHz "741-type" amplifier can represent a real limitation for audio applications, unless the performance requirements are modest.

In order to obtain a higher loop gain at the upper audio frequencies, it is necessary to increase the gain-bandwidth product to significantly above 1 MHz, since it has been shown that a 1-MHz gain-bandwidth product can be marginally adequate at low gains. This becomes even more important in the cases of high-gain, wide-bandwidth stages. A 60-dB amplifier requires a 10-MHz gain-bandwidth product just to realize a gain of 1000 in a bandwidth of 10 kHz. To provide adequate loop gain in such an amplifier requires a gain-bandwidth product of 100 MHz or better. It should be obvious by now that a high-gain-bandwidth product is one factor that is fundamental to high-precision, high-gain, ac amplifiers.

A more general picture of the interrelationship between open-loop response, gain-bandwidth product, loop gain, and closed-loop response is shown in Fig. 2-2. With this graph, the requirements for any audio-frequency amplifier can be quickly analyzed in terms of required open-loop gain and gain-bandwidth product. The upper-frequency limit of the amplifier being designed is plotted as a vertical line that extends to a height in decibels equal to the desired closed-loop gain, plus the loop gain necessary to maintain the accuracy required at this frequency. For example, if a 60-dB-gain amplifier is required to have 1% accuracy at a frequency of 10 kHz, a feedback of 40 dB is necessary. Thus, the line would extend to 60 + 40 = 100 dB at 10 kHz. This is the actual open-loop gain required of the amplifier at this frequency for this amount of feedback.

At this point on the graph of Fig. 2-2 (point A), the frequency-limit line intersects the horizontal line of the required gain (100 dB) and also interests a line sloping at 20 dB/decade (6 dB/ocave), which is the required gain-bandwidth curve. Following this sloping line down to where it intercepts the frequency axis gives the required gain-bandwidth product, which in this case is 1000 MHz.

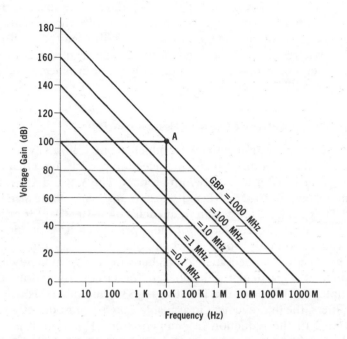

Fig. 2-2. Graph for determining the required gain-bandwidth
product (GBP).

The selection of an amplifier can now be made by choosing a device that will provide 100 dB minimum gain at a frequency of 10 kHz. The reader will note that in many cases the low-frequency gain of a particular op amp will exceed 100 dB, and then will roll off toward zero at frequencies above some corner frequency. But in terms of providing a required gain-bandwidth product, all that is needed is the computed value of open-loop gain at the highest frequency. Any additional gain at lower frequencies is a bonus—one that serves to increase the low-frequency accuracy and fidelity of the circuit.

The example given represents an extreme case, since few IC op amps can provide a 1000-MHz gain-bandwidth product. It was chosen specifically to illustrate the importance of gain-bandwidth product, because the requirements used as an example are not unrealistic. A 60-dB, 10-kHz-bandwidth amplifier is a common requirement for a microphone preamplifier. Since a single IC type may not be able to furnish the required gain-bandwidth product (and accuracy), the use of two cascaded stages will ease the specification requirements for each amplifier. In this example, the use of two 30-dB stages with an open-loop gain of 70 dB each (30 + 40) at 10 kHz will reduce the gain-bandwidth product requirement to approximately 32 MHz—which is a possibility, for instance, with the 5534 device.

2.2.1 The Benefits of Custom Compensation

Higher effective gain-bandwidth product can be realized by several methods, the most direct being the selection of an IC type that has an inherently high gain-bandwidth product. The 318 and 5534, for example, feature 10–15-MHz unity-gain frequencies, while many of the FET types have unity-gain frequencies of 5–10 MHz; for example, the 34081 (8 MHz). Some of the types which have nominally low gain-bandwidth products, when compensated for unity gain, can be custom-compensated for higher effective gain-bandwidth product at a particular gain chosen for circuit operation. For example, this is true of the TL080, 344, 531, and others. For these amplifiers, the improvement in available gain is almost directly proportional to the reduction in compensation. This option is also available with high-speed types such as the 2625, 2525, and 5534. Further, there is also what is commonly called the *decompensated* amplifier. This is one that is stable at some minimum gain *higher* than unity (usually with no provision for any adjustment to compensation). Examples are the 538, 357, OP-37, and 34080 types, which are stable at minimum gains of 5, 5, 5, and 2, respectively.

Fig. 2-3 shows the open-loop response curves for some of these amplifiers. These curves illustrate the improvement in gain available with the lowering of compensation values and represent the manufacturer's recommended values for various closed-loop operating gains. The degree of improvement varies from one op-amp type to another, as can be noted from the various performance figures.

In evaluating these various open-loop response patterns, the key thing to look for is high available gain, *at the closed-loop gain appropriate to the application.*

The 2625, as one example, has a gain (unity-gain compensated) of 70 dB at 10 kHz (20-pF curve). If it were to be used at a gain of 5, however, unity-gain compensation would *not* be required and C_1 could be removed, resulting in the open-loop curve that would yield

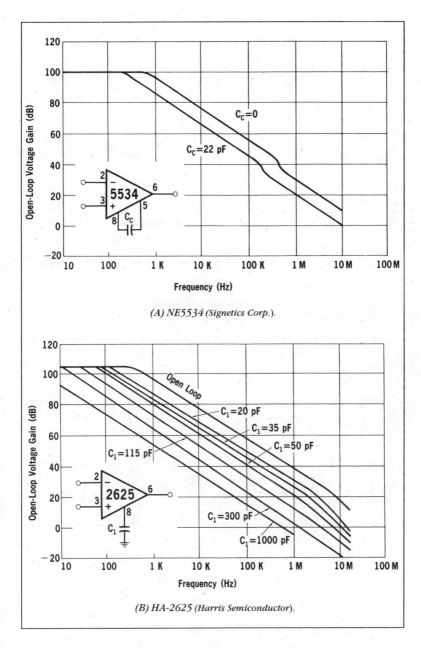

(A) NE5534 (Signetics Corp.).

(B) HA-2625 (Harris Semiconductor).

Fig. 2-3. Frequency-response characteristics of various IC amps.

IC Op-Amp Parameters Important in Audio Applications

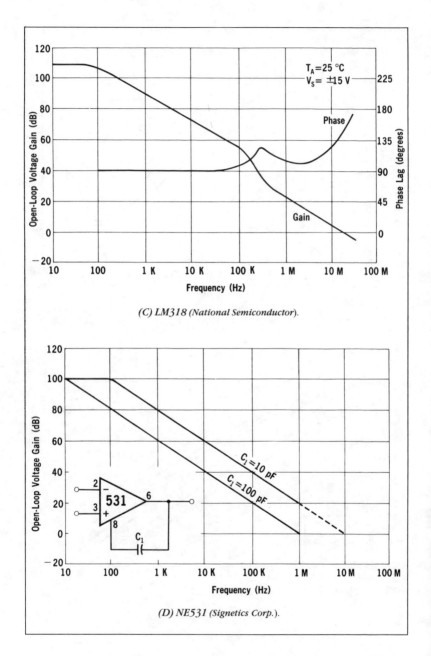

(C) LM318 (National Semiconductor).

(D) NE531 (Signetics Corp.).

Fig. 2-3. (cont.) Frequency-response

IC Op-Amp Parameters Important in Audio Applications

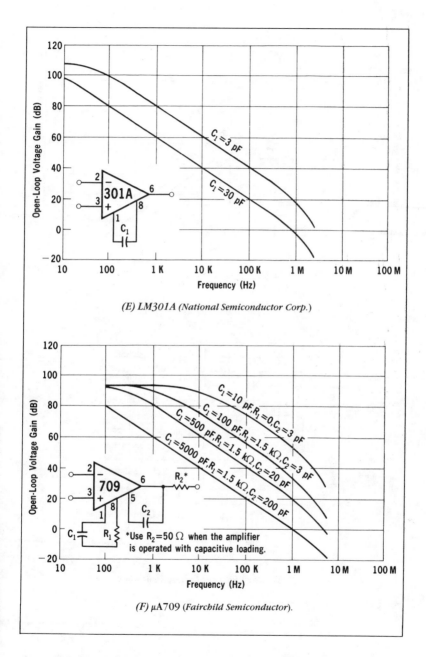

(E) LM301A (National Semiconductor Corp.)

(F) μA709 (Fairchild Semiconductor).

characteristics of various IC amps.

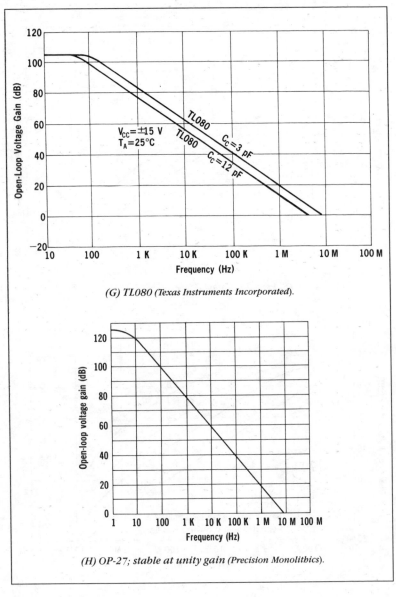

(G) TL080 (Texas Instruments Incorporated).

(H) OP-27; stable at unity gain (Precision Monolithics).

Fig. 2-3. (cont.) Frequency-response

IC Op-Amp Parameters Important in Audio Applications

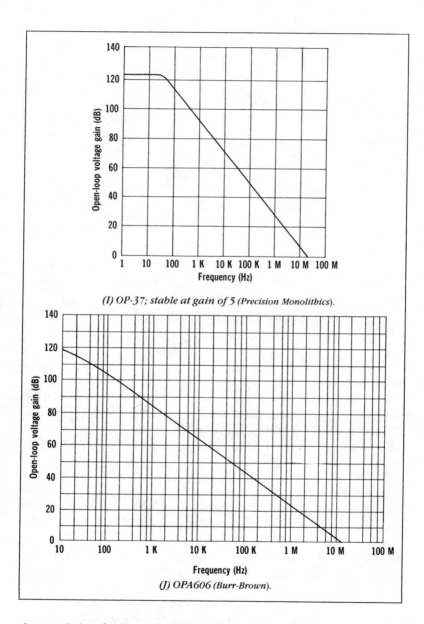

(I) OP-37; stable at gain of 5 (Precision Monolithics).

(J) OPA606 (Burr-Brown).

characteristics of various IC amps.

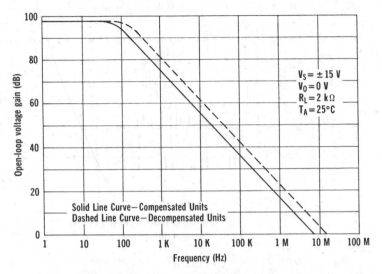

(K) MC34080 series (Motorola Semiconductor Products Inc.).

**Fig. 2-3. (cont.) Frequency-response characteristics
of various IC amps.**

80 dB at 10 kHz. This represents a 100-MHz gain-bandwidth product, which is an excellent figure for an IC op amp. Similar statements can be made regarding other devices, for example the 531 (Fig. 2-3D) and the 301A (Fig. 2-3E). The 301A response, shown in Fig. 2-3E, is also characteristic of the more recent 344 (see device data sheet).

Not all op amps "open up" for high gains as the frequency-compensation capacitance is reduced. This statement is most true in the case of devices using low-value capacitors, such as the 301A and 748, the TL080 and 344. An interesting point in this regard is the "obsolete" 709; its response is shown in Fig. 2-3F. The increase to high-gain-bandwidth product at high gains is because of the relatively high (initial) value capacitances, and is quite effective for this device.

An interesting pattern of behavior can be noted in the 5534 and 318 devices—the fact that *greater* gain is available at audio frequencies other than that implied by their high unity-gain frequency. This is due to their open-loop rolloff "bump" at about 200 kHz.

Other devices useful for audio applications are the low-noise

OP-27 (Fig. 2-3H) and the low-noise OP-37 (Fig. 2-3I), with responses as noted. The OP-27 is stable down to unity-gain, while the closely-related OP-37 is stable at a minimum gain of 5. It has a very high GBP—over 50 MHz at audio frequencies. Some JFET devices with high GBPs are the OPA606 (Fig. 2-3J) and the Motorola MC34080 series (Fig. 2-3K).

Another highly important result of reduced compensation in ac applications is increased slew rate. This aspect of the optimization of audio-amplifier performance is covered in more detail in Section 2.3, and, in many cases, it is more important than the bandwidth increase. The FET-input amplifiers are notable in this parameter, with very high slew rates achieved. Also notable are bipolars with high dynamic-range inputs (and high slew rates), such as the HA2525, the LM318, and such units as the NE530 and NE5535.

Optimizing loop gain in ac applications is not a completely straightforward matter, since the response of a number of different amplifiers must be carefully studied to determine their suitability. The graph of Fig. 2-2 is helpful in this respect; it indicates at a glance what gain is required at which frequency. Thereafter, the amplifier that satisfies the requirements is selected by noting the particular gain curve appropriate for the required gain level. To illustrate, suppose that an amplifier is required to have a loop gain of 20 dB at 10 kHz with 1% accuracy. From Fig. 2-2, we can see that this represents an open-loop gain of 60 dB at 10 kHz, or a gain-bandwidth product of 10 MHz. Inspection of the various curves in Fig. 2-3 reveals that for 20-dB compensation, several amplifiers are suitable. Selection from this list is then made on the basis of suitability for other considerations, such as input current, power requirements, slew rate, linearity, cost, availability, etc.

2.2.2 Determining the Necessary Compensation

Since correct frequency compensation is so important for optimum ac performance, it follows that no more compensation should be used than is necessary to ensure adequate stability. The manufacturer's recommended compensation values given in Fig. 2-3 provide ac stability under the worst-case conditions of temperature and supply-voltage variations, so they can be used with confidence for the gains specified. However, there is a difference between the inverting and noninverting configurations in the required compensation values. This should be understood in applying the gain values of Fig. 2-3.

Unless otherwise specified, the manufacturer's unity-gain compensation values are for noninverting configurations (Fig. 2-4A), where β is unity, or feedback is 100%. This is the worst case insofar as compensation requirements are concerned, since there is no attenuation in the feedback path. When the amplifier is stabilized for this condition ($\beta = 1$), it will be stable for *all* feedback conditions, since there can be no more than 100% feedback. In Fig. 2-4A, C_C represents the capacitance value (or values) recommended by the manufacturer to ensure stability under the condition of 100% feedback. Examples of "C_C" are the 20-pF capacitor used with the 2625 and the 22-pF capacitor used with the 5534.

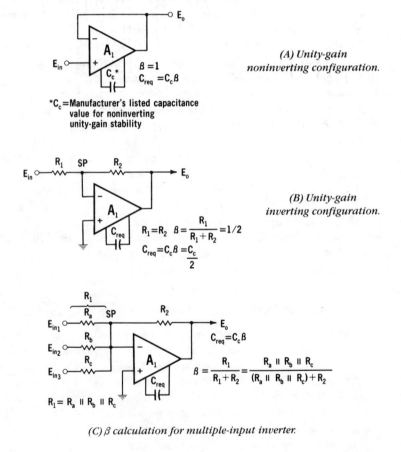

(A) Unity-gain noninverting configuration.

*C_c = Manufacturer's listed capacitance value for noninverting unity-gain stability

(B) Unity-gain inverting configuration.

(C) β calculation for multiple-input inverter.

Fig. 2-4. Determining optimum compensation capacitances for

Less compensation is necessary when β is less than unity, or feedback is less than 100%. This is illustrated in the inverting configuration of Fig. 2-4B, where the feedback situation is different from that of the follower of Fig. 2-4A. The stage gain is still unity since $R_1 = R_2$, but the feedback signal from E_o back to the summing point undergoes an attenuation of 2 to 1 because of the two resistors. This is just another way of saying that for this stage, $\beta = 0.5$. But the compensation requirements of a feedback amplifier are dictated by the value of β regardless of the configuration. In general, the relationship between C_c and C_{req} is

$$C_{req} = C_c\beta \qquad \text{(Eq. 2-1)}$$

where

C_{req} is the capacitance value for stability for a given β,
C_c is the capacitace value for unity-gain stability,
β is as given in Equation 2-2.

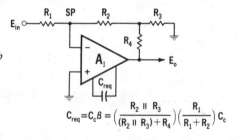

(D) β calculation for inverter with multiple-divider feedback.

$$C_{req} = C_c\beta = \left(\frac{R_2 \parallel R_3}{(R_2 \parallel R_3) + R_4}\right)\left(\frac{R_1}{R_1 + R_2}\right)C_c$$

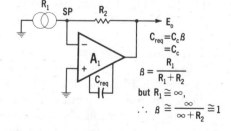

(E) β calculation for inverter with high-impedance source.

$$C_{req} = C_c\beta = C_c$$
$$\beta = \frac{R_1}{R_1 + R_2}$$
but $R_1 \cong \infty$,
$$\therefore \ \beta \cong \frac{\infty}{\infty + R_2} \cong 1$$

various amplifier configurations and feedback networks.

The equation for calculating β is

$$\beta = \frac{R_1}{R_1 + R_2} \qquad \text{(Eq. 2-2)}$$

Therefore, the compensation capacitance required for unity-gain stability for the inverting stage of Fig. 2-4B is one half of that required for the noninverting stage of Fig. 2-4A.

It should be noted that R_1 in the circuit of Fig. 2-4B represents the total resistance seen from the summing point to ground (looking back through the E_{in} source impedance, which is assumed to be low). Thus, when there are multiple inputs as in Fig. 2-4C, an equivalent resistance must be calculated for R_1 before the β calculation is made.

Similarly, the feedback is not always through a single resistance as represented by R_2 in Figs. 2-4B and C. In some configurations, the feedback is taken from a voltage divider, as in Fig. 2-4D. In this case, the feedback signal is attenuated twice—once through the divider

$$\frac{R_2 \parallel R_3}{(R_2 \parallel R_3) + R_4}$$

and once through the divider

$$\frac{R_1}{R_1 + R_2}$$

β, in this case, is the composite attenuation of the two divider networks:

$$\beta_{comp} = \left(\frac{R_2 \parallel R_3}{(R_2 \parallel R_3) + R_4} \right) \left(\frac{R_1}{R_1 + R_2} \right) \qquad \text{(Eq. 2-3)}$$

A special case of feedback is illustrated by the current-to-voltage converter of Fig. 2-4E. In this configuration, amplifier A_1 is fed from a high-impedance source, such as the collector of a transistor (as in a D/A converter). In such cases, the source impedance represented by R_1 is so much greater than R_2 that it offers little divider action with R_2; thus, the feedback becomes essentially 100% and unity-gain compensation is required.

In determining the required compensation for any feedback network, the β divider must be analyzed to determine the loss of feedback signal. This is true for any op-amp configuration—inverter, follower, subtractor, etc. Using this type of analysis, the exact compensation values can be calculated. With reference to the response curves of Fig. 2-3, it can be seen how the feedback effects of β determine the scaling of compensation capacitances. In general, this is a direct 1:10 ratio between unity gain and the first decade (gain of 10), or the ratio of the two β values. Beyond the first decade, this relationship does not hold precisely, because of the effects of stray capacitance, which will vary from device to device.

As stated previously, the manufacturer's compensation values are for the noninverting configuration. The inverting configuration uses lower values, and, in the case of the unity-gain inverter where β = 0.5 (Fig. 2-4B), the values are halved. However, at higher inverting gains (10, for example), the β scaling may not hold, depending on the particular amplifier used. In these cases, optimum compensation can be verified by experiment, or a conservative approach can be taken by using the compensation values listed for a noninverting gain of 10, which will always ensure stability.

2.2.3 Loop Gain and the Effects of β on Bandwidth

A better appreciation of the importance of optimum-frequency compensation in wideband ac amplifiers may be gained by an examination of Figs. 2-5 and 2-6. Fig. 2-5 is a Bode plot for a typical unity-gain inverter using a 1-MHz gain-bandwidth-product op amp. The β of 0.5 for a unity-gain inverter results in a noise gain $(1/\beta)$ of 2. This is shown on the plot as a dashed line at the + 6-dB level. The loop gain is the amount of gain available from the level of the noise gain up to the intersection of the open-loop response curve. Thus, at 10 kHz on the 1-MHz gain-bandwidth product curve, the available loop gain is 40 dB – 6 dB, or 34 dB. However, by custom-compensating this amplifier for the noise gain of 6 dB, the effective gain-bandwidth product is extended to 2 MHz. This restores the available loop gain to 40 dB.

The interplay between noise gain, compensation, and bandwidth is even more effectively illustrated in Fig. 2-6. This is a Bode plot for a 10-input unity-gain inverter, a very common audio application. Even though the circuit operates with unity gain for each of the 10 inputs, the noise gain is 11 (21 dB) because of the attenuation of the feedback signal by the equivalent resistance for the input (summing) network. This noise gain is sketched on the Bode plot as a dashed line at a gain of 21 dB. With unity-gain compensation, the op amp has a gain-bandwidth product of 1 MHz and an open-loop gain of

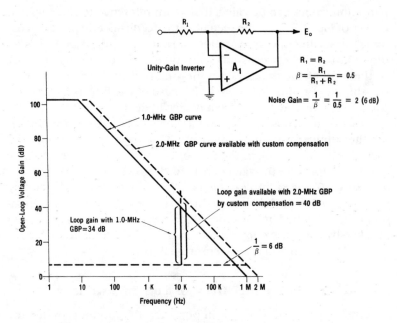

Fig. 2-5. Bode plot illustrating the effects of custom compensation on a simple unity-gain inverter.

40 dB at 10 kHz. Since the noise gain is 21 dB, the available loop gain at 10 kHz is only 19 dB—not a very respectable figure. By choosing custom compensation for a gain of 20 dB based on the noise gain, the effective gain-bandwidth product for this amplifier will be increased to 10 MHz, and 39 dB of loop gain will be realized instead of 19 dB—an obviously desirable situation.

The compensation requirements of an op-amp audio stage should be determined with care, particularly when lower-bandwidth general-purpose types are to be used. It has been shown that these types seldom have an excess of gain-bandwidth, a fact that can lead to difficult problems at high frequencies. Also, it is important to remember that compensation requirements are more accurately determined by the noise gain $(1/\beta)$ rather than by the closed-loop gain of the circuit—the two are not always the same. In the following discussion on slew rate, it will be seen that this statement regarding optimum compensation is also true for other reasons.

One further point concerning the effect of β on frequency response: There is a "shrinkage" of available bandwidth resulting

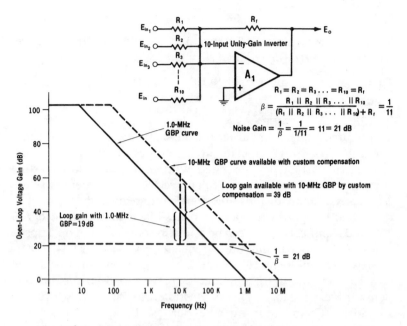

Fig. 2-6. Bode plot illustrating the effects of custom compensation on a 10-input unity-gain inverter.

from the noise gain. The maximum available bandwidth will be no greater than that point where the noise-gain curve intersects the open-loop curve. In Fig. 2-6, the $1/\beta$ curve intersects the 1-MHz open-loop curve at 100 kHz, and this will be the bandwidth. This is in sharp contrast to what might be expected from the 1-MHz unity-gain frequency. The point is that the noise gain not only determines the loop gain but also determines the resultant bandwidth. Thus, optimizing the loop gain also optimizes the bandwidth at the same time. The 10-MHz custom-compensated case of Fig. 2-6 will have a 1-MHz bandwidth.

2.3 SLEW RATE

A highly important factor in the ac performance of an IC op amp is the slewing rate of the amplifier. For a sine-wave signal, the relationship between slew rate (SR), full-power frequency response (f_p), and peak output voltage (E_{op}) in terms of signal parameters is

$$SR = 2\pi E_{op}f_p \qquad \text{(Eq. 2-4)}$$

With an output swing of 10 V (peak) and a full-power frequency response of 20 kHz, the required slew rate is

$$SR = 6.28 \times 10^1 \times 2 \times 10^4$$
$$= 1.256 \times 10^6 \text{ V/s}$$
$$= 1.256 \text{ V/}\mu s$$

This figure is the minimum acceptable slew rate for full-power output at 20 kHz. However, many op-amp types cannot meet this figure, particularly when operated with unity-gain, noninverting compensation. Also, the term "full power" is a misnomer in a sense, as it tends to imply distortionless output. In reality, operation of an op amp at full-power frequency creates distortion on the order of 1%, and significant levels can be found in some types of op amps to as low as one fourth full-power frequency response (or less).

Slew-rate limiting occurs because of the limited ability of the internal bias circuits of the amplifier to charge and discharge the compensating capacitance. This is illustrated in Fig. 2-7, which is a simplified schematic of a general-purpose IC op amp (such as a 301A) with an external compensation (C_c) of 30 pF. Transistors Q_3 and Q_4 represent the bipolar input differential stage, which is fed by a constant emitter current (I_E) of approximately 20 μA. In normal operation, this stage is balanced, with Q_3 and Q_5 conducting one half of I_E, and Q_4 and Q_6 conducting the other half. The stage will remain balanced as long as the amplifier is operating linearly. However, when the amplifier is driven to an output rate of voltage change (slew rate) faster than it can respond to, it can no longer operate linearly but can only attempt to follow at its maximum rate of change, or slewing rate. This is illustrated by the input (E_{in}) and output (E_o) waveforms in Fig. 2-7, for a square wave.

Current, I_E, and compensating capacitance, C_c, set the slewing rate of the amplifier, since I_E is the maximum current that the input differential pair can deliver to charge C_c. The slewing rate in terms of *circuit* parameters is then given by

$$SR = \left(\frac{I_E}{C_c}\right) \text{ V/s} \qquad \text{(Eq. 2-5)}$$

In this example, if $I_E = 20$ μA and $C_c = 30$ pF, then

$$SR = \frac{2 \times 10^{-5}}{3 \times 10^{-11}}$$
$$= 0.67 \times 10^6 \text{ V/s}$$
$$= 0.67 \text{ V/}\mu s$$

With the current mirror "gain" of Q_5-Q_6 very close to unity, the positive and negative rates of slewing in a 301A will be very nearly equal.

Slew rate can be increased in a number of ways, with the most direct way being to reduce the value of compensation capacitance. This is possible at higher closed-loop gains, which is verified by the increased slewing rates possible for custom-compensated types, such as the 301A, 344, or TL080. Internally compensated types,

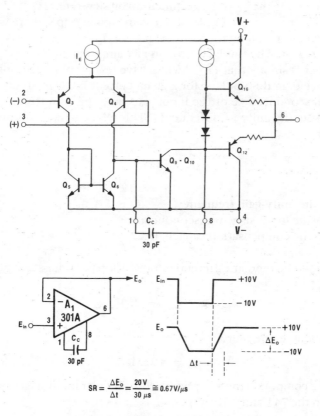

$$SR = \frac{\Delta E_o}{\Delta t} = \frac{20 \text{ V}}{30 \ \mu s} \cong 0.67 \text{V/}\mu s$$

Fig. 2-7. Simplified schematic of a 301A op amp illustrating slew-rate limitations.

such as the 741, 4558 or 4136, have constant slewing rates, because their compensation capacitance is fixed. If the slewing rate of a particular internally compensated amplifier is insufficient for a particular application, then an alternative amplifier must be selected.

Since the slewing rate of an op amp is tied to the value of compensation capacitance, it follows that the worst case of slew rate occurs when the largest compensation capacitance is used—in unity-gain noninverting configurations with maximum feedback. For amplifying configurations which must operate at full output voltage at high frequencies with unity-gain stability, the most effective device solution is, therefore, an inherently high slew-rate device.

The use of recently developed high-performance FET-input op amps, rather than bipolar op amps, is an effective design method for circumventing the input-stage limitation on slew rate. If Q_3 and Q_4 in Fig. 2-7 were p-channel FETs rather than bipolar pnp's, there would be much less of a limitation on the current, I_E.

The reason why this is true for an FET amplifier and not a bipolar amplifier is simply that FET devices have less input-stage transconductance than do bipolars, for a given current level. In an op amp, the transconductance of the input stage and the compensation capacitor set the unity-gain frequency. This relationship is simply

$$f_t = \frac{g_m}{2\pi C_c} \qquad \text{(Eq. 2-6)}$$

where

f_t is the unity-gain frequency,
g_m is the input-stage transconductance,
C_c is the compensation capacitance.

In a simple bipolar differential transistor pair, input-stage g_m is

$$g_{m_b} = \frac{q}{2kT} (I_E) \qquad \text{(Eq. 2-7)}$$

or at room temperature,

$$g_{m_b} = 19.2(I_E) \qquad \text{(Eq. 2-8)}$$

For a compound (npn + pnp cascode) bioplar input stage, such as used in the 741 and 301A types, g_m is

$$g_{m_{BC}} = \frac{q}{4kT} (I_E) \qquad \text{(Eq. 2-9)}$$

or, $g_{m_{BC}} = 9.6(I_E)$ (at room temperature). For a p-channel JFET pair as is typically employed in some FET devices, g_m is

$$g_{m_f} = 1.5(I_E) \qquad \text{(Eq. 2-10)}$$

The constant in this equation represents a design-process-dependent constant, and will vary from one particular device to another.

To illustrate the difference, we can select two op amps (one bipolar and one FET) with the same nominal unity-gain frequency. From this, it can be seen that widely differing levels for I_E (and, thus, slew rate) will result. For example, the 301A achieves a 1-MHz unity-gain frequency with $I_E = 20$ μA and $C_c = 30$ pF, while a TL070 (or TL080) FET amplifier has an I_E of 200 μA, with a 47-pF compensation capacitance required to achieve a 1-MHz unity-gain frequency.

The corresponding slew rates for the 301A and TL070 for these conditions are 0.67 and 4.3 V/μs, however, or about a factor of six times better for an FET device, for the same bandwidth. This is due to the lower gm/I_E ratio for the FET, which, in turn, allows a greater I_E/C_c* ratio, and, thus, a higher slew rate.

For an identical compensation capacitance of 30 pF, the TL070 achieves a 6.7-V/μs slew rate, or 10 times the 301A Slew rate. For this operating condition, its bandwidth will be about 1.6 MHz, or appreciably better than the 301A.

It should be thoroughly understood that the dramatic increase in slew rate which is evident in an FET-input op amp is due to the inherent difference between the gm of FET devices versus that of bipolar devices. In general, the lower gm allows a higher slew rate to be achieved, for a comparable bandwidth and stability margin, because it allows I_E to increase.

Although gm can also be reduced in bipolar transistor input stages, most directly by simple emitter degeneration, this approach has drawbacks for high-quality use. By increasing the total emitter current, I_E, in a degenerated bipolar amp, slew rate can be raised. Examples of such an approach are contained in such ICs as the 1456, 1436, 343, and 344, with the best examples being the 318 the 2525. The main disadvantage is that the addition of the emitter resistors raises the input noise over that of a straightforward differential pair. This can be a disadvantage for low-level audio uses.

---

*See Reference 26 in Chapter 1.

An advantage of the emitter-degenerated bipolar-transistor input stage is very good linearity for large input signals. Consequently, such input stages can have extremely good open-loop linearity characteristics, which is, of course, an advantage for audio applications. The 318 device is a good example of such, with an open-loop distortion that is only on the order of 0.1%. The low-transconductance FET amplifiers, for example, the 34080 series and the AD711 types, also tend to have excellent linearity for large input signals.

The (open loop) voltage dynamic range for an op-amp input stage can be related to the previously discussed design parameters of g_m and I_E. Thus, this voltage can also be related to GBP and SR. This voltage, V_{th}, is the voltage which (if exceeded) will cause the amplifier to slew limit. For many, it may be easier to visualize the input overload phenomena of the op amp when it is expressed in terms of input voltage (as opposed to SR and GBP—even though they are all related).

V_{th} is related to the amplifier input-stage operating current (I_E) and transconductance (g_m) as

$$V_{th} = \frac{I_E}{g_m} \qquad \text{(Eq. 2-11)}$$

For the 301 or 741 type of amplifier, the g_m is

$$g_{m_{(301)}} = \frac{I_E}{4V_T} \qquad \text{(Eq. 2-12)}$$

Expressed in terms of V_{th}, the 301 amplifier has a V_{th} of

$$V_{th_{(301)}} = \frac{I_E}{g_m} = 4V_T \qquad \text{(Eq. 2-13)}$$

At room temperatures, this works out to a V_{th} of approximately 104 mV. Therefore, it will only take about 100 mV (peak) of differential input voltage to slew limit a 301- or 741-type op amp.

By contrast, FET-input input amplifiers typically have five or more times V_{th}, when compared to bipolar amps. This is because their transconductance is many times lower, thus tending to raise the V_{th}. Bipolar-input amplifiers with emitter degeneration, such as the 318 and 2525, also show high figures for V_{th}.

A general expression for V_{th} in terms of SR and GBP is

$$V_{th} = \frac{SR}{2\pi GBP} \qquad \text{(Eq. 2-14)}$$

where
  SR is in V/μs,
  GBP is in MHz.

This expression can be used to compare amplifiers for V_{th} when the SR and GBP parameters are known but the exact input-stage design is not known. (A more detailed discussion of V_{th} can be found in Part III of Reference 33.)

Different op-amp designs attack the slew-rate problem in various ways, with differing degrees of success. A brief summary of the slew-rate capabilities of various devices is given in Table 2-1. Note that many devices are capable of higher slew rates with reduced compensation.

Table 2-1. Typical Slewing Rates of Various IC Op Amps for Various Compensation Conditions (V/μs)

Device	Av = +1	Reduced Compensation
5534	6	13, Av = 3
2625	7	30, Av = 5
318	70	
OP-27	2.8	
OP-37	NA	17, Av = 5
AD711	20	
OPA606	30	
MC34080 series	25	34081, 34082, 34084
	50	34080, 34083, 34085
1456 (1436)	2.5	
343	2.5	
344	2.5	30, Av = 10
2645	5	
3140	9	
TL070, TL080	13	40, Av = 10
TL071, TL081	13	
351, 411	13	
771–774 series	13	
301A, 741	0.6	10, feedforward (301A)
4136, 4558	1	
HA4741	1.6	
4605	4	
4625	NA	25, Av = 10

In most cases, an adequate slewing rate can be provided by one of the devices listed in Table 2-1. In certain configurations, however, there are additional options with particular devices. The 301A, for example, can be used with *feedforward compensation,* which enables it to slew at 10 V/μs as a unity-gain inverter and extends its unity-gain bandwidth to 10 MHz.

Another useful option is commonly termed the *input compensation,* and is available with externally compensated (or decompensated) op amps. Input compensation is a technique that allows a low-signal-gain amplifier to be compensated for greater *high-frequency* gain. This permits a faster slewing rate and a greater loop gain at high frequencies. Since the compensation requirements for stability are governed by the relative phase of the $1/\beta$ curve and the open-loop gain, it follows that crossing the $1/\beta$ curve over at higher closed-loop gains (or high frequencies) will allow less compensation and, thus, a faster slewing rate (as well as a greater loop gain if the $1/\beta$ curve is tailored properly).

In applying input compensation, an amplifier type that lends itself to appreciable increases in slewing rate and gain-bandwidth product with reduced compensation should be used. Some examples are the 357, the OP-37, and others to lesser extents, in a circuit such as shown in Fig. 2-8. The input network that provides the increased gain consists of R_1 and C_1. Resistors R_1 and R_f set the gain of the network for high frequencies, while C_1 limits the lower frequency at which this gain is active. Finally, a small feedback capacitor, C_f, is used to increase the phase margin in the crossover region.

Input compensation is most useful where the highest speed is necessary for a low-signal gain, such as the inverter shown in Fig. 2-8. The technique does have a drawback, however, and that is an increase in high-frequency noise due to the higher gain at high frequencies.

Slew rate is a highly important audio circuit design parameter, because the slew-rate limit of an op amp is determined by a nonlinearity—most often clipping (hard overload) in the input stage. Therefore, power bandwidth is a highly different type of relative-bandwidth quality indicator than is the more familiar small-signal bandwidth. There is an inherent nonlinearity and distortion associated with slew rate and full-power frequency response that must be considered for high-quality results.

An important factor that should be appreciated concerning slew

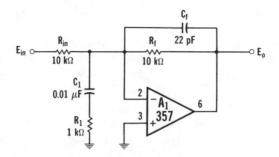

To use input compensation:

(1) Compensate amplifier for a higher gain which yields the desired slewing rate, or use a decompensated amplifier.

(2) Select $\dfrac{R_f}{R_1}$ for this compensation.

(3) Select $C_1 = \dfrac{1}{2\pi f_1 R_1}$ where, $f_1 = 1/10$ of crossover frequency (f_c) of $1/B'$ curve.

(4) Select C_f for clean settling.

Fig. 2-8. Use of input compensation to achieve a faster slewing rate and a greater high-frequency loop gain.

rate is that its effect upon signal fidelity is both level- and frequency-dependent. Often, in view of a confining limit, these two parameters can be traded off, with a net reduction in distortion as a result. This may already be evident from Equation 2-4, but some sample performance data will bring this point into focus.

In practice, distortion due to power bandwidth or low slew rate will usually be the limiting factor on circuit performance, particularly for high-voltage output circuits. High-slew-rate, high V_{th} linear-input IC devices are the key to achieving superlative audio performance for such conditions.

For those relatively new to feedback theory and/or op-amp technology, it might seem that the very high levels of feedback possible could render virtually any source of distortion negligible. While this is to a large degree true at low frequencies (< 1 kHz) for virtually any device, it is not at all so at high frequencies. This is because slew-rate limiting represents a form of total dynamic overload within an amplifier, and any amount of feedback (even 100%) cannot correct the nonlinearity of clipping. It is helpful, perhaps, if slew-rate limiting is viewed as another form of clipping; being *a rate of change* limit, analogous (as an absolute maximum) to amplifier limiting for peak voltage swing.

High feedback factors, as may be provided by high device gain-bandwidth product, can minimize the effects of nonlinearities as the slew-rate limit is *approached.* Performance examples (to follow) will illustrate how this occurs in practice. Since slew rate and bandwidth are closely related in many respects, it is important to appreciate how each can affect actual device performance in terms of nonlinearity. Some special test procedures have been evolved to maximize sensitivity to slew-induced distortion (SID) detection, and they are briefly discussed in this section.

Slew-induced distortion[*] is a general term which is intended to mean the distortion products generated by an amplifier as the signal rate of change (as measured at the output) approaches and coincides with the device slew-rate limit. The distortion can be measured by a number of high-frequency test methods, and will generally show a rapid rise as the slew-rate limit is reached. Some suitable methods are swept-frequency total harmonic distortion, two-tone high-frequency intermodulation distortion, and the sine-square inter-modulation distortion test. Typical results for these methods are discussed below.

Since slew rate is worst (lowest) at unity-gain compensation, it follows that a unity-gain-compensated device will show (when tested) the most slew-induced distortion. The general test circuit of Fig. 2-9 can operate a unit under test (UUT) with unity-gain compensation (appropriate for this test). The device is operating in the inverting mode, because many devices exhibit different (usually lower) slew rates for the noninverting connection (a separate test can check for the different slew rates). The device is operated without heavy loading, to minimize nonlinearities within the output stage.

Some generally typical results of performance, as tested by the swept-frequency total harmonic distortion method, are shown in Fig. 2-10. In Fig. 2-10A, a 0.5-V/μs 741 device is tested at 7 V, 2 V, and 1 V rms. As can be noted, the fixed slew rate allows lower distortion to higher frequencies, for lower output levels. Fig. 2-10B shows a number of devices with different slew rates, for a common 7-V test

---

[*]See References 31-33 at the end of the chapter.

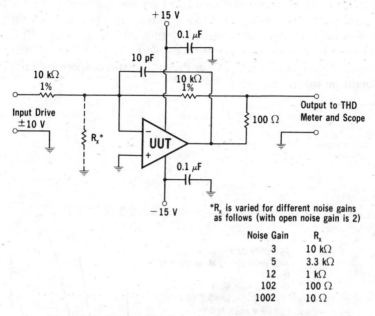

+15 V

0.1 μF

10 pF

10 kΩ
1%

10 kΩ
1%

Input Drive
±10 V

R$_x$*

UUT

100 Ω

Output to THD
Meter and Scope

0.1 μF

−15 V

*R$_x$ is varied for different noise gains
as follows (with open noise gain is 2)

Noise Gain	R$_x$
3	10 kΩ
5	3.3 kΩ
12	1 kΩ
102	100 Ω
1002	10 Ω

Fig. 2-9. Test circuit for slew-induced distortion (SID).

level, with the higher slew-rate devices performing appreciably better.

Curves for a two-tone 1:1 high-frequency intermodulation distortion test for a number of devices with various slew rates are shown in Fig. 2-11. For this test, the two high-frequency tones are spaced 100 Hz apart at a 20-V p-p level and are swept from 5 to 50 kHz. The linear higher-slew-rate devices perform much better for this test as well, and the best of them show no more distortion than that of the test-setup residual.

There has evolved a school of thought that views high-frequency high-level distortion in terms of "transient" distortion, or *transient intermodulation distortion* (TIM). Although there have been special tests designed to test for such distortion in amplifiers, the pattern of resultant behavior is much like other test methods; that is, as the signal rate of change approaches the amplifier slew rate, there is a sharp increase in the distortion observed. Some representative results of this method are shown in Fig. 2-12.

The basic test method for transient intermodulation distortion is a sine-square intermodulation distortion test,[*] where a 3.18-kHz square wave is linearly added to a 15-kHz sine wave, in a 4:1 ratio. The resultant composite signal is band-limited to either 30 kHz (TIM30K) or 100 kHz (TIM100K). (*Note:* The interested reader should consult the references at the end of the chapter for further details on this technique.)

---

[*]See Reference 38 at the end of the chapter.

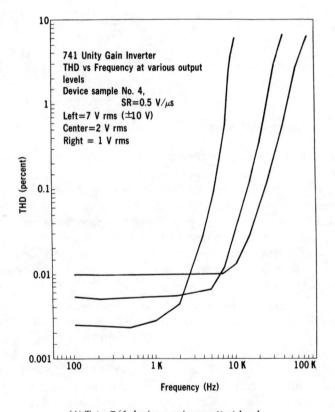

(A) Type-741 device, various output levels.

Fig. 2-10. Slew-induced distortion measured

IC Op-Amp Parameters Important in Audio Applications

To assess the degree of distortion in a transient intermodulation distortion test, the amplifier output signal is observed on a spectrum analyzer, over the 20-kHz audio range. In Fig. 2-12A, the transient intermodulation distortion performance of two IC op amps is shown for the same test conditions. The upper trace, which shows strong transient intermodulation distortion, is a 0.5-V/μs 741 device. The bottom trace, which is essentially a duplicate of the input spectrum, is for a 10-V/μs NE536 device. The main parameter difference between the two amplifiers is their slew rates.

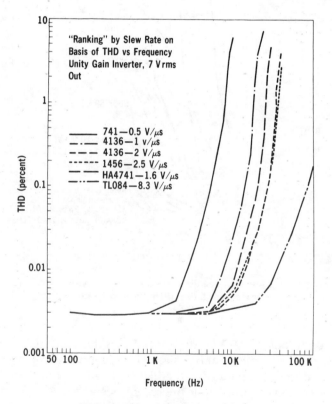

(B) A 7-V rms output, various devices.

by total harmonic distortion method.

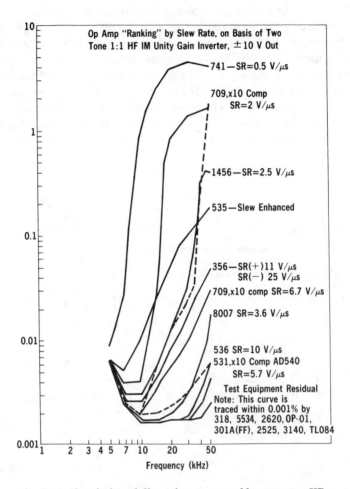

Fig. 2-11. Slew-induced distortion measured by two-tone HF
intermodulation distortion method.

In Fig. 2-12B, the performance of a 301A IC is shown, for slew-rate conditions of 0.9 V/µs (top) and 7 V/µs (bottom), respectively. The higher slew-rate condition shows negligible transient intermodulation distortion, indicating the higher slew rate (due to reduced compensation) as the key to increased performance. The reader should appreciate the fact that increasing the noise gain (decreasing feedback) with the objective of decreasing the compensation (so as to *increase* slew rate) can make a net *increase* in performance, in

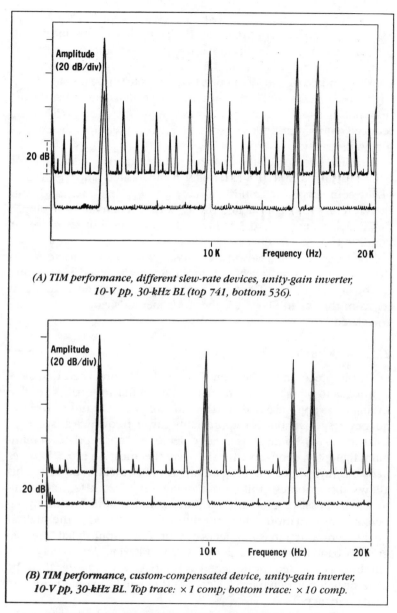

(A) TIM performance, different slew-rate devices, unity-gain inverter, 10-V pp, 30-kHz BL (top 741, bottom 536).

(B) TIM performance, custom-compensated device, unity-gain inverter, 10-V pp, 30-kHz BL. Top trace: ×1 comp; bottom trace: ×10 comp.

Fig. 2-12. Slew-induced distortion measured by transient intermodulation distortion method.

some cases. This can be explained as follows.

If an amplifier slew limits when subjected to a specific signal (Fig. 2-12B, top trace), the performance increase allowable by increasing the slew rate (Fig. 2-12B, bottom trace) will often improve the situation, even though there is *less* overall feedback. At first this may seem contrary to feedback theory, as it seems to imply that less feedback is better. Less feedback is not better *in general* for lower distortion, but in a specific case as described here, it *can be better* if the reduced compensation increases slew rate, and removes the confining nonlinearity.

It should be appreciated that this optimized compensation is, of course, available only on externally compensated amplifier types. Fixed compensation amplifiers have a fixed slew rate, and can, therefore, *not* be manipulated thusly. A fixed compensation amplifier, which is slew limited for a low gain condition, will get worse for conditions of less feedback.

The three test methods just discussed will all show increases in distortion as the slew rate of the amplifier is approached by the slope of the signal. If data from the three methods are normalized in terms of this, as in Fig. 2-13, the three methods can be seen to be correlated.

2.3.1 A Criterion for Slew Rate

From the preceding discussion, it should be appreciated that slew limiting is to be prevented in an audio amplifier for quality results. Inasmuch as appreciable distortion not only exists at full-power frequency response, but for appreciably lower frequencies (see Figs. 2-10 and 2-11), some conservative derating is appropriate. A minimum figure for a conservative slew-rate specification is *0.5 V/μs per peak output volt,* or, expressed as a power bandwidth, 80 kHz. This allows distortionless full-output operation to 20 kHz, and minimizes the possible generation of intermodulation distortion by supersonic information. This criterion can be relaxed if the highest quality reproduction is not necessary, or if the input signals are specifically band limited, such as by low-pass filtering. Alternately, if an amplifier is selected (or designed as such) for a V_{th} *greater* than the peak-peak input-signal level, slew limiting will be avoided (and linearity enhanced).

The following section goes further into test methods that can be used for slew-induced distortion detection and characterization.

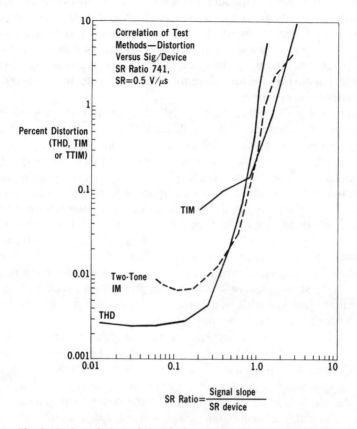

Fig. 2-13. Correlation of slew-induced distortion test methods.

The references listed at the end of the chapter will also be helpful in this regard.

2.4 DISTORTION

As has just been touched upon in the previous section, and which certainly can be generally appreciated, the distortion performance of an IC op amp is of fundamental importance for audio use. Distortion can result from many different factors, including both the inherent nonlinearities of the device and also how it is used within an actual circuit. It is important that the user of these devices appreciate how the various considerations that affect distortion are interrelated, beginning with the device itself. Accordingly, this section discusses a general method of characterizing the distortion of a given IC op amp in a standard manner. The method can be used to generate data for any op amp, but, in the course of discussing it here, typical distortion performance for many of the devices featured in this book are presented.

There are many different methods of distortion analysis that can be used to evaluate an audio amplifier. Unfortunately, none seems to be universally applicable for exposing various sorts of circuit defects. A modified total harmonic distortion analysis technique has been used by the author with good success, and it is presented here because it is well understood and equipment for it is readily available. All of the tests discussed here can be performed with a total harmonic distortion oscillator/analyzer test set, such as those manufactured by Hewlett-Packard, Sound Technology, Tektronix, etc., and a lab oscilloscope. A minimal amount of specialized test circuitry is necessary, consisting mostly of test sockets for the unit under test, some passive components, and appropriate switches. Standard lab-type plug-in IC breadboards are suitable and convenient for this use, for low-volume testing.

Table 2-2 briefly outlines each test in the series, which consists of tests A through G. Each test has a circuit configuration associated with it. These are shown in Fig. 2-14 for tests B through G; the test circuit for test A was previously shown in Fig. 2-9.

As may be appreciated, each test in the series is designed to pinpoint a particular distortion mechanism that can exist in a given de-

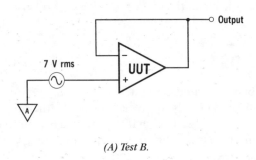

(A) Test B.

Fig. 2-14. Test circuit configurations for

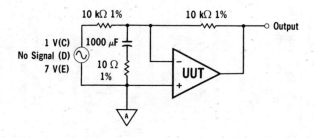

(B) Tests C, D, and E.

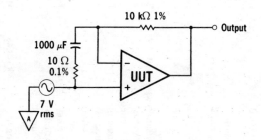

(C) Test F.

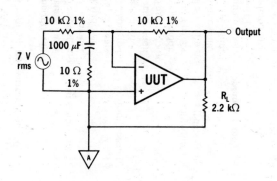

(D) Test G.

total harmonic distortion test series.

Table 2-2. THD Test Series for IC Op-Amp Audio Characterization

Test No.	Test for	General Conditions	Load	Frequency	Remarks
A	SR (general)	Unity-gain inverting with unity-gain compensation; full-rated output voltage.	open	100 Hz–100 kHz (or to fp)	Checks SR independent of CM and output nonlinearities.
B	SR (common mode)	Unity-gain noninverting with unity-gain compensation; full-rated output voltage.	open	100 Hz–100 kHz (or to fp)	Checks input CM SR, if different than in test A.
C	Small-signal bandwidth	60-dB noise gain, inverting unity signal gain, compensation as appropriate; 1 V rms out.	open	10 Hz to −3-dB point	Checks amplifier GBP to determine open-loop frequency response.
D	Noise	60-dB noise gain, compensation as appropriate; $R_s = 10 \, \Omega$ (or as appropriate), no signal applied.	open	N.A.	Checks equivalent input noise for low R_s, extrapolate to $nV/\sqrt{Hz}$.
E	Transfer linearity	60-dB noise gain, inverting unity signal gain, compensation as appropriate; full-rated output voltage.	open	10 Hz to one half −3-dB frequency	Checks basic transfer linearity of amplifier, independent of test A or B.
F	Input nonlinearity	60-dB noise gain, noninverting unity signal, compensation as appropriate; full-rated output voltage.	open	10 Hz to one half −3-dB frequency	Checks input-stage nonlinearity, independent of tests A, B, and E.
G	Output nonlinearity	60-dB noise gain, inverting unity signal gain, compensation as appropriate; full-rated output voltage, rated R_L.	2 k (or as appropriate)	10 Hz to one half −3-dB frequency	Checks output-stage nonlinearity, independent of tests A, B, E, and F.

vice. This is done through a series of controlled closed-loop tests, and the resulting data can be used to predict performance of a given unit. This will become more obvious as some examples are discussed.

To begin the discussion of the tests, we will review performance data for a 741 op amp, which is quite poor in terms of audio quality. The data are plotted in Fig. 2-15; Fig. 2-15A is the data for the 741 device under discussion.

The first test of the series, Test A, is intended to yield the basic slew-induced distortion characteristic of the op amp, exclusive of any common-mode (CM) or output effects. The heavy feedback forces the device to maintain a flat voltage output up to the power bandwidth (i.e., it is forced, by the high feedback factor, to slew), and the slew-induced distortion generated can be measured under controlled repeatable conditions.

Before proceeding with the total harmonic distortion series of tests—in particular, tests A and B—it is highly useful to measure and record the actual slew rate of the unit under test. This is done by driving the device in the appropriate circuits for tests A and B with a square wave, and measuring the (+) and (–) slew rates. This should be done for both the inverting (test A) and noninverting (test B) modes, for many op amps differ in slew rates between input modes.

The oscilloscope photographs of Fig. 2-16 illustrate this problem, and were taken from the 741 being tested. Note in this double-exposure photograph that the inverting response (rising slope at beginning) is fairly symmetrical, but the noninverting response is markedly different. This sort of misbehavior shows up in test results (and is also audible). The 4136 slewing characteristics shown in Fig. 2-16B are much more desirable, and quite symmetrical.

With the slew-rate checks completed, the total harmonic distortion tests can begin, starting with test A (Fig. 2-15). The data is plotted on log-log coordinates; 3 × 5 cycles is usually adequate for most devices.

Test A is a full output-voltage-level total-harmonic-distortion sweep, which is done using the circuit in Fig. 2-9. Data are taken from 100 Hz up to the 1% distortion-level frequency, at full-power frequency response. Here full-power frequency response is 10.8 kHz for the 741 under test. The general similarity of this curve to those of Fig. 2-10 should be obvious.

Test B is done with the op amp strapped for unity gain, as in Fig.

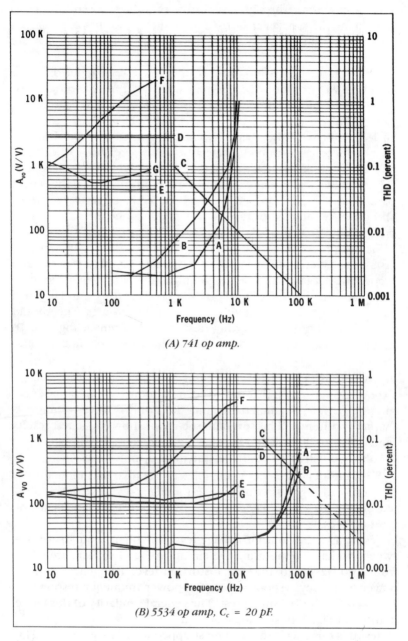

(A) 741 op amp.

(B) 5534 op amp, C_c = 20 pF.

Fig. 2-15. Total harmonic

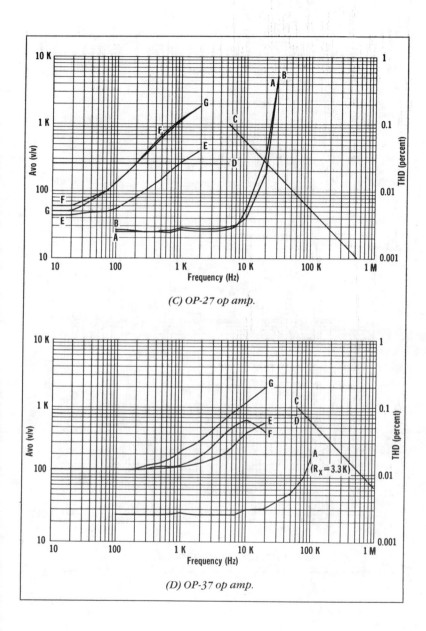

(C) OP-27 op amp.

(D) OP-37 op amp.

distortion test series.

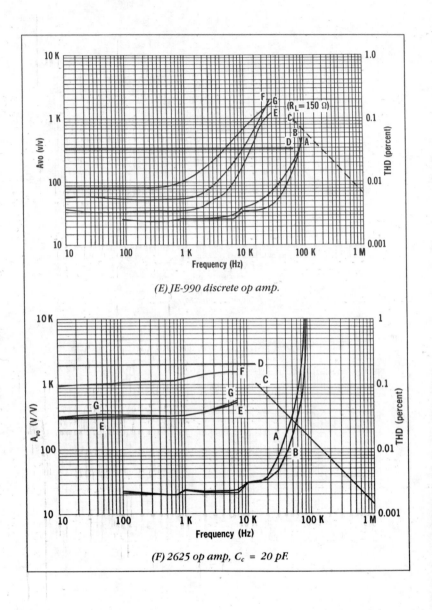

(E) JE-990 discrete op amp.

(F) 2625 op amp, C_c = 20 pF.

Fig. 2-15. (cont.) Total harmonic

IC Op-Amp Parameters Important in Audio Applications

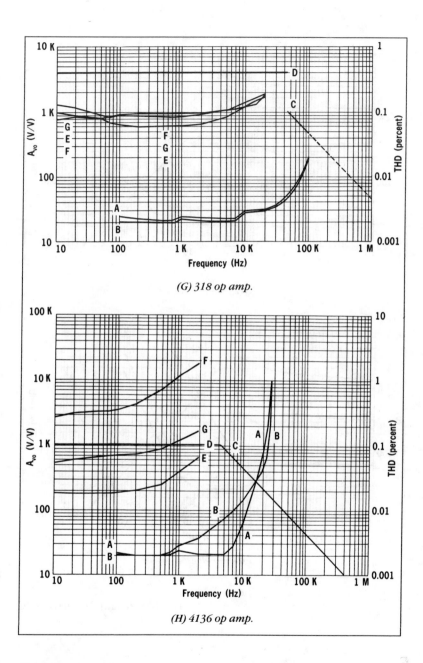

(G) 318 op amp.

(H) 4136 op amp.

distortion test series.

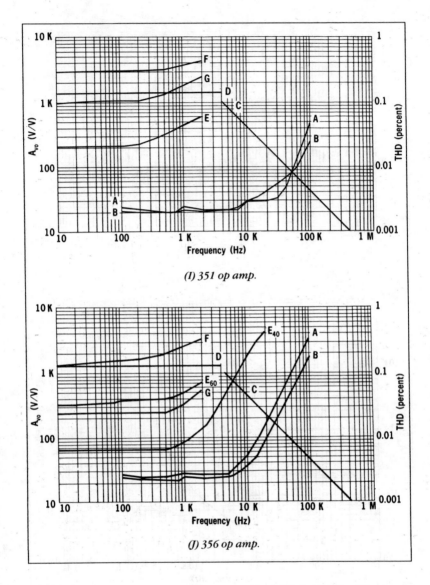

(I) 351 op amp.

(J) 356 op amp.

Fig. 2-15. (cont.) Total harmonic

IC Op-Amp Parameters Important in Audio Applications

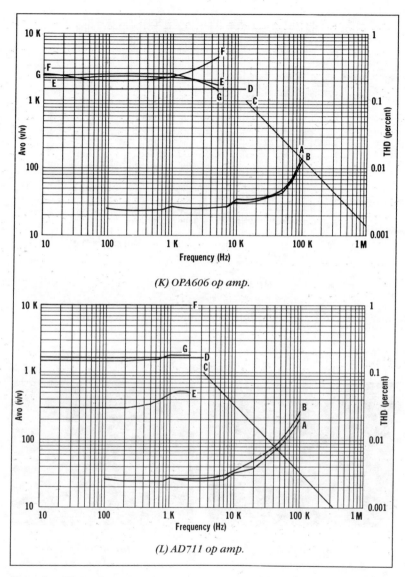

(K) OPA606 op amp.

(L) AD711 op amp.

distortion test series.

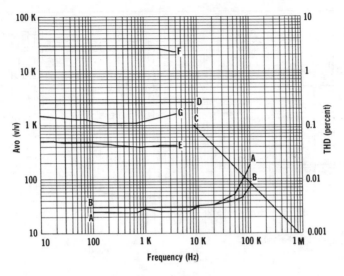

(M) MC34080 series op amp.

Fig. 2-15. (cont.) Total harmonic distortion test series.

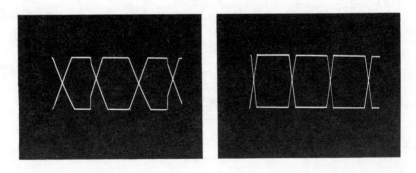

(A) Nonuniform,
also asymmetric slewing, 741.

(B) Uniform,
also symmetric slewing, 4136.

**Fig. 2-16. Slew characteristics between (+) and (–) input
modes—double exposure.**

IC Op-Amp Parameters Important in Audio Applications

2-14A, and the frequency sweep is repeated. For this condition, two possible new nonlinearities may be exposed. One is a general input-stage common-mode nonlinearity, which is evident here starting at 200 Hz, and rising 6-dB per octave. This nonlinearity is a result of a poor input-stage common-mode rejection ratio (CMRR), and it typically produces second-harmonic distortion products. It is present to at least some degree in almost every IC op amp, and is well controlled in only the best. Test F will further quantify this type of distortion.

It can be noted that there is a slight difference in full-power frequency response between the A and B curves, with curve B here at a lower frequency. This is brought about by the fact that the op amp has a different slew rate for the inverting connection than the noninverting one; as a result, full-power frequency response will also differ. Again, it is stressed that this is not uncommon, particularly in the 741, 301A, and similar units.

It is helpful to appreciate what different types of distortion will generate in terms of distortion products. Often, the *character* of the distortion products is a helpful clue to pinpointing the mechanism that is the source of the trouble. The distortion output of the analyzer can be used for this purpose, and the distortion products displayed on a dual-trace scope along with the output signal of the unit under test.

Fig. 2-17 shows two examples of slew-induced distortion produced by the 741 unit being tested. In Fig. 2-17A, the total harmonic distortion is about 3%, and the linear slopes of the sine wave are readily visible. Note the distortion products are third harmonic, and the slew limiting is fairly symmetrical. The amplifier here is past its slew-limit frequency. In Fig. 2-17B, the condition is test B, which, as noted, produces asymmetric slewing (which is noticeable) and also asymmetric distortion products. Note that full-power frequency response is lower here.

Fig. 2-18 shows a more typical slew-induced distortion photograph taken with a symmetrical slew rate, and a total harmonic distortion equal to 1%. Note that evidence of slew limiting is subtle with regard to the sine wave; the linear slopes are just discernible.

Fig. 2-19 shows low-level slew-induced distortion for the same device, taken at a lower frequency, where total harmonic distortion is 0.02%. Note that there is no visible indication whatsoever from the sine wave. With a symmetric slew characteristic (as here), the distortion products will be predominantly third harmonic.

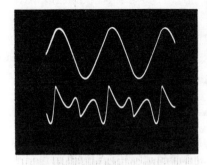

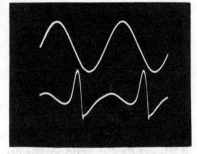

(A) Gross slew-induced distortion;
test A: f = 11.8 kHz, THD = 3%.

(B) Asymmetric slew-induced distortion;
test B: f = 9.5 kHz, THD = 1%.

Fig. 2-17. The 741 slew-induced distortion.

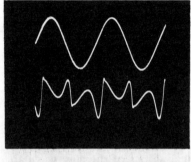

Fig. 2-18. The 4136 high-level slew-induced distortion; test A: f = 18.4 kHz, THD = 1%.

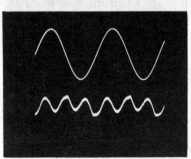

Fig. 2-19. The 4136 low-level slew-induced distortion; test A: f = 10 kHz, THD = 0.02%.

It should be noted that total harmonic distortion curves A and B (Fig. 2-15), which are taken at rated output (7 V), may represent overly pessimistic data if a device is to be used at low levels. They can, of course, be repeated at low levels, as appropriate to an intended application. This general comment can be extended to many

IC Op-Amp Parameters Important in Audio Applications

of these tests; they are basically intended to show worst-case data and can often be improved for more specific cases.

To measure the small-signal bandwidth of an op amp, test C (Fig. 2-14B) connects the unit under test in a 60-dB gain configuration and sweeps the input drive up in frequency until the output drops 3 dB below a 1-V reference level. This frequency, when multiplied times the gain factor ($\times$ 1000), represents the gain-bandwidth product (GBP) of the device. Here, a frequency of 1 kHz was measured for the 741 op amp, which extrapolates to the 1-MHz gain-bandwidth product of the device. A 6-dB-per-octave curve (C) is drawn downward from this point (Fig. 2-15A), and represents the open-loop gain characteristic of the device. The gain at any frequency can be read on the left scale. The 3-dB point (and gain-bandwidth product) can, of course, be varied in externally compensated types, and this technique can measure the resulting bandwidth improvement.

Curve D is a noise floor curve (in reality) and represents the residual noise level of the device with no input, referred to 1 V. When combined with the bandwidth measured in test C, this noise reading can be extrapolated to the input noise level of the device in $nV/\sqrt{Hz}$, or noise in a 20-kHz bandwidth. This is discussed further in the next section. To emphasize the fact that the noise level is as measured in the bandwidth C, curve D is extended to the 3-dB point (1 kHz here). The distortion products should be checked visually to verify the presence of a "noise only" condition in this test. Note that objectionable noise products, such as popcorn noise or l/f noise, can be readily spotted in this display. A white-noise spectrum will appear as shown in Fig. 2-20 (even with an input signal in most cases; as the distortion will usually be below the noise level for this test).

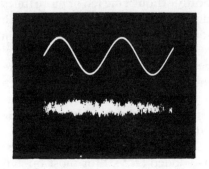

Fig. 2-20. The 741 noise-limited THD; test D: f = 100 Hz, THD (noise) = 0.07%.

Curve E (Fig. 2-14B) is taken with the amplifier driven in an inverting 60-dB gain configuration, with rated output level. Since the bandwidth of the device is drastically reduced (usually) at 60-dB gain, a 100-Hz reference frequency is appropriate for level set. Total harmonic distortion is then measured, from 10 Hz up to a frequency that is one half that measured in test C. Harmonic attenuation by the bandwidth rolloff will make higher-frequency total harmonic readings inaccurate.

This test measures the basic voltage-transfer linearity of the op amp, without consideration of loading or common-mode voltage. For the higher-quality devices, actual distortion for this condition will be less than 0.1% and it will usually disappear into the noise level for lower output voltages. An ideally behaving device would have comparably low distortion and noise, such that this test would barely differentiate between actual distortion and noise, with the composite near 0.01%. Although the 741 device used here is reasonably low in distortion for test E, it is desired that this type of characteristic be available up to 10 kHz (or more). Only linear wide-bandwidth devices can provide this level of performance. Typical output and distortion products for this test are shown in Fig. 2-21A, using a 741 for the device under test.

Test F is also performed at a 60-dB gain level, but with full-rated common-mode voltage applied in a noninverting hookup (Fig. 2-14C). This test fully stresses the input stage for common-mode nonlinearity and amplifies the distortion by 60 dB. Although this test cannot be directly compared to most noninverting amplifiers (which will see much smaller than full-rated input voltage), it still is useful for relative comparison of devices. This performance area is, as stated previously, a most common weak point of IC op amps, with the distortion being ten or more times worse for test F than test E. As can be noted here, this 741 has a noninverting total harmonic distortion of 2% at 500 Hz, while the inverting mode produces only 0.04%. Distortion products for this test are shown in Fig. 2-21B, and, as can be noted, it is (typically) second harmonic. Clearly, this is one op-amp performance area which bears close scrutiny as to device characteristics. Also, it should be appreciated by the reader that, wherever possible, inverting amplifiers should be considered if the ultimate in linearity is an objective.

Test G (Fig. 2-14D) is similar to test E, but with a standard output load added (2.2 kΩ for most op amps). This may not seem like a stringent test, but it exposes a commonly weak area of IC perform-

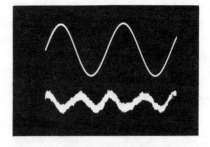

(A) Voltage transfer; test E:
f = 100 Hz, THD = 0.02%.

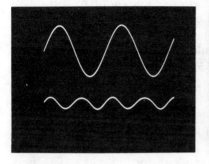

(B) Input CM; test F: f = 100 Hz,
THD = 0.5%.

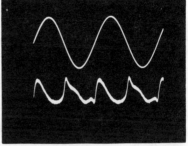

(C) Output; test G: f = 100 Hz,
THD = 0.1%.

Fig. 2-21. 741 nonlinearity.

ance. It is not uncommon to see a three to five times increase in total harmonic distortion for this condition, and only the best devices will show negligible increases in total harmonic distortion for this test. The 741 device of this example is an average performer in this regard. Note that thermal effects can often be seen as increased low-frequency total harmonic distortion in this test, as is noted in this case. The distortion products typically produced with output non-linearity are shown in Fig. 2-21C. As can be noted, they are sharper in waveshape, indicating higher-order harmonics. This type of distortion is more objectionable, and often shows up as crossover distortion, even at low gains.

The remaining performance data of the various IC op-amp devices illustrate various patterns of behavior, both good ones and those that show specific examples of problem areas.

The performance of the 5534 op amp is plotted in Fig. 2-15B, and is highly exceptional in almost every regard. The A and B slew-induced distortion tests show a pattern of total harmonic distortion that is essentially the residual of the equipment, except at the very highest frequencies. Note that the B-test distortion level, as the frequency approaches 100 kHz, is lower than that of the A test, as it should be, due to greater feedback.

The bandwidth of the 5534 device is exceptionally wide, and as the C curve indicates, the gain-bandwidth product is 27 MHz. Note that this is greater than the unity-gain frequency of the device, which is 10 MHz, due to the "bump" in the open-loop rolloff (see Fig. 2-3A). Also note the fact that a device does *not* have a constant 6-dB/octave rolloff, as indicated by a *dashed* C curve, here above 100 kHz where the transition from a 27- to 10-MHz gain-bandwidth product occurs. The reader should also note that an even greater bandwidth is possible with the 5534 device, by reducing the value of C_c.

The very low distortion characteristics of the 5534 op amp are illustrated by curves E and G; as curve G implies, the very low impedance of the output stage of the 5534 allows this to be achieved independent of loading.

There is appreciable common-mode distortion in the 5534 amp, as indicated by curve F. Below 2 kHz, however, it is still better than most amplifiers, and even the fraction of a percent observed at 10 kHz will be strongly reduced by the higher-than-typical feedback factors possible with the 5534 device, due to its unusually high-gain bandwidth product.

The OP-27 and OP-37 devices are illustrated in Figs. 2-15C and 2-15D, respectively. These two units are similar to one another, except that one is unity-gain compensated (the OP-27) and the other is compensated for a gain of 5 (the OP-37). They have a noise performance that is better than the 5534, but with less output drive.

Tests A and B for the OP-27 show its lower SR (vis-a-vis the 5534), while test A for the OP-37 excells due to the device's exceptionally high GBP and high SR. Tests E, F, and G show low distortion at low frequencies, but increasing with frequency, and with some loading effect (test G). Neither device has the load-drive capability of the 5534 op amp.

Where wholesale improvements in both load drive and input-noise voltage are sought, discrete op-amp circuits, such as the JE-

990,[*] can be used. The THD test under discussion can also be used with such modular amplifiers, with the results shown in Fig. 2-15E. In general, the performance of this circuit is superior to most IC op amps, in most categories. This, however, is not without price (in terms of volume and cost). The JE-990 circuit can be useful at the limits of performance where present IC op amps fall short. It is unity-gain stable, and can operated from supplies of ± 24 V.

The 2625 op amp, whose curves are illustrated in Fig. 2-15F, is another exceptionally good performer with regard to audio applications. An interesting pattern can be noted in the slew-induced distortion data of this device. Curve B indicates a slightly higher slew rate, as evidenced by a slightly higher full-power frequency response. As the full-power frequency response of the device (approximately 90 kHz) is approached, the B curve shows 6 dB less total harmonic distortion at a given frequency, as the feedback theory would predict. At lower frequencies, these curves are at near residual level.

The single most-outstanding characteristics of the 2625 amplifier is its exceptionally high linearity and the ability to maintain this linearity in the presence of a load. The E and G curves reflect this, being virtually identical. Curve F indicates the presence of some common-mode distortion, but of a moderate degree. The gain-bandwidth product of the 2625 op amp is 14 MHz for this condition of unity-gain compensation (C_c = 20 pF). The gain-bandwidth product of this device can be extended appreciably, by reducing the value of C_c.

Fig. 2-15G illustrates the performance of a 318 op amp, which is exceptional in a number of regards. As can be noted, the slew-induced distortion of this device is virtually nonexistent due to the high slew rate and bandwidth. Curves A and B are essentially at the test equipment residual, all the way to 100 kHz. The gain-bandwidth product (also exceptional, being 46 MHz at audio frequencies) reduces above 100 kHz, as noted.

Perhaps the most-significant unique characteristic of the 318 amplifier is the fact that it shows little or no change in total harmonic distortion between the inverting and noninverting modes, or with loading. Tests E, F, and G are very close in performance and are, in fact, largely dominated by noise rather than actual distortion.

---

[*]See Reference 20 at the end of the chapter.

The preceding factors make the 318 op amp a good choice when lowest distortion is the prime criterion and lowest noise is a secondary requisite.

The 4136 op amp, shown in Fig. 2-15H, is interesting in a number of ways, as it illustrates several different forms of distortion. In regard to curves A and B, it can be noted that the distortion that predominates actually varies according to frequency. Curve B shows that common-mode distortion, as is indicated by a 6-dB/octave rise between 1 kHz and 15 kHz, is appreciable in this amplifier. Note that curve A shows *less* distortion in this range, even with 6 dB less feedback! Above 15 kHz, the dominant nonlinearity is slew-induced distortion and, here, the greater feedback of the curve-B condition is effective. Note that the slew characteristic of this amplifier is uniform between test conditions A and B, as they merge at a single frequency.

For the higher-gain tests, the 4136 device shows a reasonable total-harmonic-distortion level in the E test, with some loading effects in test G. Curve F confirms the presence of common-mode nonlinearity that is suggested in test B, as it shows as much as a 20:1 degradation over the inverting case. An amplifier such as this should be applied carefully, with regard to noninverting-mode operation.

The 351 amplifier shown in Fig. 2-15I is another interesting example of different behavior patterns. This device has a high slew rate, and good input-stage distortion characteristics. A trace of common-mode nonlinearity is evident above 10 kHz, but at just detectable levels. The high-frequency performance of this device is nearly as good as the 318 and 5534 units, and, in general, is quite high. At higher gains, the input common-mode nonlinearity also shows up, as the difference between curves E and F. Some output stage loading is also evident. Overall, however, this is still a good-to-excellent op amp, depending upon which single performance parameter is most important. The 351 op amp represents one of the better second-generation FET-input op amps, and its characteristics may also be found in the 353 and 347 units, and, also, the TL070 and TL080 device series, as well as others, such as the 771–774 series. To some extent, the type of performance shown here is also generally evident in other second-generation JFET devices, but individual performances will, of course, vary from one design to another.

The 356 op amp shown in Fig. 2-15J illustrates a pattern of behavior that is nonideal in terms of audio performance. For this device, both A and B tests show relatively strong levels of total harmonic distortion, which also rise at 12 dB per octave. This distortion is not slew-induced distortion as the device has a high slew rate that is actually comparable to the 351 amp. An internal frequency-dependent asymmetry causes a second-order nonlinearity that shows up as second-harmonic distortion, beginning below 10 kHz. The rise of this distortion with frequency, combined with the normal 6-dB/octave gain rolloff, combines (apparently) to result in the 12-dB/octave rise in total harmonic distortion. Obviously, such a characteristic is not as desirable as the more often seen 6-dB/octave rise in total harmonic distortion (see the 351 data), and this makes it harder to control overall performance.

The fact that the total harmonic distortion is "second harmonic" is evident from the distortion shown Fig. 2-22. The 60-dB-gain condition curves do not reflect the complete picture of this unique and rapid rise in total harmonic distortion, as they are bandwidth limited to frequencies lower than those at which it occurs. For this reason, an additional E-mode test is plotted, for a gain of 40 dB (E40). This curve also shows the 12-dB/octave rise in total harmonic distortion, up to 20 kHz (one half the −3-dB frequency for this condition).

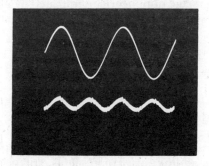

Fig. 2-22. The 356 asymmetric
THD; test A: f = 20 kHz,
THD = 0.015%.

For these reasons, it is recommended that an op amp, such as the 356, be applied with caution to audio signal-path circuitry. Another device of the same family, the 357, is not restrictive in terms of frequency-dependent nonlinearity, as its gain-bandwidth product is five times higher. It is, however, applicable to minimum gains of 5, as opposed to the minimum gain of the unity of the 356. The 357 unit can be an effective performer at gains of 5 to 20.

An interesting amplifier that has recently been developed is the OPA606 device, which uses an FET-input topology similar to the 356 type(s). The OPA606, shown in Fig. 2-15K, does not have the same second-harmonic distortion problem of the 356 amplifier. It also has an appreciably higher SR of 30 V/µs and a GBP of 13 MHz, both desirable for audio circuitry. As can be noted from tests A and B, the distortion is near the residual level, to as high as 100 kHz.

Other recently developed FET-input amplifiers useful for audio applications are the AD711 and the MC34080 series (their curves are shown in Figs. 2-15L and 2-15M, respectively). Both of these devices have an SR of 20 V/µs or more, and they have 4- and 8-MHz bandwidths, respectively.

From an overall point of view, there are several main items that should be apparent from the preceding discussion. One is that while no single op amp is absolutely perfect, many do exhibit excellent performance, and this performance can be tested in a straightforward manner, enabling relative quality comparisons to be made. The different sources of distortion that are seen in op amps can be individually stressed, so as to assess their individual meaning to a given use.

Although most op amps have one or more individual defects, these do not necessarily defeat use of the device. For example, output-stage nonlinearity can be eliminated by buffering, and input stage nonlinearity eliminated by use of the inverting mode. The application examples that follow will stress some examples of these solutions.

2.5 NOISE

Although not specifically stated as one of the primary characteristics of an ideal op amp, it is desirable that noise-free operation be one of its virtues. However, practical amplifiers degrade the input signal by adding noise components. This noise is nearly random in nature and determines the ultimate lower limit of signal-handling capability. It is specified as equivalent input noise and, like the other input-error factors, is increased by the noise gain of the stage. Unlike the other input parameters, however, input noise specification and control is by no means a straightforward process. It involves the interpretation of a number of involved specifications, as well as an understanding of the basic physics of its mechanism, to yield maximum performance. Disregarding the basic rules of noise-performance optimization, however, can result in signal-to-noise ratios that may be short of maximum by an order of magnitude or more.

A circuit model for the discussion of input-referred noise components is shown in Fig. 2-23. Similar to bias current and offset voltage, the noise generators of an amplifier are modeled as a series-voltage noise generator, e_n, and as shunt-current noise generators, i_n+ and i_n-. These generators represent the mean values of voltage and current noise that are referred to the input of the amplifer. They are specified in terms of noise density in volts-squared or amperes-squared per hertz of bandwidth. To these generators must be added two other noise sources—the thermal noise of the source resistances seen by the amplifier, which is R_{eq} and $R_{in} \parallel R_f$.

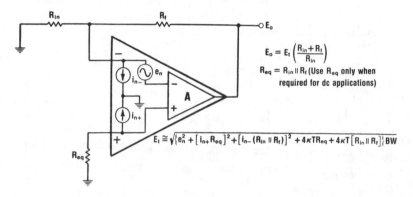

$$E_o = E_t \left(\frac{R_{in} + R_f}{R_{in}} \right)$$

$R_{eq} = R_{in} \parallel R_f$ (Use R_{eq} only when required for dc applications)

$$E_t \cong \sqrt{\left\{ e_n^2 + \left[i_{n+} R_{eq} \right]^2 + \left[i_{n-} (R_{in} \parallel R_f) \right]^2 + 4\kappa T R_{eq} + 4\kappa T \left[R_{in} \parallel R_f \right] \right\} BW}$$

Fig. 2-23. Input-current and voltage-noise errors.

Thus, a real amplifier has five potential sources of noise that have to be considered for minimization. First, there is the thermal noise of (possibly) two source resistances seen by the inputs, which is an irreducible minimum, existing even with an ideal (noiseless) amplifier. For audio applications, where lowest noise is of greater concern than lowest dc offset, a bias-compensation resistor, such as R_{eq}, should *not* be used. This will reduce noise by the simple elimination of an unnecessary noise source. Next, there are the noise-current and noise-voltage generators. For low values of source resistance, the effect of i_n is often at a minimum. Under such conditions, which are usually typical for audio applications, e_n will dominate as the source of amplifier noise. As the source resistance is increased, the effect of i_n becomes larger until, at high source resistances, $i_{n+} R_{eq}$ and $i_{n-} (R_{in} \parallel R_f)$ are the dominant components of amplifier input noise. Thus, in specifications, these two parameters are detailed separately, with e_n specified at a low-source resistance and i_n specified at a high-source resistance. Both e_n and i_n are given in terms of spectral density, measured with a narrow-bandwidth filter at a series of points across the useful spectrum of the amplifier. Data are given either in terms of e_n (or $e_n{}^2$) or i_n (or $i_n{}^2$) versus frequency, with typical graphs as shown in Figs. 2-24A and 2-24B. These particular curves are given in $e_n/\sqrt{Hz}$ and $i_n/\sqrt{Hz}$, but other manufacturers sometimes choose to display the same information in terms of $e_n{}^2/Hz$ and $i_n{}^2/Hz$. Conversion between the two may be accomplished by simply squaring or extracting the square root as appropriate. When comparing such data in graphical form, however, it should be noted that variations in terms of $e_n{}^2$ will appear exaggerated over the same data expressed in terms of e_n. This clearly emphasizes the need for comparison of data on the same basis.

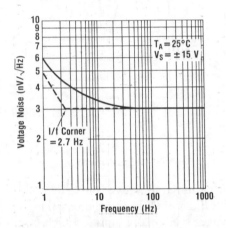

(A) Input-noise voltage density.

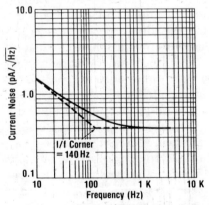

(B) Input-noise current density.

Fig. 2-24. Typical op-amp noise-performance specifications—

Although the spectral densities of both e_n and i_n are obviously not flat in the examples given (nor are they in general), it is not unreasonable to select a mean value for e_n and i_n if their total variation across the frequency range of the amplifier is within the same order of magnitude. An accurate calculation of total rms noise would involve integration across the bandwidth of the amplifier. The simplified approach given here will yield order-of-magnitude estimates of noise performance that are adequate for comparison purposes. Thus, given values of e_n, i_n, and bandwidth, the total noise of the circuit can be approximated as follows:

$$E_t \cong \sqrt{\{e_n^2 + [i_{n+}R_{eq}]^2 + [i_{n-}(R_{in} \parallel R_f)]^2 + 4\kappa T R_{eq} + 4\kappa T[R_{in} \parallel R_f]\}BW} \qquad \text{(Eq. 2-15)}$$

where

E_t is the total circuit noise,
e_n is the amplifier noise voltage in $V/\sqrt{Hz}$,
i_n is the amplifier noise current in $A/\sqrt{Hz}$ (i_{n+} or i_{n-}),
R_{eq} and $R_{in} \parallel R_f$ are the source resistances ($R_{eq} = R_{in} \parallel R_f$),
κ is Boltmann's constant (1.38×10^{-23} J/K),
T is the absolute temperature (in Kelvins),
BW is the noise bandwidth in Hz.

It is obvious from this expression that as e_n and i_n are reduced, the total noise approaches the thermal noise of R_s. A further point is that total noise is proportional to R_s and bandwidth. An illustration of

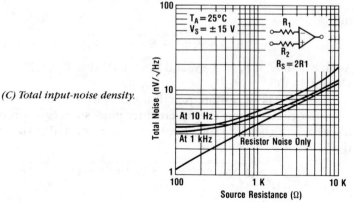

(C) Total input-noise density.

OP-27 amplifier. *(Printed with permission from Precision Monolithic Inc.).*

this is given in Fig. 2-24C, a plot of the wideband noise performance of the same amplifier, with the individual noise components shown in Figs. 2-24A and B. Such a plot is typically given for IC amplifiers and may, in fact, be adequate information for comparative evaluation.

In choosing an amplifier, the requirements will often dictate a certain source resistance from which the amplifier must work. This will dictate which noise generator is dominant and, therefore, which specification must be minimized—e_n or i_n. In general, low-input-current amplifiers, such as the FET types or the low-bias-current bipolar types, will have lower current noise, thus tending to be quieter with source impedances above 10,000 ohms. Below 10,000 ohms, the advantage swings to the bipolar types, which have lower voltage noise. In any instance, absolute minimum values of feedback resistance should be used so that R_s is composed largely of generator resistance. This means that the feedback resistances used should be low in relation to the generator resistance. Another consideration is that the noninverting configuration has less noise gain than the inverting configuration for low signal gains; therefore, it offers a distinct advantage in signal-to-noise ratio (at high gains, however, this advantage diminishes).

Equation 2-15 also illustrates (indirectly) another property of noise behavior and calculations. This is the rms addition property of unrelated noise voltages, used to arrive at a total noise voltage.

For instance, if there are two noise voltages whose sum is to be calculated, voltage E_1 and E_2, it is done as follows:

$$E_{total}^2 = E_1^2 + E_2^2 + \ldots E_n^2 \qquad \text{(Eq. 2-16)}$$

or

$$E_{total} = \sqrt{E_1^2 + E_2^2 + \ldots E_n^2} \qquad \text{(Eq. 2-17)}$$

As an example, if $E_1 = 1\ \mu V$, and $E_2 = 1\ \mu V$ also, E_{total} will be 1.414 μV (not 2 μV).

Likewise, taking a more practical example, suppose we had an amplifier circuit where there were three noise sources (expressed in nV/$\sqrt{Hz}$), which were 3 nV/$\sqrt{Hz}$, 1.3 nV/$\sqrt{Hz}$, and 4 nV/$\sqrt{Hz}$, respectively. Their sum would be

$$E_{total} = \sqrt{(3 \times 10^{-9})^2 + (1.3 \times 10^{-9})^2 + (4 \times 10^{-9})^2}$$
$$= 5.2\ nV/\sqrt{Hz}$$

This is a realistic example, as it could represent an OP-27 (noninverting) op amp (3 nV/√Hz), with a 100-ohm-feedback resistance, fed from a 1000-ohm source. The net noise of such a configuration would be 5.2 nV/√Hz. (A 5534 amplifier would yield similar results).

It should be always borne in mind that the total noise of an amplifier working from a given source resistance will therefore be dictated by a number of factors, many of which are under the designer's control. Source resistance or feedback resistor noise can be readily determined by a nomograph, such as shown in Fig. 2-25, where resistance is charted in nV/√Hz (curve A), or noise in a 20-kHz bandwidth (curve B). A chart such as this can be an invaluable reference for low-noise design, in determining the relative weights of the various noise sources.

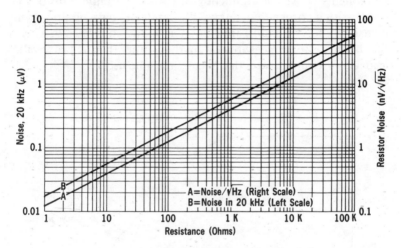

Fig. 2-25. Resistor thermal noise.

To minimize total noise, it should be obvious from Equation 2-15 that as many components within the radical as possible are to be either minimized or eliminated. In a case where it is desirable to characterize the noise performance of a given op amp, the source resistance should be held to an absolute minimum for measurement of e_n, or at a defined value for measurement of i_n. Examples of both will be covered shortly.

In audio work, it is usually e_n that is the more important of the two, inasmuch as source resistances are always held to low values for low-noise amplifiers, and, under such conditions, only e_n will be significant. The noise-characterization procedure presented here measures op-amp e_n, basically, and i_n, optionally.

Noise of an op amp can be measured simply by placing the device in a high-gain configuration, with a defined source resistance, and measuring the output rms noise in a defined bandwidth. Of course, appropriate shielding, screening, and power-supply noise-isolation techniques must be used so as not to contaminate the reading with noise components external to the unit under test.

Two fundamental properties of noise behavior should be appreciated before noise measurements are attempted. First, bandwidth as related to the measurement of noise is not the same as 3-dB bandwidth, for fundamental reasons. Noise bandwidth is measured ideally by an infinitely fast rolloff filter, which rejects all noise components above the frequency of cutoff. A simple 6-dB/octave rolloff with a corner frequency will, of course, pass significant information above its cutoff frequency, as shown in Fig. 2-26. Therefore, if noise is to be measured by anything other than a "brickwall," or ideal noise filter, correction factors must be used.

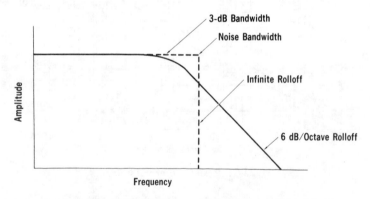

Fig. 2-26. Relationship between noise bandwidth and
3-dB bandwidth.

For a single-pole 6-dB/octave rolloff, the relationship is

$$\text{noise bandwidth} = 1.57\ f_c \qquad \text{(Eq. 2-18)}$$

where
f_c is the 3-dB small-signal bandwidth.

Faster slope filters afford greater accuracy, as they approach the ideal noise-bandwidth filter function.[*]

Another point is that noise should be measured by an *rms responding* voltmeter for best accuracy, because of the crest factor of noise voltages. Typical sine-wave-calibrated average-responding meters will read 1 dB low on noise, compared to a true rms meter. They can still be used, however, if they have adequate bandwidth (10 times measurement or better), and if a correction factor is used. The correction factor is + 1 dB (or 113%). Mathematically, this is expressed as

$$E_{rms\ (corrected)} = 1.13\ E_{reading\ (average)} \qquad \text{(Eq. 2-19)}$$

Crest-factor errors can be miniminizing by avoiding near full-scale readings, which can overload on noise peaks and can cause errors.[†]

The following discussion of op-amp noise is based on measurement of noise in a defined 3-dB bandwidth. When a true rms meter is not available, correction factors should be added for best accuracy of results (when applicable).

A simplified noise-measurement system, as noted in the previous section, can use data from the previously described total-harmonic-distortion test series, by reducing this data to equivalent input noise. This procedure is best explained with typical performance data; such a discussion follows immediately. An alternate (and more general) system, which gives direct reading results, is also described.

2.5.1 Measurement of e_n (Simplified Method)

Both the OP-27/37 and the 5534 devices are low-noise op amps, and their data will be used first for comparison.

From test C (Fig. 2-15C), the 3-dB bandwidth for the OP-27 device, for the 60-dB gain condition, was found to be 5.4 kHz. The noise voltage measured (test D) 0.025 referred to 1 V, or 250 μV. Both of these figures must be corrected before their reduction to equivalent input noise.

---

[*]If a great number of high-accuracy, highly repeatable measurements are to be performed, a committed 20-kHz noise-bandwidth filter should be considered. See Reference 19 at the end of the chapter.
[†]For a thorough discussion of noise-measurement techniques, see Reference 43 at the end of the chapter.

The bandwidth is corrected to noise bandwidth (BW noise) by multiplying by 1.57, which yields

$$BW \text{ Noise} = 1.57 \ (5.4 \text{ kHz}) = 8.5 \text{ kHz}$$

The noise voltage is corrected for rms by multiplying by 1.13

$$\text{Noise (rms)} = 1.13 \ (250 \ \mu V) = 280 \ \mu V$$

The 280 μV is noise as referred to the amplifier *output*; to relate it to input, it must be divided by the stage gain of 1000. This yields

$$\text{Noise (rms)} = \frac{280 \ \mu V}{1000} = 0.280 \ \mu V$$

This noise voltage is referred to a noise bandwidth of 8.5 kHz. To reduce it to a nV/$\sqrt{Hz}$ figure, the 0.280-μV input noise must be divided by the square root of the bandwidth. This gives

$$e_n = \frac{0.280 \ \mu V}{\sqrt{8500}} = 3 \text{ nV}/\sqrt{Hz}$$

As can be noted, this figure agrees with the typical noise voltage as given in the data-sheet information of Fig. 2-24. Similarly, the data for the 5534 or the OP-37 can be so analyzed.

The preceding series of steps will most probably seem tedious and cumbersome of taken sequentially. They can be combined in a simple equation, which will give e_n as a result.

$$e_n = \frac{1.13\% \text{ noise from ``D''}}{100,000\sqrt{1.57} \text{ (bandwidth from ``C'')}} \qquad \text{(Eq. 2-20)}$$

With this, only the noise in percent (referred to 1 V) and the 3-dB bandwidth from step D are needed. (Note that if a true rms responding meter is used, the 1.13 correction factor becomes 1.)

As an example, the "C" and "D" measurements of the OPA606 FET-input op amp (Fig. 2-15K) are 13.5 kHz and 0.15%, respectively. Substitution in Equation 2-20 yields an e_n of 11.6 nV/$\sqrt{Hz}$ for this device (which compares well with the data sheet). The very lowest noise voltage of all the amplifiers is achieved by the JE-990, and is in the vicinity of 1 nv/$\sqrt{Hz}$.

The just described method for measurement of e_n is a simplified one, and its main attractiveness is that it can be accomplished with the same basic test setup as the total-harmonic-distortion test series.

While it produces reasonably accurate results for e_n, it is not suitable for i_n measurements, because of bandwidth limitations. The following method is recomended as generally more useful for both e_n and i_n measurement, and uses a test circuit expressly designed for the purpose for the purpose of noise measurement.

2.5.2 Measurement of e_n (General Method)

A more general circuit that is optimized in terms of convenience and greater accuracy is the noise test circuit of Fig. 2-27. This circuit measures both e_n and i_n, and provides a direct voltmeter reading of e_n in $V/\sqrt{Hz}$.

As can be seen, this circuit is different from the previous one in that it uses a two-stage amplifier and an *external* noise-bandwidth defining filter. The external filter fixes the measurement noise bandwidth, simplifying measurement and data reduction. The two-stage amplifier operates the unit under test in a wideband gain-of-11 mode, allowing accurate definition of the noise bandwidth by the post filter-amplifier stage.

It will be noted that the overall gain of this circuit is 58.05 dB, and that it has a 20-kHz noise bandwidth. The seemingly odd gain is for the purpose of direct calibration of the voltmeter used, in $V/\sqrt{Hz}$.

The voltage noise output of this circuit will be of the same general form as Equation 2-20, and is rewritten here as

$$e_n = \frac{1.13 \ (\% \ \text{noise})}{(100) \ \text{gain} \ \sqrt{\text{noise bandwidth}}} \qquad \text{(Eq. 2-21)}$$

Note that for this equation, when the bandwidth is 20 kHz and the gain is 799 (or 58.05 dB), the 1.13 constant divides out, which results in a 1% full-scale reading of 100 $nV/\sqrt{Hz}$. This is, of course, very useful, as the various voltmeter percent ranges can be used to read e_n directly, with appropriate scale factors. The scale factors for this circuit, as applicable to a 1-V reference level, are shown in Table 2-3, for an e_n dynamic range of 3 to 300 $nV/\sqrt{Hz}$.

This circuit must be calibrated before use, to ensure an accurate gain of 58.05 dB and a 12.7-kHz 3-dB bandwidth (20-kHz noise bandwidth). The simplest way to do this is to trim the 1-kHz gain against a reference attenuator of 799/1 (such as the 7980 and 10-ohm resistors) to provide an overall input-output gain of unity.

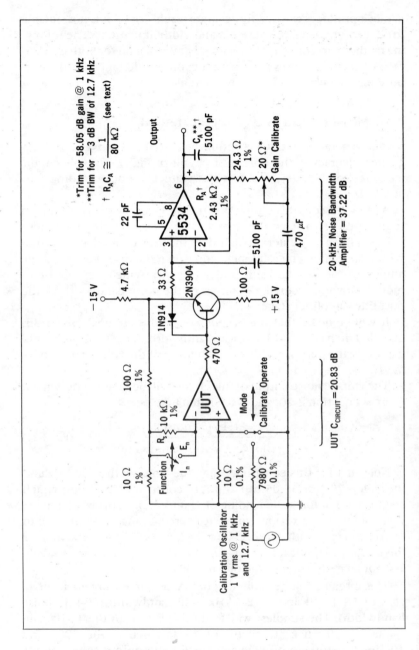

Fig. 2-27. Test circuit for measurement of e_n and i_n.

IC Op-Amp Parameters Important in Audio Applications

Table 2-3. Voltmeter Calibration in V/√Hz

dB/Volts Scale		Equivalent Full Scale nV/√Hz[*]
%	dB	
3.0	−30	300
1.0	−40	100
0.3	−50	30
0.1	−60	10
0.03	−70	3

[*]Assumes 12.7 kHz 3-dB bandwidth, 58.05-dB gain referred to 1-V rms = 100% (or 0 dB).

After gain calibration, the capacitance, C_A, is trimmed to provide a 3-dB bandwidth of 12.7 kHz. The circuit is then ready for use.

Measurement of e_n is quite simple; insert the unit under test into the fixture, apply power, and adjust the voltmeter scale for a usable reading. The circuitry will be accurate to op-amp UUT e_n levels of about 3 nV/√Hz; below this, the 9.09-Ω equivalent feedback source resistance begins to introduce error. (The 10 Ω and 100 Ω UUT feedback resistance can be reduced, in principle. This is not necessarily justified until 1-nV/√Hz IC op amps need testing!)

2.5.3 Measurement of i_n

With the same circuit, i_n is measured by inserting a known value of source resistance in the input of the unit under test. Here a 10-kΩ value resistor is used. This value must be excessively high ($\gg$ 100 kΩ) or it will limit the unit-under-test bandwidth and yield a lower than actual i_n, or the circuit may oscillate. Also, the value must not be too low or it will obscure i_n, due to the fact that as R_s is lowered, the noise output approaches e_n. The 10-kΩ value used here is a median one that gives good accuracy and also simplifies data reduction. Very-low-bias-current amplifiers will require higher resistances—up to 100 kΩ (or more).

Since it is impossible to isolate, i_n cannot be measured directly, as can e_n. It can be measured indirectly, however, and it is such a procedure that is now used here. When an amplifier is operated in such a circuit as used here, there will be three input-referred noise components. These are e_n (as just measured), the thermal noise of R_s, and the noise voltage across R_s due to i_n, i_nR_s. From these three components, the voltage due to i_n must be isolated, and then i_n can be calculated by dividing by the value of R_s.

The total input-noise voltage, E_t, can be expressed as

$$E_t = \sqrt{E_1^2 + E_2^2 + E_3^2} \qquad \text{(Eq. 2-22)}$$

where

E_1 is e_n,
E_2 is the thermal noise of R_s,
E_3 is $i_n R_s$.

E_1 has already been measured and E_2 can be calculated from the relationship

$$E_2 = \sqrt{1.656 \times 10^{-20} R_s} \qquad \text{(Eq. 2-23)}$$

or you can use the nomograph (in Fig. 2-25). The voltage desired is E_3, and E_t is the voltage measured from the i_n test (in $V/\sqrt{Hz}$).

To isolate E_3, Equation 2-22 can be rewritten as

$$E_3 = \sqrt{E_t^2 - (E_1^2 + E_2^2)} \qquad \text{(Eq. 2-24)}$$

Since

$$E_3 = i_n R_s$$

then

$$i_n = \frac{\sqrt{E_t^2 - E_1^2 - E_2^2}}{R_s} \qquad \text{(Eq. 2-25)}$$

As an example of the i_n measurement technique, a 5534 op amp measured an E_t voltage of 15 $nV/\sqrt{Hz}$ for the i_n test, and it had previously measured 3.35 $nV/\sqrt{Hz}$ in the e_n test. The calculation of i_n proceeds as follows:

$$E_1 = 3.35 \times 10^{-9}$$

$$E_2^2 = 1.656 \times 10^{-16}$$

$$E_t = 15 \times 10^{-9}$$

Substituting into Equation 2-25

$$i_n = \frac{\sqrt{(15 \times 10^{-9})^2 - (3.5 \times 10^{-9})^2 - (1.656 \times 10^{-16})}}{10^4}$$

$$= 0.7 \ pA/\sqrt{Hz}$$

This result, as can be noted, is higher than the data-sheet values typical for i_n, which is 0.4 pA/$\sqrt{\text{Hz}}$. This is not necessarily an atypical result, from two standpoints. One of these is the general trend of i_n, which shows a stronger low-frequency rise in noise than e_n. The factor which is probably most predominant, however, is an inverse correlation of i_n and e_n, as is peculiar to the 5534 op amp. In this device, e_n is an inverse function of emitter current (and, thus, base current, also), while i_n will be a direct function of emitter current (and base current). The result is that device samples which show very low e_n levels will tend to have higher i_n levels (such as is the case here). Conversely, higher values of e_n will tend to reflect lower i_n values. The general trend of this behavior pattern should also be theoretically true for other bipolar op amps, but it does not surface as readily since very few other devices approach the level of performance evident in the 5534 amplifier.

It should appreciated by the reader that for low-noise audio circuits, i_n can often be a specification of academic interest. This is simply because low-noise designs will seek to minimize noise resistance in general, which, in turn, minimizes the significance of i_n. For example, the 5534 unit under discussion would generate an additional noise voltage due to i_nn when working from a 1-kΩ source resistance of

$$
\begin{aligned}
E_{noise} &= i_n \times 1000 \\
&= \left(0.7 \times 10^{-12} \ \frac{A}{\sqrt{\text{Hz}}} \right) (1000) \\
&= 0.7 \times 10^{-9} \ \frac{V}{\sqrt{\text{Hz}}}
\end{aligned}
$$

The 0.7 nV/$\sqrt{\text{Hz}}$ is, of course, insignificant when compared to the 3.35-nV/$\sqrt{\text{Hz}}$ noise of the 5534, and the 4-nV/$\sqrt{\text{Hz}}$ noise of a 1-kΩ R_s.

The relative importance of i_n becomes increasingly significant as source resistance becomes larger. The curves of Fig. 2-24C illustrate this, in principle. As is discussed later on, it can also be used in conjunction with e_n to calculate an optimum source resistance which will result in the lowest additional noise, beyond that of the source resistance itself. When noise must be minimized, with source resistances appreciably higher than (about) 10 kΩ, FET-input amplifiers may be more effective.

There is one major weakness for these procedures; this is the fact that e_n and i_n are seldom *uniform* over a frequency spectrum, and these simple tests do not allow for this—they simply give an "average" e_n or i_n for the measured bandwidth. The most-common form of noise pattern that can invalidate this form of measurement is severe 1/f, or other low-frequency noise. However, such cases can usually be spotted from the "distortion components" scope display, and from erratic voltmeter behavior.

An important basic point that should be appreciated from the preceding is that a noise measurement by itself is usually meaningless, unless the bandwidth is accounted for. Only when the bandwidths of two different measurements are *equal* can noise data be directly compared. For, example, the 4136 op amp (Fig. 2-15H) and 351 op amp (Fig. 2-15I) have equal bandwidths; therefore, the lower "D" level measurement of the 4136 can be justifiably interpreted to mean a lower e_n. In this case, the e_n of the 4136 unit is 14 nV/$\sqrt{Hz}$, and for the 351, it is 19 nV/$\sqrt{Hz}$. These figures are reasonable when compared to the data-sheet values, but somewhat high due to the 1/f noise of the two devices. Typically, data-sheet noise specifications are given at 1 kHz, which is almost always lower than the 10–100-Hz noise. Note that *both* e_n and i_n can exhibit 1/f behavior.

2.6 REFERENCES

1. Allen, P.E. "Slew Induced Distortion in Operational Amplfiers." *IEEE J. Solid State Circuits,* Vol SC-12 #1, February 1977.

2. *Applications Manual for Computing Amplifiers.* Philbrick Researches, Inc., Dedham, MA, 1966, 1984.

3. Baxendall, P.J. "Audio Power Amplifier Design." *Wireless World,* January 1978.

4. Cherry, E. M. "Three Audio Amplifier Dragons." *Monitor-Preceedings of the IREE* (Australia), Vol 37 #12, December 1976.

5. Daughtery, D. G. "Design Considerations for Linear Transistor Audio Power Amplifiers." Ph.D. dissertation, University of Wisconsin, 1964.

6. _____, and Greiner, R. A. "Some Design Objectives for Audio Power Amplifiers" *IEEE Transactions on Audio and Electroacoustics,* Vol. AU-14 #1, March 1966.

7. Davis, W. F. and Vyne, R. L. "Design Techniques for Improving the HF Response of a Monolithic JFET Operational Amplifier." *ISSC Journal,* Vol SC-19 #6, December 1984.

8. Dobkin, R. C. "Feedforward Compensation Speeds Op Amp." *National Semiconductor LB-2,* April 1969. National Semiconductor Corp., Santa Clara, CA.

9. _____. "LM118 Op Amp Slews 70 V/μs." *National Semiconductor LB-17,* September 1971, National Semiconductor Corp., Santa Clara, CA.

10. _____. "Op Amp Circuit Collection." *National Semiconductor Application Note AN-31,* February 1970. National Semiconductor Corp., Santa Clara, CA.

11. Erdi, G., Schwartz, T., Bernardi, S., and Jung, W. "Op Amps Tackle Noise—and for Once, Noise Loses." *Electronic Design,* December 12, 1980.

12. Giles, J. N. *Fairchild Semiconductor LIC Handbook.* Fairchild Semiconductor, Mountain View, CA, 1967.

13. Gittleman, R. "Applications of the Audio Operational Amplifier to Studio Use." *Journal of the AES,* Vol. 17 No. 3, June 1969.

14. Greiner, R. A. "Amp Design and Overload." *Audio,* November 1977.

15. Hamm, R. O. "Tubes vs. Transistors—Is There an Audible Difference?" *Journal of the AES,* Vol. 21 #4, May 1973.

16. Hearn, W. E. "Fast Slewing Monolithic Operational Amplifier." *IEEE Journal of Solid State Circuits,* Vol. SC-6 #1, February 1971.

17. Holman, T. "New Factors in Phonograph Preamplifier Design." *Journal of the AES,* Vol. 24 #4, May 1976.

18. Jelsing, T. "Causes and Elimination of TID." *AES preprint #A-5,* AES Zurich Convention, March 1976.

19. Jensen, D. "A 20 kHz Low Pass Filter for Audio Noise Measurements" *Recording Engineer/Producer,* December 1977.

20. _____. "JE-990 Discrete Operational Amplifier." *Journal of the AES,* Volume 28 #1 & 2, January/February 1980.

21. Jung, W. G. *IC Op-Amp Cookbook, Third Edition.* Howard W Sams & Co., Indianapolis, IN, 1986.

22. _____. "IC Op Amps for Audio." Parts I & II, *The Audio Amateur,* issue #2, 1973 Series; issues #1 and #2, 1974 Series.

23. _____. "Improve Op Amp Audio Circuits." *Electronic Design,* September 27, 1973.

24. _____. "Let's Put Function Generators to the Test." *Broadcast Engineering,* December 1975.

25. _____. "New IC Approach to Audio Power." *Broadcast Engineering,* October 1972.

26. _____. "Optimizing IC Amp Speed." *db, The Sound Engineering Magazine,* January 1973.

27. _____. "Slewing Induced Distortion." *Hi Fi News and Record Review,* November 1977.

28. _____. "Slewing Rate Important for Audio Amps?" *Electronic Design,* May 24, 1977.

29. _____. "Slew Rate Tests for Distortion in Audio Circuits." *Broadcast Engineering,* August 1977.

30. _____. "The Pitfalls of the General Purpose IC Operational Amplifier as Applied to Audio Signal Processing." *Journal of the AES,* Vol. 21 No.9, November 1973.

31. _____, Stephens, M. L. and Todd C.C. "Slewing Induced Distortion and Its Effect on Audio Amplifier Performance—With Correlated Measurement/Listening Results." Presented at 57th AES convention, May 1977, preprint #1252.

32. _____, Stephens, M. L. and Todd, C.C. "Slewing Induced Distortion in Audio Amplifiers." 4-part article series, *The Audio Amateur,* February 1977. (Available in reprint.)

33. _____, Stephens, M. L., Todd, C. C. "An Overview of SID and TIM." Parts I through III, *Audio,* June, July, and August, 1979.

34. Kesner, D. A. "Simple Technique for Extending Op Amp Power Bandwidth." *Motorola Application Note AN-459,* May 1971. Motorola Semiconductor Products, Inc., Phoenix, AZ.

35. Leach, W. M. "Build a Low TIM Amplifier." *Audio,* February 1976.

36. _____. "Suppression of Slew Rate and Transient IM Distortions in Audio Power Amplifiers." *Journal of the AES,* Vol. 25 Nos. 7 & 8, July/August 1977.

37. _____. "Transient IM Distortion." *Audio,* February 1975.

38. Leinonen, E., Otala, M., and Curl, J. "Method for Measuring Transient Intermodulation Distortion (TIM)." *Journal of the AES,* Vol. 25 #4, April 1977.

39. Lohstroh, J. and Otala, M. "An Audio Power Amplifier for Ultimate Quality Requirements." *IEEE Transactions on Audio and Electroacoustics,* Vol. AU-21 #6, December 1973.

40. Losmandy, B. J. "Operational Amplifier Applications for Audio Systems." *Journal of the AES,* Vol. 17, No. 1, January 1969.

41. Maxwell, J. "The Low Noise JFET, The Noise Problem Solver." *National Semiconductor AN-151,* September 1975.

42. McClain, E. F. Jr. "Intermodulation Distortion Produced by Out-of-Band Program Components." *Journal of the AES,* Vol. 24 #2, March 1976.

43. Motchenbacker, C. D. and Fitchen, F. C. *Low Noise Electronic Design.* Wiley & Sons, NY, 1973.

44. Naryanan, S. "Transistor Distortion Analysis Using Volterra Series Representation." *Bell System Technical Journal,* Vol. 46, pp. 991-1024, May/June 1967.

45. Nelson, C. "Super-Match Transistor Pair." *National Semiconductor Application Note.*

46. Otala, M. "Circuit Design Modifications for Minimizing Transient Intermodulation Distortion In Audio Amplifiers." *Journal of the AES,* Vol. 20 #5, June 1972.

47. _____. "Transient Distortion in Transistorized Audio Power Amplifiers." *IEEE Transactions on Audio and Electroacoustics,* Vol. AU-18 #3, September 1970.

48. _____, Ensomaa, R. "Transient Intermodulation Distortion in Commercial Audio Amplifiers." *Journal of the AES,* Vol. 22 #4, May 1974.

49. _____, Leinomen, E. "The Theory of Traansient Intermodulation Distortion." *Monitor-Proceedings IREE,* Vol. 37, March 1976. pp. 53-59.

50. Roberge, J. K. *Operational Amplifiers—Theory and Practice.* Wiley & Sons, NY, 1975.

51. Schmoock, J. C. "An Input Stage Transconductance Reduction Technique for High Slew Rate Op Amps." *IEEE JSSC,* Vol. SC-10 #6, December 1975.

52. Schrock, C. "The Tektronix Cookbook of Standard Audio Tests." *Tektronix Application Note,* February 1975.

53. Sherwin, J. "Noise Specs Confusing?" *National Semiconductor AN-104,* 1975.

54. Solomon, J. E. "The Monolithic Op Amp: A Tutorial Study." *IEEE Journal of Solid State Circuits,* Vol. SC-9 #6, December 1974.

55. Stout, D. F. and Kaufman, M. *Handbook of Operational Amplifier Circuit Design.* McGraw Hill, NY, 1976.

56. Stuart, J. R. "An Approach to Audio Amplifier Design." Parts 1, 2, & 3, *Wireless World,* August, September, & October 1973.

57. Sundqvist, B. "Transient Intermodulation in Amplifiers. *Wireless World,* Vol. 83, No. 1494, pp. 37-39. February 1977.

58. Thomsen, C. and Moller, H. "Swept Electroacoustic Measurements of Harmonic Distortion, Difference-Frequency and Intermodulation Distortion." *AES preprint #1068,* Fall Convention, 1975.

59. Tobey, G. E., Graeme, J. G., and Huelsman, L. P. (Ed). *Operational Amplifiers—Design and Applications*. Burr-Brown Research Corp., McGraw-Hill Book Co., NY, 1971.

60. Tremaine, H. M. *The Audio Cyclopedia*. Second Edition, Howard W. Sams & Co., Indianpolis, IN, 1969.

61. Vander Kooi, M. K. "Predicting Op Amp Slew Rate Limited Response." *National Semicondutor LB-19,* August 1972, National Semiconductor Corp., Santa Clara, CA.

62. Widlar, R. J. "Monolithic Operational Amplifiers—The Universal Linear Component." *National Semiconductor Application Note AN-4,* April 1968, National Semiconductor Corp., Santa Clara, CA.

63. Manufacturer's Data Sheets:

Analog Devices	{ AD711 (712)	Operational Amplifiers
Burr-Brown	OPA606	Operational Amplifier
Motorola Semiconductor Products Inc.	{ MC34080 (series)	Operational Amplifiers
Precision Monolithics	{ OP-27, OP-37	Operational Amplifiers
Signetics	NE5534	Operational Amplifer

THREE

The Basic Op-Amp Configurations Translated to Audio Applications

Audio-frequency voltage amplifiers fall into two general categories: (1) low-gain amplifiers, such as inverters, followers, buffers, summers, difference amplifiers, etc., and (2) high-gain amplifiers, such as preamps, booster amplifiers, line amplifiers, etc. The approach taken in this discussion is to first illustrate the basic op-amp configurations translated to audio performance (and also for single power-supply operation), and then illustrate the different options available in more-specialized and/or higher-performance circuitry.

3.1 THE INVERTING AMPLIFIER

The inverting amplifier applied to audio use is shown in Fig. 3-1. The basic inverter is shown in Fig. 3-1A and can be recognized as being similar to the standard dc inverter but with C_1 added in series with R_1. This makes the stage responsive to ac input signals at frequencies where $X_{C_1} < R_1$. The lower cutoff frequency is determined by C_1 and R_1 as

$$f_c = \frac{1}{2\pi R_1 C_1} \qquad \text{(Eq. 3-1)}$$

This is simply the frequency at which $X_{C_1} = R_1$. In the example shown, this frequency is 1.59 Hz. The inclusion of C_1 makes the dc gain of the stage unity, since $R_1 = \infty$ at dc. Gain within the normal passband is simply $-R_2/R_1$. The stage does not amplify offset or low-frequency noise, because of the inclusion of C_1.

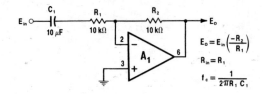

(A) Basic inverter.

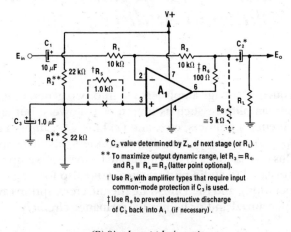

* C_2 value determined by Z_{in} of next stage (or R_L).

** To maximize output dynamic range, let $R_3 = R_4$, and $R_3 \parallel R_4 = R_2$ (latter point optional).

† Use R_5 with amplifier types that require input common-mode protection if C_3 is used.

‡ Use R_6 to prevent destructive discharge of C_2 back into A_1 (if necessary).

(B) Single-supply inverter.

Fig. 3-1. The inverting amplifier applied to audio use.

The direct ground on the noninverting input of A_1 biases the output terminal at a dc potential that is very close to zero. There will be a small offset voltage equal to the unamplified input offset voltage of A_1. With typical input offset voltages less than ± 5 mV, the voltage drop due to $I_{bias} R_2$ will become dominant when either R_2 or I_{bias} is high, such as in the case of bipolar op amps. With FET-input devices, the bias current can be neglected, for all practical purposes.

Note that the normal "bias compensation" resistor, which would be used at the ($+$) input, is *not* used, due to its undesirable noise contribution. For higher input impedance(s), R_1 (and R_2) can be raised to 100 kΩ (and C_1 can be reduced), with the use of an FET op amp such as the TL071.

So far, most of the op-amp configurations that have been discussed have utilized symmetrical power supplies of ± 15 V, and this is always assumed when the supply connections are not explicitly shown. In many instances, however, it may be desirable to operate the op amp from a single-supply potential and ground (common). The inverter of Fig. 3-1A is shown in single-supply form in Fig. 3-1B. The feedback and input connections in this circuit are the same as in Fig. 3-1A, and the same relationships apply.

In an op-amp configuration using a single supply, it is desirable to operate the output at one half the supply potential ($1/2$ V+ or $1/2$ V−) for maximum undistorted output. In Fig. 3-1B, divider R_3-R_4 provides a bias that references the noninverting input of A_1 to the $1/2$ V+ potential. Because of C_1, the dc gain of the circuit is unity; therefore, the output of A_1 is automatically biased to $1/2$ V+ for any value of supply voltage. Any noise on the supply line will also be divided by two at the R_3-R_4 junction and will be amplified by the noise gain of A_1. In cases where noise is a problem, an ac bypass capacitor (C_3) can be used (and increased, where noise is a problem).

An output capacitor (C_2) will normally be needed for single-supply operation, since the output is biased at a dc level. The value of C_2 is determined by the desired low-frequency rolloff and the input impedance of the next stage. If electrolytic capacitors are used for C_1, C_2, and C_3, proper polarity must, of course, be observed (as shown). Some op amps, such as the 358 or 324 types, will require an output "pulldown" resistor (R_B). The value can be adjusted for minimum crossover distortion while feeding the load.

Although a positive supply is used in Fig. 3-1B, the circuit could also be operated from a negative supply simply by grounding R_3 and the positive supply terminal of A_1 (pin 7), and then applying a V− potential to R_4 and the negative supply terminal of A_1 (pin 4). Also, the polarity of capacitors C_1, C_2, and C_3 must be reversed when operating the circuit from a negative supply.

The ac inverting configurations of Figs. 3-1A and B can be modified into summing inverters simply by connecting additional input networks (same as R_1-C_1) to the inverting input of A_1. The component values shown in Fig. 3-1 are intended only as general examples; they can be used with virtually any op amp for A_1. However, certain op-amp types (such as the low-bias-current types) will permit a wider latitude of resistance values. FET units, for example, allow R_1 and R_2 to range up into the megohm values, if desired.

3.2 THE NONINVERTING AMPLIFIER

The noninverting amplifier applied to audio use is shown in Fig. 3-2. Fig. 3-2A is the basic inverting stage with ac coupling. Stage gain above the lower cutoff frequency is determined in the same manner as for the standard noninverting stage, which is

$$\frac{E_o}{E_{in}} = \frac{R_1 + R_2}{R_1} \qquad \text{(Eq. 3-2)}$$

There are two low-frequency rolloffs in this stage because of R_1-C_1 and R_3-C_2. The rolloff due to R_1-C_1 acts in a manner identical to the rolloff caused by R_1-C_1 in the inverter of Fig. 3-1, and should be used as the predominant rolloff in order to minimize the low-

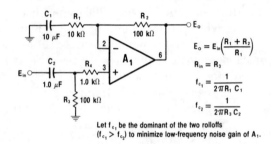

$$E_o = E_{in}\left(\frac{R_1 + R_2}{R_1}\right)$$

$$R_{in} = R_3$$

$$f_{c_1} = \frac{1}{2\pi R_1 C_1}$$

$$f_{c_2} = \frac{1}{2\pi R_3 C_2}$$

Let f_{c_1} be the dominant of the two rolloffs $(f_{c_1} > f_{c_2})$ to minimize low-frequency noise gain of A_1.

(A) Basic noninverting stage.

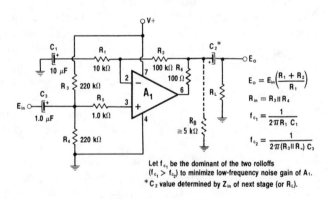

$$E_o = E_{in}\left(\frac{R_1 + R_2}{R_1}\right)$$

$$R_{in} = R_3 \| R_4$$

$$f_{c_1} = \frac{1}{2\pi R_1 C_1}$$

$$f_{c_2} = \frac{1}{2\pi (R_3 \| R_4) C_3}$$

Let f_{c_1} be the dominant of the two rolloffs $(f_{c_1} > f_{c_2})$ to minimize low-frequency noise gain of A_1.
* C_2 value determined by Z_{in} of next stage (or R_L).

(B) Single-supply noninverting stage.

Fig. 3-2. The noninverting

frequency noise gain of A_1. The R_3-C_2 rolloff frequency can be five to ten times lower than the R_1-C_1 rolloff frequency unless it is desired to have the low-end response roll off more rapidly.

The noninverting amplifier in single-supply form is shown in Fig. 3-2B. Resistors R_3 and R_4 bias the noninverting input (and the output) of A_1 to $1/2$ V + (or $1/2$ V–), and the input signal is applied to this junction. As in the single-supply inverter of Fig. 3-1B, proper capacitor polarity must be observed if electrolytic types are used. The optional pulldown resistor (R_B) should be used, if necessary, for lowest distortion.

Operation of this circuit from a negative supply is possible by grounding R_3 and the positive supply terminal of A_1 (pin 7), and, then, applying a V– potential to R_4 and the negative supply terminal of A_1 (pin 4).

Unlike the inverter of Fig. 3-1B, supply-noise decoupling cannot be applied directly to the noninverting input of A_1 in the circuit of Fig. 3-2B because this would bypass the signal as well as the noise. In order to decouple supply noise in the noninverting amplifier, the circuit of Fig. 3-2C should be used. In this circuit, resistor R_5 is

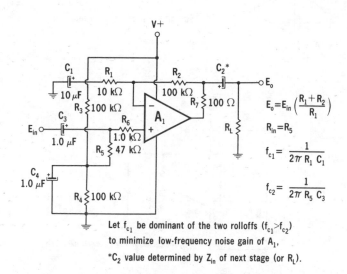

Let f_{c1} be dominant of the two rolloffs (f_{c1}>f_{c2}) to minimize low-frequency noise gain of A_1,

*C_2 value determined by Z_{in} of next stage (or R_L).

(C) Single-supply noninverting stage with noise decoupling.

amplifier applied to audio use.

added to isolate R_3 and R_4 from E_{in}, and the supply noise is bypassed by capacitor C_4 without affecting the input signal.

3.3 THE VOLTAGE FOLLOWER

The voltage follower used for audio applications has some unique considerations of its own; therefore, it is discussed separately in this section and is illustrated in Fig. 3-3. The basic follower, with ac coupling, is shown in Fig. 3-3A. The output of A_1 is dc referenced at zero potential by the ground connection from R_1 and the input signal that is ac coupled through C_1. The low-frequency cutoff is determined by C_1 and R_1. The shunting effect of R_1 lowers the input impedance of the stage, which is in contrast to the dc follower, where the input impedance is extremely high. Thus, the naturally high input impedance of the follower configuration can be compromised with ac coupling unless R_1 is high.

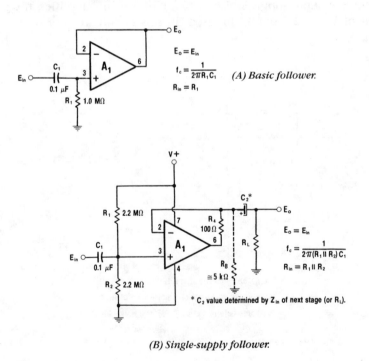

(A) Basic follower.

(B) Single-supply follower.

Fig. 3-3. The voltage follower

If R_1 is made very high (above 1 MΩ, for example), it can create an excessive dc output offset unless A_1 has low input-bias current. The use of low-bias-current op amps, such as one of the FET types, will minimize dc offset due to bias current, and will allow bias resistances up to 10 MΩ. Note that common-mode nonlinearity can be a problem in this circuit with certain amplifier types; therefore, the device used should have low common-mode distortion (see Section 2.4).

A voltage follower converted to single-supply operation is shown in Fig. 3-3B. Resistors R_1 and R_2 bias the noninverting input (and the output of A_1) to ½ V+ (or ½ V−), and the input signal is applied to this junction. This circuit can also be operated from a negative supply by grounding R_1 and the positive supply terminal of A_1 (pin 7), and, then, applying a V− potential to R_2 and the negative supply terminal of A_1 (pin 4). Supply-noise decoupling in the voltage follower is accomplished as shown in Fig. 3-3C.

3.4 THE DIFFERENTIAL AMPLIFIER

A differential amplifier, which is applied to audio use, is shown in Fig. 3-4. The basic differential amplifier is shown in Fig. 3-4A and

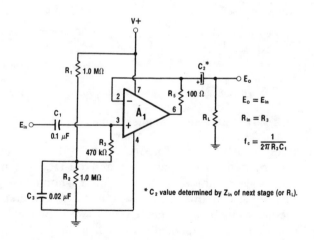

(C) Single-supply follower with noise decoupling.

applied to audio use.

The Basic Op-Amp Configurations Translated to Audio Applications 105

can be recognized as being similar to the standard dc differential amplifier, but with coupling capacitors C_1 and C_2 added in series with the two inputs.

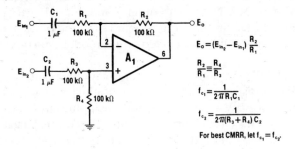

$$E_o = (E_{in_2} - E_{in_1}) \frac{R_2}{R_1}$$

$$\frac{R_2}{R_1} \equiv \frac{R_4}{R_3}$$

$$f_{c_1} = \frac{1}{2\pi R_1 C_1}$$

$$f_{c_2} = \frac{1}{2\pi (R_3 + R_4) C_2}$$

For best CMRR, let $f_{c_1} = f_{c_2}$.

(A) Basic differential amplifier.

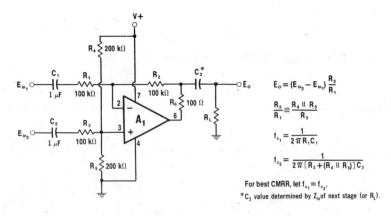

$$E_o = (E_{in_2} - E_{in_1}) \frac{R_2}{R_1}$$

$$\frac{R_2}{R_1} \equiv \frac{R_4 \parallel R_5}{R_3}$$

$$f_{c_1} = \frac{1}{2\pi R_1 C_1}$$

$$f_{c_2} = \frac{1}{2\pi [R_3 + (R_4 \parallel R_5)] C_2}$$

For best CMRR, let $f_{c_1} = f_{c_2}$.
*C_3 value determined by Z_{in} of next stage (or R_L).

(B) Single-supply differential amplifier.

Fig. 3-4. The differential amplifier applied to audio use.

This circuit will have two low-frequency rolloffs, f_{c_1} and f_{c_2}, which are determined by the capacitances and resistances seen at the two inputs. For best common-mode rejection, f_{c_1} should be equal to f_{c_2}. The dc output level of this circuit is automatically centered when R_4 is made equal to R_2. The resistance ratios should be matched, as noted, for best results. In practically, this will be best accomplished via the use of a common ratio-matched array of values for R_1–R_4. Alternately, use fixed resistances for R_1–R_3, and trim R_4 for best CMRR at 100 Hz.

A differential amplifier converted to single-supply operation is shown in Fig. 3-4B. As far as signal considerations are concerned, this circuit is the same as the basic circuit of Fig. 3-4A. Resistors R_4 and R_5 bias the noninverting input (and the output) of A_1 to $1/2$ V+ (or $1/2$ V–). Since these two resistors are of equal value, they also help to preserve the common-mode rejection of the stage.

The basic ac op-amp circuits of Figs. 3-1 through 3-4 are intended primarily to illustrate the configuration differences over the fundamental dc circuits. In essence, the design equations for both the dc and ac circuits are the same except for the differences due to ac coupling and the low-frequency rolloff. The more elaborate audio circuits to follow will in some manner be a variation of the basic ac configurations. Although the component values shown are only intended as examples, they will work well with virtually any op amp if it is properly compensated for the noise gain used.

3.5 MODIFICATIONS OF THE BASIC CONFIGURATIONS

There are many useful variations of the basic configurations that can be implemented as elements of larger-scale circuits. The circuits discussed in this section are designed to perform some specific function in addition to the basic one on which they are based.

3.5.1 Noninverting Stages with Increased Input Impedance

In many circumstances, the bias resistance in shunt with the (+) input of noninverting stages may represent an undesirable load on the source. A technique to increase the effective bias resistance is illustrated in Fig. 3-5.

A circuit that increases the input impedance of a voltage follower is shown in Fig. 3-5A. In this circuit, resistor R_1 is bootstrapped for ac signals by the feedback from the output of A_1 through capacitor C_2. Capacitor C_2 causes the same voltage to appear at both ends of R_1, which drastically lowers the signal current in R_1, thereby effectively increasing the input impedance to many megohms and restoring the high-impedance virtues of the follower configuration.

The same principle applied to a noninverting amplifier is shown in Fig. 3-5B. In this circuit, R_3 is the bias resistance, which is returned to R_1 rather than directly to ground. As far as dc is concerned, this connection has no effect. But for ac signals, the voltage at the

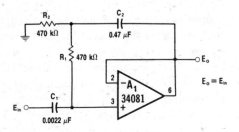

(A) Bootstrapped voltage follower.

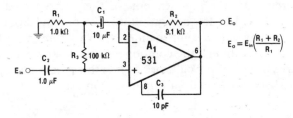

(B) Bootstrapped noninverting amplifier.

Fig. 3-5. High-input-impedance noninverting stages.

junction of R_2, R_3, and C_1 is the same as that at the (–) input (for frequencies where $X_{c_1} \ll R_1$). Thus, for ac, little voltage drop appears across R_3, which effectively raises its value and the input impedance of the stage. A 531 device, compensated for a gain of 10, is used effectively here. Another effective device for this circuit is the FET-input 357. If very low noise is a requirement, the OP-37 can be useful.

3.5.2 Inverting Amplifier with Increased Input Impedance

One of the fundamental disadvantages of the inverting amplifier is its restriction on input impedance, which is the value of the input resistor used. The only way to raise the input impedance (short of buffering, which requires an extra amplifier) is to raise the value of the input resistor. However, this can create problems when the feedback resistor is raised by the same ratio. Feedback resistances in excess of 1 MΩ can cause dc stability problems as well as gain error, due to the shunting effect of the internal input resistance (r_{in}) of the amplifier. In standard configurations, this restricts the use of high feedback resistances to amplifiers having FET inputs, as noted previously.

These problems are solved in the inverting amplifier circuit of Fig. 3-6, which provides a 1-MΩ input impedance while using a 301A general-purpose op amp. The value of feedback resistor R_4 is made one tenth that of R_1, or 100 kΩ. This attenuates E_{in} by a ratio of 10:1 at the junction of R_2 and R_3. However, the output divider of R_4 and R_3 in parallel with R_2 make up the loss and restores the gain to unity, since E_o will be 10 times the voltage at the R_2-R_3 junction.

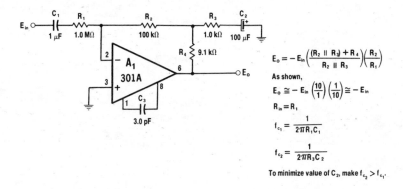

$$E_o = -E_{in}\left(\frac{(R_2 \parallel R_3) + R_4}{R_2 \parallel R_3}\right)\left(\frac{R_2}{R_1}\right)$$

As shown,

$$E_o \cong -E_{in}\left(\frac{10}{1}\right)\left(\frac{1}{10}\right) \cong -E_{in}$$

$$R_{in} = R_1$$

$$f_{c_1} = \frac{1}{2\pi R_1 C_1}$$

$$f_{c_2} = \frac{1}{2\pi R_3 C_2}$$

To minimize value of C_2, make $f_{c_2} > f_{c_1}$.

Fig. 3-6. High-input-impedance inverting amplifier

In this circuit, the 301A bipolar op amp operates with a noise gain of 20 dB due to the divider in the feedback loop. Therefore, a 3-pF compensation capacitor is used to optimize the high-frequency loop gain. If desired, gain can be increased by changing either the R_3-R_4 divider or R_2. Another effective device for this circuit is the 344 (usable at high voltages), the TL080, or the 34080. (The latter two devices are FET-input types.)

This circuit has two low-frequency rolloffs: f_{c_1} due to R_1-C_1 and f_{c_2} due to R_3-C_2. From the standpoint of component economy, the dominant rolloff should be f_{c_2}. This minimizes the value of capacitor C_2.

3.6 REFERENCES

1. Jung, W.C. "An IC Op Amp Update." *Ham Radio,* March 1978.

2. _____. *IC Op-Amp Cookbook, Third Edition.* Howard W. Sams & Co., Indianapolis, IN, 1986.

3. _____. "IC Op Amps for Audio, Parts I and II." *The Audio Amateur,* issues 2/75, 1/74, and 2/74.

4. _____. "Improve Op Amp Audio Circuits." *Electronic Design,* September 27, 1973.

FOUR

Practical Audio Circuits
Using IC Op Amps

In this chapter, we will discuss a variety of practical audio circuits in which specific IC op-amp types are utilized. These circuits include standard voltage amplifiers with optimized frequency and gain performance; power amplifiers; and microphone, phono, and tape preamplifiers.

4.1 STANDARD AUDIO-FREQUENCY VOLTAGE AMPLIFIERS

The operation of IC op-amp audio voltage amplifiers, which have stage gains of from 0 dB to 60 dB in both the inverting and noninverting configurations, will be considered in this section. With reference to the discussions on gain-bandwidth product and slewing rate in Chapter 2, the circuits presented here will be performance optimized for these parameters. The reader can choose a configuration, select feedback and compensation values from simple, easy-to-read charts, and then use these amplifiers as "gain blocks" in larger systems. Although specific amplifier types are recommended, the charts can be applied to any IC type, provided the compensation is adjusted accordingly.

4.1.1 Low-Noise Voltage Amplifiers

A circuit for noninverting audio voltage amplifiers, using the 5534, OP-27, and OP-37 low-noise op amps, is shown in Fig. 4-1. It will be noted that this circuit is both general and specific. Components such as C_1, R_1, and R_2 are general devices and apply to any amplifier used in these applications. Gains from 0 dB to 60 dB are set up by selecting these components from the tabulated values given in the chart in Fig. 4-1. In this chart, C_1 varies as a function of stage gain to keep the low-frequency cutoff point constant. The C_1 values shown are for a low-frequency rolloff of 1.59 Hz (to prevent cumulative rolloffs with cascaded stages),[*] but the reader can, of course, choose C_1 for any suitable rolloff. C_2 provides a high-frequency rolloff at 160 kHz.

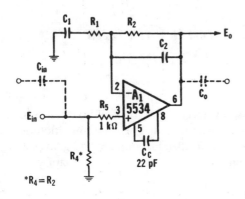

Fig. 4-1. Circuit diagram and tabulated feedback/ compensation values for optimized noninverting audio voltage amplifiers using the 5534 op amp.

Stage Gain (dB)	Feedback †			Compensation †
	C_1	R_1	R_2	C_2
0	0	∞	0	0
20	100 μF	1 kΩ	9 kΩ	100 pF
40	1000 μF	100 Ω	9.9 kΩ	100 pF
60	1000 μF	100 Ω	9.99 kΩ	10 pF

†See text for detailed discussion of component values.

For optimum performance, values for the gain-determining resistors, R_1 and R_2, should be as close as possible to the tabulated values. These are precise theoretical values for operating gains of from 0 dB to 60 dB in 20-dB steps. For gains intermediate to those listed, R_1 and R_2 can be determined using the appropriate gain equation consistent with the ranges given in the chart. A 30-dB inverting amplifier, for

---

[*]This general rationale is carried through in the discussion of other circuits, as they are always used in conjunction with other circuits, which *also* have rolloffs.

Practical Audio Circuits Using IC Op Amps

example, would require an R_1 value lower than the 20-dB value of 1 kΩ by a factor of 3.16, or 316 Ω. For best stability and accuracy, close-tolerance metal-film resistors should be used for R_1 and R_2. In less critical applications, the closest 5% carbon-resistor type can be used (but with proportionately reduced performance with regard to accuracy, stability, and noise).

A 5534 amplifier can be used for all the gains listed and will provide the greatest output for low-impedance loads. The OP-27 and OP-37 amplifier types can also be used, for specific gain levels. The OP-27 is useful at low gains, and the OP-37 at higher gains (to take advantage of its greater bandwidth).

Input/output coupling capacitors, C_{in} and C_o, may or may not be needed, dependent upon the interfacing required. It is preferable that these be film-type units, such as polypropylene, if they are used. C_1 will necessarily be an electrolytic type, because of the large electrical size required for a long time constant (with R_1 being a low value, for low noise). C_2 should, preferably, be a polystyrene type.

All of the amplifiers shown here are excellent devices from an all-around standpoint, having very low noise and the ability to drive output loads to levels of more than ± 10 V. If the 5534 amplifier is used, loads down to 600 ohm can be driven.

A potential undesirable side effect of the increased bandwidth and high-frequency gain of such amplifiers is that they are more susceptible to oscillation. In order to minimize this potential problem, good high-frequency construction techniques, such as those used in video circuitry, should be employed. These include the use of good-quality local rf-bypass capacitors on power-supply leads, short and direct signal paths, low-inductance ground paths, and a minimum of capacitive loading. If these considerations are observed, excellent high-frequency performance can be attained with these devices.

For a great many higher-level, moderate-gain applications, low offset and high input impedance may be the primary selection criteria. The circuit of Fig. 4-2 shows how low-offset, high-speed, FET-input op amps can be used in a simple high-performance non-inverting stage.

In this circuit, any of the FET amplifiers listed will have over a 20-V/μs slew rate and a very wide bandwidth. Input current will be 50 pA (or less), allowing direct connection to virtually any source (i.e., volume controls, etc.). Noise will not be as low overall as it is with the bipolar amps, but it is lowest with the OPA606 unit. Offset will be no more than 11-mV (with a 1-mV offset device). As shown,

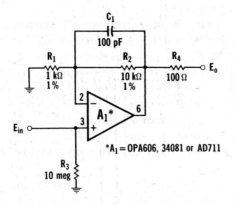

Fig. 4-2. A high-performance
noninverting circuit.

$*A_1 = OPA606, 34081$ or AD711

the bandwidth will be 160 kHz, as established by $C_1 \cdot R_2$. R_4 provides
load isolation for driving the capacitance of long cables.

4.2 SERVO-CONTROLLED STAGES

With multiple stages of audio-frequency gain, the accumulation of
DC offsets of the various amplifiers can lead to problems. The classi-
cal solution to decoupling the offset of stage(s) has been to employ
coupling capacitors, at the input or output (or both). Typically, this
has been the employment of large value electrolytic capacitors (100
to 1000 μF) when operating into low impedances.

Modern low-bias-current, low-offset-voltage, op amps allow for
the simple elimination of coupling capacitors in many instances. For
example, the use of very-low-bias-current, low-offset-voltage, FET-
input amplifiers in the circuit of Fig. 4-2 will not generally require
capacitive coupling. This is one approach to the elimination of
coupling capacitors, which, of course, simplifies this circuit. A more
general approach which has come into vogue in recent years[*] is the
use of a *servo amplifier* stage, for output DC-offset elimination.
Two examples of servo circuits, for noninverting and inverting
stages, are shown in Fig. 4-3.

4.2.1 Noninverting Servo Amplifier

The circuit of Fig. 4-3A is a basic noninverting audio voltage-
amplifier gain stage (A_1), with a noninverting integrator feedback

---

[*]See Reference 16 at the end of the chapter.

Practical Audio Circuits Using IC Op Amps

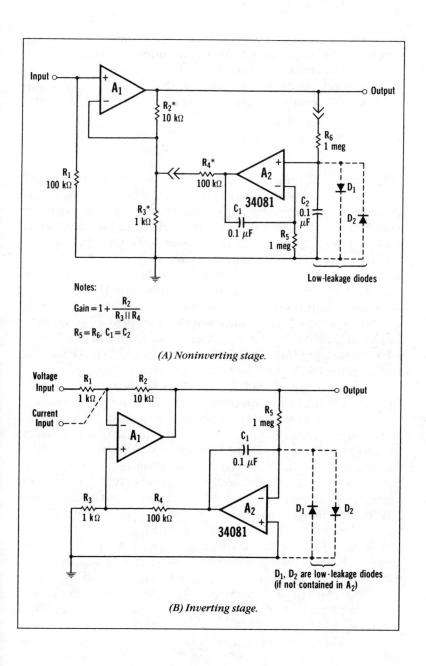

(A) Noninverting stage.

Notes:

$$\text{Gain} = 1 + \frac{R_2}{R_3 \| R_4}$$

$R_5 = R_6,\ C_1 = C_2$

(B) Inverting stage.

Fig. 4-3. Servo-corrected stages.

stage connected around it (A_2). For normal audio-range input signals, the gain of this stage is defined conventionally—that is, it is the ratio of the feedback resistance (R_2) to the resistance from the (–) input to ground, plus 1. In this instance, the resistance to ground is made up of the parallel equivalent resistances of R_3 and R_4; basically,

$$\text{Gain} = 1 + \frac{R_2}{R_3 \parallel R_4}$$

R_5-C_1 and R_6-C_2 form the integration time constants, which are set equal in this form of integrator. The DC feedback from stage A_2 is applied to the (–) input of A_1, via R_4. By virtue of the integrator stages' infinite DC gain, the overall loop will force the output of A_1 to a very low DC level. In practice, the residual DC output offset of A_1 becomes essentially the offset voltage of A_2.

The DC feedback resistor, R_4, is chosen to be several times higher than R_2, while the integrator time constant sets the basic low-frequency rolloff point. In this example, the rolloff is set at about 0.16 Hz. Low-leakage clamping diodes are used across C_2 to prevent a possible latchup. Servo amplifier A_2 should be a low-offset-voltage, low-input-bias-current, FET-input device, such as either the AD711 or the 34081 (or their dual equivalents, for stereo).

The exact circuit around A_1, as well as A_1 itself, can take many forms, which are, in fact, much more complex than in this basic example. The servo loop can still operate as described, however, and, indeed, will even correct offset errors that are due to A_1, as well as any varying DC input level to A_1. For example, this servo technique can be useful as a continuous correction factor for a relatively high-bias-current, high-offset-voltage, bipolar op amp, such as the 318- or 2525-type op amps. Insofar as the details of the circuit design are observed, care should be taken to ensure that the worst-case offset to be corrected is within the range of the values assigned for R_2-R_4, as well as the supply voltages used for A_1 and A_2. High-quality components, such as low-leakage film capacitors with a high-quality dielectric, should be used in the integrator (such as polypropylene capacitors, along with metal-film resistors). Since these components represent high-impedance, lead lengths should be minimized around A_2, and the assembled circuit should be carefully cleaned of any flux residue (which could introduce leakages, or other spurious behavior). The outside foils of C_1 and C_2 should be connected to AC ground. The clamping diodes can be other types with low-leakage characteristics (≤ 100 pA). If LEDs are used as shown, they should be shielded from light (to prevent photocurrents).

As noted for AC-gain calculations, the servo input resistor, R_4, appears in parallel with R_3. This lowers the effective value of R_3 as noted in Fig. 4-3. In this example, the gain error is 1%, for the values shown (vis-à-vis R_3 considered alone).

4.2.2 Inverting Servo Amplifier

An inverting type of servo amplifier is shown in Fig. 4-3B; it uses the more familiar form of inverting integrator for feedback. In this circuit, A_1 is a basic inverting gain stage, with a gain of R_2/R_1. The DC feedback from the A_2 integrator stage is applied to A_1 through the divider, R_4-R_3. With the time-constant values shown and the scaling of R_4-R_3, the circuit of Fig. 4-3B has a low frequency cutoff of 0.16 Hz.

Input clamp diodes which are low-leakage types are recommended for this circuit, along with the use of quality film components for R_5 and C_1, as before. Again, the range of R_4, with regard to R_2, should be about ten times as large (with R_1 and R_3 equal), and the supply voltage used for A_1-A_2 should be sufficient enough to accommodate the worst DC offset of A_1 that can be expected.

This circuit will also work with a wide range of inverting stages which are more complex than that shown. Note that, in principle, a noninverting integrator could also be used, with DC feedback to the R_1-R_2 junction. The inverting integrator is more simple overall, however, and it eliminates one RC network. Note also that a current source can be used as an input (shown dotted), such as a D/A converter.

Examples of some complete servo-connected stages are shown in several of the applications elsewhere in this chapter and throughout the book.

4.3 AUDIO AMPLIFIERS WITH INCREASED POWER OUTPUT

Although IC op amps are extremely useful in audio applications because of their high gain, small size, low cost, and general versatility, most of them are not capable of delivering more than a few milliwatts of power to a load. The standard ± 10-V output swing into the rated 2000-ohm load represents only about 25 mW of power, which is quite modest. Audio applications that require greater power often demand voltages and currents far in excess of what the standard op amp can deliver. For some of these applications, specialized IC types can be used, but, in general, some means of increasing both the output voltage swing and the output current capability is necessary in order to take full advantage of the high-gain properties of IC op amps. In this section, we will examine a number of power applications, ranging from a simple headphone driver to a single-supply speaker amplifier.

4.3.1 Headphone Drivers

The first power application to be examined involves the use of an IC op amp to drive one or more sets of headphones. Virtually any standard op amp can be used to drive a single set of high-impedance (2000 Ω) headphones at a 25-mW level. All that is necessary is to select a suitable configuration and provide the required gain. The IC type can be chosen almost from convenience or personal preference, since most standard types can deliver 25-mW into 2000 Ω.

However, when a number of high-impedance headphones (or a smaller number of low-impedance types) are to be driven, the power requirements exceed the output capabilities of the standard op-amp types. One type of circuit that is suited for this application is a *buffered output* standard IC op amp. Fig. 4-4 illustrates a 300-mW output circuit that is useful as a headphone driver, and capable of driving loads down to 150 ohms at levels up to ± 10 V.

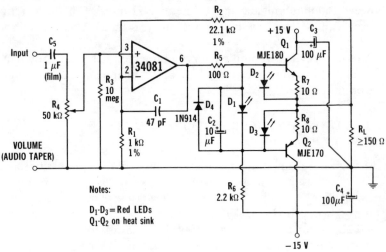

Fig. 4-4. Headphone driver.

The key to this circuit's operation lies in the output-stage biasing by D_1 (a red LED) and emitter resistors R_7-R_8. A quiescent current of about 15 mA is set by the voltage across resistors R_7-R_8. Individual clamp diodes, D_2-D_3, limit the maximum output current to 100 mA in Q_1 and Q_2. Since the output transistors dissipate approximately $1/2$ watt, they should be mounted on a small heat sink.

Because of its class-A output-stage operation at low levels, this circuit is very linear. Maximum gain is 23 times (27 dB), as set by R_1-R_2. Although shown here in the context of a headphone driver, this basic circuit is easily adaptable to many other applications.

4.3.2 Line Amplifiers

A standard audio-signal processing circuit is the *line* or *program-distribution* amplifier. This is typically a noninverting stage with a high input impedance, flat frequency response, voltage gains from 20 to 50 dB, power outputs from + 20 to + 30 dBm (dB referred to 1 mW), and very low distortion and noise characteristics. These requirements are restrictive in terms of standard op-amp performance because the voltage (and current) swings for the power levels quoted are beyond the range of IC power supplies. Therefore, the use of booster techniques becomes necessary in order to satisfy the increased voltage and current demands while maintaining low distortion and noise.

The primary consideration is that of increasing the current output of the op amp to a level that can drive a 600-ohm or 150-ohm load with negligible distortion. Although some op amps with well-designed output stages can come close to delivering a + 20-dBm signal into a 600-ohm load just as they stand, it is generally not good practice to operate them this way; it deteriorates the linearity of the op-amp output stage and also reduces the open-loop gain of the op amp due to the loading. The 5534 device is a notable exception to this general rule and can drive 600-ohm loads directly. The OP-27 and OP-37, while comparable to or better than the 5534 on input noise, cannot drive low-impedance loads nearly as well.

A good general solution is to provide an external current-gain buffer stage, which isolates the load currents from the gain stage, and allows it to operate at maximum gain and deliver its full unloaded output voltage with good linearity. The following circuits illustrate examples of this principle; one key to better sound using IC op amps.

With multiple op amps now commonly available, advantage can

be made of their high performance/price ratio to implement circuits that would not be considered using single-type devices. Fig. 4-5 is an example of this. It employs three sections of a quad FET-input amp, the 774, as an output buffer. The fourth section is used as a conventional 20-dB voltage-gain stage. The paralleled stages are connected as unity-gain followers, with current-summing output resistors to force equal current distribution. This technique increases the already considerable output drive of a single 774 section by a factor of 3, allowing lower impedance loads to be driven. The circuit can drive 150-ohm loads at levels up to 7 volts without clipping, a power level of 326 mW (+ 25 dBm). Distortion remains low, on the order of 0.02% below 10 kHz.

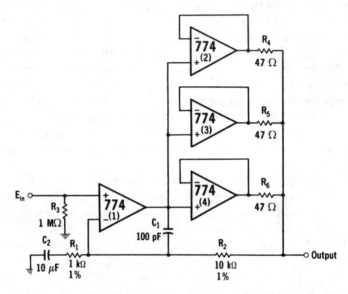

Fig. 4-5. Parallel-stage buffer.

It should be noted that the circuit can be adapted to other gains by adjustment of R_1, or can further increase power by paralleling more sections, connected in a similar fashion. Gain resistors R_1-R_2 are metal-film types for best stability, and C_2 can be varied for the desired low-end rolloff.

Because some FET-input amplifier types have common-mode restrictions on (–) swings (and are, therefore, subject to latch-up), substitution of other quad types in place of the 774 is not recommended here.

"Universal" Line Amplifiers

Another example of how the performance of an op amp can be improved through the addition of an external buffer stage is shown by the general-purpose line amplifier given in Fig. 4-6. This circuit employs a Class-AB output stage, which greatly enhances its output capability while maintaining the high open-loop gain and linearity of the driver op amp.

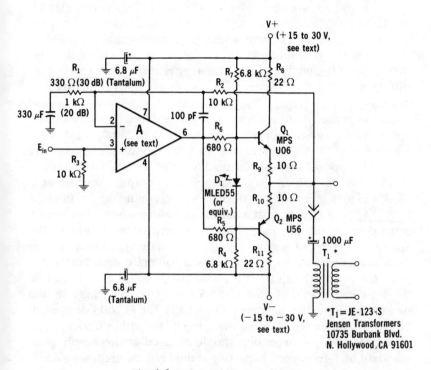

Fig. 4-6. Universal line amplifier.

The circuit is a noninverting stage with 20–30 dB of gain, capable of driving 100- to 600-ohm loads either directly, or optionally through a transformer. Transistors Q_1 and Q_2 form a complementary-symmetry Class-AB emitter follower, which provides a high-current output with minimum loading to the op amp. A floating base bias is provided for Q_1 and Q_2 by LED D_1. Resistors R_4 and R_7 provide a bias current for the LED, which allows the op amp to operate with optimum linearity. Resistors R_5 and R_6 prevent parasitic oscillations in Q_1 and Q_2, while R_8 and R_{11} provide short-circuit protection.

Power output is dependent upon the supply voltage used; with ± 22-V supplies, the circuit can typically deliver 10-V rms into a 100-ohm load (+ 30 dBm) with good linearity. Linearity, particularly high-frequency total harmonic distortion, is strongly dependent upon the slew rate of the device used. For higher voltage operation, such as ± 28 V, high-voltage op amps must be used, such as the 2645- or 344-type units.

For supplies in the range of ± 15 V to ± 22 V, many more standard devices can be used. The highest performer in terms of linearity in this circuit is the 5534 amp, which has a total harmonic distortion of less than 0.02% to 20 kHz, driving 100 ohms. Other devices, such as the 318 and 2625 amps, do not perform quite as well, but, still, they are of good quality. Also usable are the TL080 and 357 devices.

Although the circuit is presented as a "universal" one, it can be optimized for a given supply voltage. Resistors R_7 and R_8 are selected for a 3.3-mA LED bias current, and the values shown are appropriate for ± 22-V operation. Resistor R_1 adjusts the circuit gain, for either 20 or 30 dB, as shown. Note that when an output transformer is used, a coupling capacitor is necessary to decouple the DC offset.

Fig. 4-7 is a circuit with a similar output capability, but with a servo control added. A pair of op amps are used for A_1 and A_2, the amplifier/driver and servo integrator, respectively. Output current drive is achieved here with the use of a 100-mA output buffer, A3. With the use of the LT1010 IC, loads of 75 ohms and up can be driven. For this level of power, the 5-pin (TO-220) package should be used, along with a heat sink. Optionally, the EL2003 device can be used, at somewhat lower power levels. For either device, however, heavy supply bypassing should be used at the supply pins. Standard high-frequency bypassing should also be used, with A_1.

If a transformer is to be used to provide load isolation, it can be driven as shown, with no coupling capacitor necessary. With the use of servo amp A_2, the 1-mV maximum offset for A_2 prevents excessive primary DC in the transformer.

4.3.3 Single-Supply Mobile Radio Speaker Amplifier

Another audio-signal application requiring increased power output is in circuits that are used to drive speaker loads. In such applications, the load currents can reach several amperes, which means that

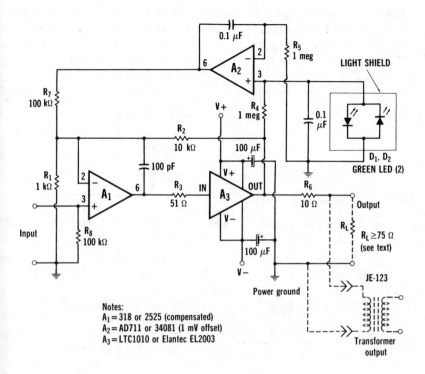

Fig. 4-7. Servo-controlled 1-watt amplifier.

Notes:
A_1 = 318 or 2525 (compensated)
A_2 = AD711 or 34081 (1 mV offset)
A_3 = LTC1010 or Elantec EL2003

multiple stages of current boost are needed between the op amp and the load.

A unique requirement in this class of amplifier is the output stage of mobile radio equipment. The available supply potential is relatively low (12 to 16 V), yet the amplifier must deliver several watts of power into the speaker, with a minimum of circuit complexity, at good efficiency, and at low overall cost.

An interesting solution to these requirements is shown in Fig. 4-8. This is an op-amp-driven, Class-B, output amplifier that can deliver 3.5 watts into a 4-ohm speaker load at 0.25% total harmonic distortion. In this circuit, A_1 is operated as a noninverting voltage amplifier driving the Darlington power transistors Q_1 and Q_2, which are connected in a complementary-symmetry, push-pull, output configuration. The circuit has a very low idle current because Q_1 and Q_2 are biased off under no-signal conditions. Transistors Q_1 and Q_2 are driven by the current flowing in the supply leads of A_1. This current develops a drive voltage across base resistors R_5 and R_6, which are selected to drop a voltage that is less the turn-on V_{BE} of Q_1 and Q_2, with no signal input and with the quiescent supply current of A_1 flowing. This maintains a low overall current consumption.

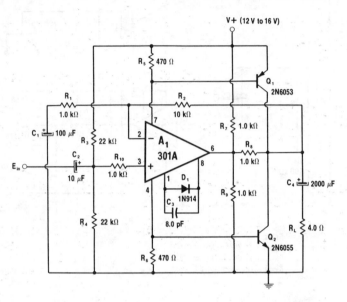

Fig. 4-8. Single-supply mobile radio speaker amplifier.

The penalty for operating Q_1 and Q_2 at zero bias is an increase in crossover distortion at low levels, since A_1 must "pulse-on" Q_1 and Q_2 alternately to form an output sine wave. However, this is not a significant factor except at frequencies above 5 kHz, since the loop gain of A_1 corrects for the crossover distortion.

The circuit can be viewed as a two-stage amplifier, with the bulk of the voltage gain supplied by the 301A first stage. The second stage, which consists of output transistors Q_1 and Q_2, has a voltage gain of approximately 3, determined by

$$\frac{R_8 + (R_7 \parallel R_9)}{R_7 \parallel R_9}$$

This is actually local feedback around Q_1-Q_2 and the output stage of the op amp. The purpose of this feedback is to scale the voltage swing, seen by the load, upward from that at the op-amp output.

Practical Audio Circuits Using IC Op Amps

With the values given, the load-voltage swing will be three times the output swing of the op amp. This allows power transistors Q_1 and Q_2 to be driven into saturation, developing nearly the full supply voltage across the load, or 3.5 W into 4 ohms with a 14-V supply.

Substitution of other op-amp types for A_1 in this circuit should be done with care. The circuit requires an op amp that has high gain at low supply voltages, which is a design feature of the 301A family. Furthermore, the op amp's supply current should be low and independent of temperature and supply-voltage variations, since this current directly affects the bias of Q_1 and Q_2. These factors are also features of the type-301A design. Finally, A_1 should be an externally compensated type, since the optimization of high-frequency loop gain in this circuit is important in minimizing crossover distortion.

Two circuit components, which are provided for safety reasons, are resistor R_{10}, which protects the input of A_1 against the discharge of C_2, and diode D_1, an antisaturation clamp which prevents possible latch-up.

4.4 AUDIO PREAMPLIFIERS

Audio preamplifiers represent the low-level end of the dynamic range of practical audio circuits using IC op amps. In general, amplifying stages that accept input signals at levels of 10 mV or less will fall into this category. In this section, we will discuss the three basic types of audio preamps: (1) microphone, (2) tape, and (3) phono.

When working signals reach a level of 1 mV, the input noise generated by the first amplifying stage in the system becomes an important consideration if a wide dynamic range and a good signal-to-noise ratio are to be preserved. For example, if the internally generated noise voltage of the input stage is 1 μV, and the input signal voltage is 1 mV, the best signal-to-noise ratio that can be expected is 60 dB. In a given application, it is usually the input voltage level that is fixed; thus, for best signal-to-noise ratio, the input noise generated by the first amplifying stage must be minimized. Minimizing the input noise of an amplifier requires an understanding of the factors that contribute to the total noise, including both the amplifier itself and the external circuit in which it is used, as previously discussed.

4.4.1 Microphone Preamplifiers

The microphone preamplifier (mic preamp) is one of the basic low-level amplification requirements. The mic preamps can have a variety of forms, considering the wide range of possible signal levels and microphone impedances. Both of these factors influence the optimum circuit for a particular application.

Single-Ended, High-Impedance, Mic Preamp

The simplest form of mic preamp is shown in Fig. 4-9. This is a non-inverting stage with a single-ended input for high-impedance microphones. It has a gain of 40 dB and, in concept, could use any op amp. The exact device used, however, can greatly affect the performance. In terms of bandwidth and loop gain, the op amp used should be a high gain-bandwidth-product type, with compensation optimized for the gain used. In terms of noise performance, the device should have as low an input noise as possible, with the circuit values adjusted so that the source impedance (mic impedance) is the dominating percentage of the overall source resistance.

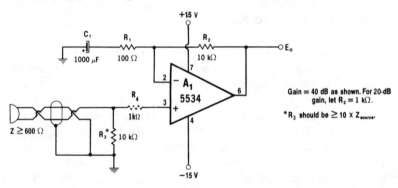

Fig. 4-9. High-impedance microphone preamplifier.

The 5534 amp is very good choice for this circuit from both a bandwidth and a noise-performance standpoint, because its high gain-bandwidth product allows high loop gain at 20 kHz and it has the lowest input noise. The OP-37 will do nearly as well, and the OP-27 works well at low gains. Other types that will also work satisfactorily in this circuit (with their appropriate compensation) are the 4625 and 4605 devices. Lower performance (but yet reasonable) can be realized with the HA4741 or the 4136 amplifiers.

In the circuit of Fig. 4-9, gain-determining resistors R_1 and R_2 are scaled such that the total resistance of $R_1 \parallel R_2$ is less than the lowest expected source impedance, which in this case is 600 ohms. This minimizes the contribution of $R_1 \parallel R_2$ to input noise. Although microphones having impedances of less than 600 ohms can be used with this circuit, noise performance will not be optimum. Succeeding circuits will illustrate alternate methods of optimizing noise performance for low-impedance microphones.

The gain of this circuit can be adjusted over a range of 20 to 40 dB by resistor R_2. Control of microphone signal level should preferably be exercised after it has undergone a stage of gain, such as in the feedback loop with R_2. Attenuation of the signal level before amplification (such as with resistive pads) should never be done, because it compromises the signal-to-noise ratio.

The circuit of Fig. 4-9 is a good one if modest performance and simplicity are required. For a bandwidth of 20 kHz with a 600-ohm source, the circuit can be expected to have an equivalent input noise of approximately 700-nV rms, when using the 5534, the OP-27, or the OP-37 op amps. Resistor R_4 can be used (with the 5534), for cases of instability, with some noise sacrifice.

Differential-Input, Low-Impedance, Mic Preamps

One problem with using unbalanced microphone lines is noise pickup due to common-mode signals coupled into the cable. The circuit of Fig. 4-10 can minimize such induced noise by cancelling it with a differential-input configuration. This circuit works best when used with low-impedance sources, such as 150-ohm (or lower) microphones.

The 5534 is also a good choice for this circuit, not only because of its wide bandwidth and good noise performance, but also because of its high ac common-mode rejection ratio. The ultimate input noise of this circuit will not be quite as low as in the circuit of Fig. 4-9, however, because R_1 and R_2 must be made higher in value. The main advantage of this circuit lies in terms of common-mode noise rejection. The degree of common-mode rejection realized is proportional to the matching of resistor ratios, as indicated in Fig. 4-10. If 0.1% resistors are used, the common-mode rejection ratio can be 100 dB; with 1% resistors, the common-mode rejection ratio can be 80 dB. To optimize common-mode noise rejection when 1% resistors are used, R_4 can be trimmed with a 10-kΩ potentiometer, as shown. An alternate (very attractive and practical) technique is to employ a matched thin-film array for the four bridge resistors. Re-

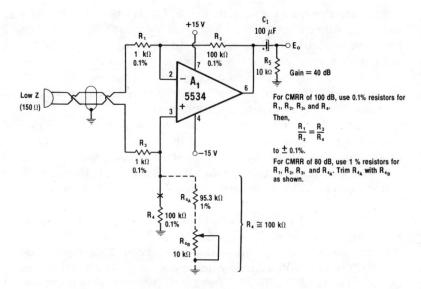

Fig. 4-10. Differential-input, low-impedance, microphone preamplifier (40-dB gain).

sistors that are ratio-matched to 0.1% (or better) are available in single arrays.

The circuit of Fig. 4-11 is similar to the basic stage of Fig. 4-10, but adds DC servo control and an AC common-mode rejection trim. The bridge resistors, R_1–R_4, should be matched generally as noted for Fig. 4-10. In this case, they provide a gain of 20 dB.

For best rejection of high-frequency CM noise, the AC balance of the bridge should be precise. Here, this is provided by similar-value capacitors, C_1 and C_2, with C_2 being variable.

A_1 can be either a 5534 amp, as shown, and (optionally) an OP-27; both provide very low noise. The output offset of this circuit will be 1 mV or less with an 34081 amp for A_2.

Transformer-Input, Low-Impedance, Mic Preamps

The best noise performance for any op amp is attained when the source resistance (R_s) is equal to the characteristic noise resistance (R_n) of the amplifier. Examples of a preamp type that takes advantage of this factor, utilizing a matching transformer (T_1), are shown in Fig. 4-12. In order to select an optimum turns ratio to match a given source resistance (R_s) to the characteristic noise resistance (R_n) of the

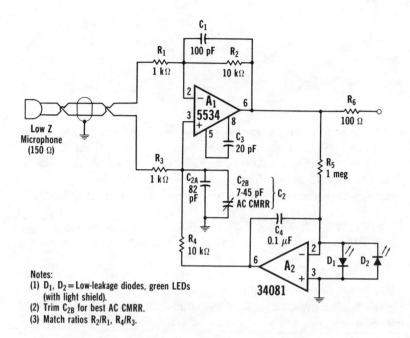

Notes:
(1) D_1, D_2 = Low-leakage diodes, green LEDs (with light shield).
(2) Trim C_{2B} for best AC CMRR.
(3) Match ratios R_2/R_1, R_4/R_3.

Fig. 4-11. Servo-stabilized microphone preamps (20-dB gain).

op amp used, R_n must first be calculated from the specified data for e_n and i_n as follows:

$$R_n = \frac{e_n}{i_n} \qquad \text{(Eq. 4-1)}$$

where
   e_n is in $V/\sqrt{Hz}$,
   i_n is in $A/\sqrt{Hz}$.

Then, the turns ratio for T_1 may be calculated as

$$\frac{N_s}{N_p} = \sqrt{\frac{R_n}{R_s}}$$

For the 5534 amp, the values of e_n and i_n are 4 nV/$\sqrt{Hz}$ and 0.6 pA/$\sqrt{Hz}$, respectively; thus,

$$R_n = \frac{e_n}{i_n}$$

$$= \frac{4 \times 10^{-9}}{6 \times 10^{-13}}$$

$$= 6.7 \text{ k}\Omega$$

Since both e_n and i_n vary with frequency, R_n will also vary with frequency. Therefore, the value calculated for R_n from data-sheet data (such as above) is most accurate at the frequency for which the data applies. If the amplifier were to be optimized for a specific frequency, then the values for e_n and i_n should be for that frequency.

However, audio amplifiers are wideband circuits, so some compromise is inevitable here. An amplifier minimum-noise-figure plot will allow graphical determination of the optimum source resistance, for least noise.

For this case, an optimum transformer turns ratio can be calculated to provide the optimum R_n to the op amp, working from a given R_s. For example, if R_s is 150 ohms, then the turns ratio for T_1 will be

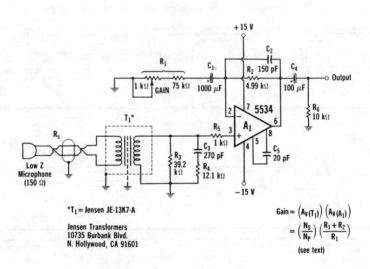

*T_1 = Jensen JE-13K7-A

Jensen Transformers
10735 Burbank Blvd.
N. Hollywood, CA 91601

$$\text{Gain} = \left(A_{V(T_1)}\right)\left(A_{V(A_1)}\right)$$
$$= \left(\frac{N_S}{N_P}\right)\left(\frac{R_1 + R_2}{R_1}\right)$$
(see text)

(A) Conventional AC coupling.

Fig. 4-12. Transformer-input, low-impedance,

Practical Audio Circuits Using IC Op Amps

$$\frac{N_s}{N_p} = \sqrt{\frac{R_n}{R_s}}$$

(Eq. 4-2)

for the 5534,

$$\frac{N_s}{N_p} = \sqrt{\frac{6.7 \times 10^3}{1.5 \times 10^2}} = \frac{6.7}{1}$$

The OP-27 or OP-37 devices can also be applied using this rating with little error.

Since transformers are catalogued and stocked in fairly narrow and specific impedance ranges, a unit with a secondary impedance of 5 to 15 kΩ will be sought (since the minimum noise impedance is reasonably broad). A suitable unit for this purpose is the Jensen JE-13K7-A. It goes without saying, of course, that T_1 must be adequately shielded and otherwise suitable for operation in low-level environments.

The use of a matching transformer allows the circuit to achieve an equivalent input noise (referred to the transformer input) that is only a few decibels above the theoretical limit, or very close to the thermal noise of the source resistance. For example, the thermal

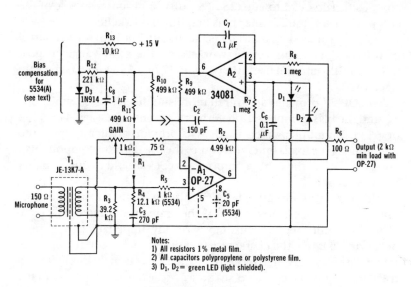

(B) Servo controlled.

microphone preamps (gain = 28 to 50 dB).

noise of a 150-ohm resistor in a 20-kHz bandwidth at room temperature is 219 μV (Fig. 2-25). The circuit will have a noise performance that is less than this ideal due to the noise-degradation factors of the transformer and the op amp.

An additional advantage of the matching transformer is the voltage gain that it provides due to the turns ratio. For a given circuit gain (A_v), this reduces the gain required from the op amp (A) to

$$A = \frac{A_v}{N_s/N_p} \qquad \text{(Eq. 4-3)}$$

Thus, the composite gain is the product of the transformer gain (N_s/N_p) and ($R_1 + R_2$)/R_1. This has the obvious advantage of allowing more loop gain, hence greater accuracy, lower distortion, etc.

In this circuit, the source resistance seen by the op amp is relatively high ($\cong 5$ kΩ); thus, the feedback resistances can be higher than in the previous circuits without deterioration of noise performance. This has the additional benefit of allowing a smaller capacitance value for C_1. The 5534 stage has a variable gain of about 5 to 60 times, which, in combination with the transformer gain, yields a composite gain of 25 to 300 (28 to 50 dB). Transient response of the composite gain (transformer plus amplifier) is excellent.

In Fig. 4-12B, a similar circuit is illustrated, but with servo control of offset added. This circuit works over the same range of gain (28 to 50 dB), and can use either an OP-27 or a 5534 unit as the gain stage (A_1).

The OP-27 provides an overall more simple circuit, in which R_5, C_5, and the bias-compensation network are not necessary. The 5534 or 5534A amplifier, when used, will provide greater output into low-impedance loads (but will require the use of these components). For best results, the other component types should be high-quality devices, as noted.

Although this circuit has been discussed in terms of a low-impedance source (microphone), the transformer-matching technique is applicable to transducers of any impedance. It is only necessary to know the characteristic noise resistance of the op amp. If this data is not given in terms of e_n and i_n, it is usually implicit from the curves of noise figure versus source resistance. The noise figure is at a minimum when $R_n = R_s$; therefore, it is only necessary to verify the source resistance for minimum noise figure, which will be very close to R_n. This value can then be used in the calculations.

4.4.2 Tape Preamplifier

A typical preamplifier application is in a tape-playback system. These circuits often operate at signal levels of 1 mV or less, which places stringent requirements on the amplifier if a good signal-to-noise ratio is to be realized. In addition to high average gain, equalized frequency response is necessary, which raises the total low-frequency gain to as high as 80 dB. Few op amps can provide adequate loop gain with low input noise under these conditions. The 5534 amp has a low-frequency gain of 100 dB and, as has already been discussed, low input noise.

The general response curve required for tape-playback equalization is shown in Fig. 4-13. Gain is at a maximum below 50 Hz (f_1), which is the lower corner frequency that begins the equalized portion of the curve. Above f_1, the response rolls off at 6 dB/octave until it reaches the upper corner frequency somewhere between f_2 and f_3. This frequency will vary according to tape speed, but a range of 1 kHz to 5 kHz covers most of the standard frequencies. Frequency f_2 (1 kHz) is also the gain-reference frequency, and the gain at this frequency may be in the range of 40 to 50 dB. The other frequency of interest is f_o, the low-end rolloff frequency, which is somewhere below 50 Hz. The choice of this frequency is left up to the personal preference of the user.

Rather than attempting to list a number of circuits covering all the possible variations in gain and high-frequency equalization, a uni-

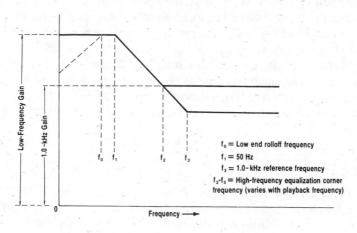

f_o = Low end rolloff frequency
f_1 = 50 Hz
f_2 = 1.0- kHz reference frequency
f_2-f_3 = High-frequency equalization corner frequency (varies with playback frequency)

Fig. 4-13. Tape-playback equalization curve.

versal circuit will be described that will accommodate a range of possible conditions. This circuit is shown in Fig. 4-14; it uses either an OP-37 or a 5534 amp in a low-noise noninverting configuration. The reader may use this circuit as it stands or may substitute fixed resistance values for specific conditions.

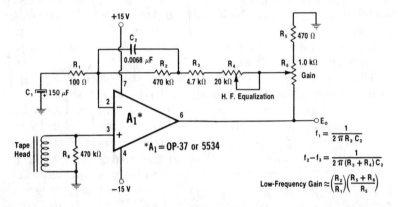

Fig. 4-14. Tape preamplifier.

The gain and equalization characteristics of this circuit are established by the feedback network consisting of R_1 through R_6, and C_1-C_2. The actions of the various components are best appreciated if analyzed individually. The value of resistor R_1 is low in comparison to the source resistance, as described previously. Capacitor C_1 and resistor R_1 set the low-end rolloff frequency, which is 10 Hz for the values shown in Fig. 4-14. The ratio of $R_1 + R_2$ to R_1 determines the gain at low frequencies. In a conventional stage, the gain would be simply $(R_1 + R_2)/R_1$, but, in this circuit, the divider R_5-R_6 adds an additional gain (variable) of 10 dB. The reason that R_6 is used to vary the gain rather than R_1 is that varying R_1 would also vary the low-end rolloff frequency. Resistor R_6 varies the gain without any frequency effects.

The reactance of capacitor C_2 begins reducing the gain from its low-frequency maximum at the frequency where $X_{c_2} = R_2$, or 50 Hz. At frequencies above 50 Hz, the gain rolls off at 6 dB/octave, following the curve of Fig. 4-13. At the frequency where $X_{c_2} = R_3 + R_4$, the high-frequency equalization corner occurs. Resistor R_4 is made variable to allow adjustment of this equalization frequency from 1 kHz to 5 kHz. Above this frequency, the amplifier gain is flat up to the

Practical Audio Circuits Using IC Op Amps

limit of the open-loop bandwidth. Resistor R_6 provides an overall gain adjustment for the circuit, varying the low-frequency gain from 70 dB to 80 dB, and varying the f_2 reference-frequency (1 kHz) gain from 44 dB to 54 dB. Resistor R_4 provides a high-frequency corner adjustment from 1 kHz to 5 kHz, which is sufficient to accommodate most playback curves. It is not recommended that other op amps be substituted for the OP-37 or the 5534 in this circuit, unless they are selected for low noise and distortion, and for high gain. For highest performance, use metal-film resistors and film capacitors.

Although a specific example is not shown here, servo control (for low-output offset) can be added to the tape preamp circuits also, using the general concepts already described.

4.4.3 RIAA Phono Preamplifiers

Another preamplifier application requiring equalized frequency response is the RIAA phono preamp. The RIAA equalization curve is shown in Fig. 4-15. Like the tape equalization curve of Fig. 4-13, this curve also indicates maximum gain below 50 Hz (f_1). Unlike the tape curve, however, the RIAA curve has two high-frequency breakpoints. Above f_1, the gain rolls off at 6 dB/octave until the first high-

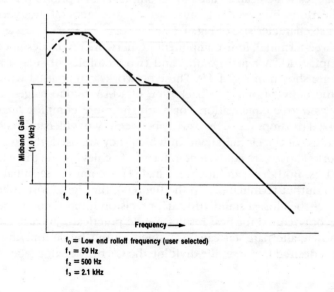

f_0 = Low end rolloff frequency (user selected)
f_1 = 50 Hz
f_2 = 500 Hz
f_3 = 2.1 kHz

Fig. 4-15. RIAA phono-playback equalization curve.

frequency breakpoint is reached at 500 Hz (f_2). The gain then remains constant until the second high-frequency breakpoint is reached at 2.1 kHz (f_3), where it again rolls off at 6 dB/octave through the remainder of the audio region. The low-end rolloff frequency (f_0) is at the option of the designer. It can be extended towards DC, or, alternately, rolled off at a low frequency below 50 Hz. This roll off, when applied, is popularly called a "rumble" filter, and it reduces the turntable-/record-induced low-frequency disturbances and lessens the possibility of system and low-frequency driver overloading.

However, the gain at the basic frequencies of f_1, f_2, and f_3 describe the RIAA curve. This curve can also be described in terms of three corresponding time constants, T_1, T_2, and T_3. These time constants are defined as T_1 = 3180 μs, T_2 = 318 μs, and T_3 = 75 μs.

The characteristic gain of an RIAA preamp is generally specified in terms of the 1-kHz reference frequency. Since the shape of the standard curve is fixed, this also defines the gain for all other frequencies. It will be noted from the RIAA curve that the gain characteristic reduces to zero at high frequencies. This implies that an amplifier with unity-gain stability is required, which is indeed true if the standard feedback configuration is used. There are many circuit approaches which can be used to accomplish RIAA phono-playback equalization, however all must satisfy the general frequency-response characteristic of Fig. 4-15.

A three-terminal, four-component RC network can be designed to accomplish RIAA equalization,* and two examples of such a network are shown in Fig. 4-16. These networks can be used with either the conventional feedback-type of RIAA phono stages (also know as *active* equalization), or, with the more complex *passive* equalized preamps (as such, usually between two wideband stages). Regardless of the circuit(s) within which they are used, the two RC networks shown are equivalent in terms of achieving the three time constants. Both have an input terminal (1), a common terminal (3), and an output terminal (2). In the figure(s), the right-most column indicates the closest standard value; precision film RC components are recommended for best results. While practical standard values are shown, alternate sets can be attained, simply by multiplying the R's by a desired factor, while dividing the C's by the same factor.

---

*See Reference 13 at the end of the chapter.

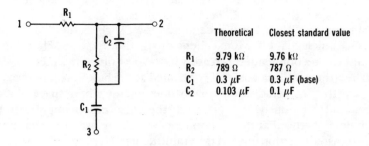

	Theoretical	Closest standard value
R_1	9.79 kΩ	9.76 kΩ
R_2	789 Ω	787 Ω
C_1	0.3 μF	0.3 μF (base)
C_2	0.103 μF	0.1 μF

(A) Example 1.

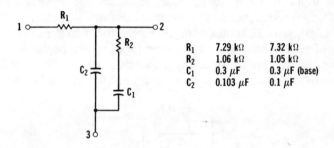

	Theoretical	Closest standard value
R_1	7.29 kΩ	7.32 kΩ
R_2	1.06 kΩ	1.05 kΩ
C_1	0.3 μF	0.3 μF (base)
C_2	0.103 μF	0.1 μF

(B) Example 2.

Fig. 4-16. RIAA networks (T_1 = 3180 μs, T_2 = 318 μs, T_3 = 75 μs).

Feedback-Equalized RIAA Phono Preamp (Active Equalization)

Fig. 4-17 illustrates two variants of a popular approach to achieving a simple RIAA phono preamp. Fig. 4-17A is a high-performance version, using precision components. Amplifier A_1 provides the gain, and equalization components R_1-R_2-C_1-C_2 form the RIAA network, providing a very accurate realization with standard component values. (The network used here is that of Fig. 4-16A, with terminals 1 and 3 common; scaled by 10).

The actual network components should be precision high-quality types, both for initial equalization accuracy and also for minimal errors from nonideal properties. High-quality metal-film resistors and film capacitors of polystyrene or polypropylene are recommended,[*] as they have low-voltage coefficients, low-dissipation factors, and

---

[*] See Reference 17 at the end of the chapter.

low-dielectric absorption. (A capacitor type which generally should be avoided is the "high K" ceramic families.)

In contrast, the "low K" ceramic types, such as the "NPO" or "COG" dielectrics, have excellent dissipation factors. While they cannot be recommended as readily as the best film types mentioned earlier (their DA is not as well controlled as the best films), they may be worth consideration for small values and/or where space is at a premium. Obviously, the quality of the equalization/amplification can be no better that the components which are used to determine the transfer function (even if the amplifier itself is perfect). Note that these comments apply to all the circuits that follow.

The input RC components, R_t-C_t, terminate the moving magnet cartridge, as recommended by the manufacturer. The values shown are typical, with C_t typically being varied for flattest response. In terms of desired amplifier parameters, for optimum performance in this circuit, they are considerably demanding. For lowest noise from the cartridge's inductive source, the amplifier should preferably

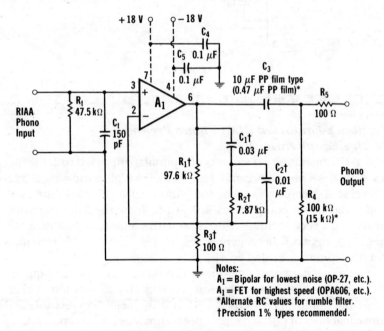

(A) High-performance circuit.

Fig. 4-17. Feedback-equalized

have a voltage noise density of 5 nV/√Hz or less, and a current noise density of 1 pA/√Hz or less. The former requirement is best met by using low-noise bipolar-input amplifiers, such as the OP-27, 5534, 5532, LM833, etc. The latter need is best met by the use of FET-input amplifiers, in general. For the desirable low-noise bipolar-input amplifiers, DC input-bias current can be a potential problem when direct coupling to the cartridge; thus, in this circuit, the low-bias-current OP-27 amplifier is suggested. The amplifier used for A_1 should have an input current of less than 100 nA, for minimum problems with the related DC offset (assuming a typical phono cartridge of about 1-kΩ resistance). FET-input amplifiers generally have negligible bias currents but they also tend to typically have a higher voltage noise. One FET-input type that is useful for A_1 is the OPA606, as it has a reasonably well-controlled noise for this type of application (although not as low as the bipolar devices mentioned).

For high-gain accuracy, particularly at high stage gains, the amplifier should have a high gain-bandwidth product; preferrably 5 MHz or more at audio frequencies. Because of the 100% feedback through the network at high frequencies, the amplifier used for A_1 must be a unity-gain-stable type. To minimize noise from sources

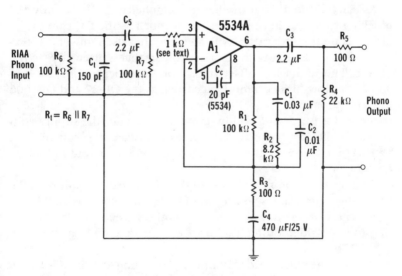

(B) General-purpose circuit.

RIAA phono preamps.

other than the amplifier, gain resistor R_3 is set to a relatively low value, which generates a voltage noise that is low in relation to that of the amplifier used. The 1-kHz gain (G) of the circuit can be calculated by the expression:

$$G = 0.101 [1 + (R_1/R_3)]$$

For the values shown, the gain is just under 100 times (or 40 dB). Lower gains can be accomodated by increasing R_3, but gains higher than 40 dB may show increasing equalization errors, dependent upon the gain bandwidth of the amplifier used. For example, R_3 can be 200 ohms for a gain of 50 times (34 dB). Dependent upon the amplifier, this circuit is capable of very low distortion over its entire range, generally below 0.01% at levels up to 7-V rms (assuming ± 15-V supplies) and higher with the ± 18-V supplies suggested.

For extended low-frequency response, C_3 and R_4 are the larger values shown, with C_3 preferably a polypropylene film type. Alternately, the smaller values for C_3 and R_4 (when applied) form a simple 6-dB per octave rumble filter, with a corner at 22 Hz. Placing a rumble filter's high-pass action after the preamp stage has the desirable property of discriminating against the RIAA-amplified LF noise components, in addition to the pickup-produced LF disturbances.

As can be noted from the figure's simplicity, C_3 is the only DC blocking capacitor in the circuit. In as much as the DC gain of the circuit is on the order of 60 dB, the amplifier used must be a low-offset-voltage device, with an offset voltage that is insensitive to the source. This implies an offset voltage on the order of 1 mV or less, and a very-low-bias-current device (such as the OP-27 and OPA606 units mentioned).

Since this is a high-gain low-input-level circuit, the supply voltages should be well regulated and free of noise, and reasonable care should be taken with the shielding and conductor routing during layout.

An alternate economy version of this circuit can be built with the higher-bias-current low-noise bipolar devices, such as the 5534, 5532, and LM833 units (which would otherwise make direct coupling to a cartridge difficult). This form of the circuit is shown in Fig. 4-17B.

It should be noted here that input AC coupling to A_1 is added with C_5, and the RIAA feedback network is AC-grounded via C_4 (a large nonpolar electrolytic type). Nearest 5%-value units are used for the network components, making this an easy to reproduce and inexpensive circuit. R_4 is shown in a value suitable for a rumble filter, but it can be increased for a lower rolloff point. In this case, the cartridge termination resistance, R_t, is made up of the parallel equivalent of R_6 and R_7.

Passively Equalized RIAA Phono Preamp

A current area of high audiophile interest is the passively equalized preamplifier circuits used for phono signal sources. A circuit topology which can be used for such RIAA phono applications is shown in Fig. 4-18. This circuit consists of two high-quality wide-bandwidth-gain blocks, A_1 and A_2, which are separated by a three-terminal network, "N." Each of the gain stages is set up for the required gain, via R_2-R_1 and R_4-R_3. Input termination, as appropriate to the particular cartridge used, is provided by R_t and C_t, which are optimized for flattest response into this passive network (as in Fig. 4-17).

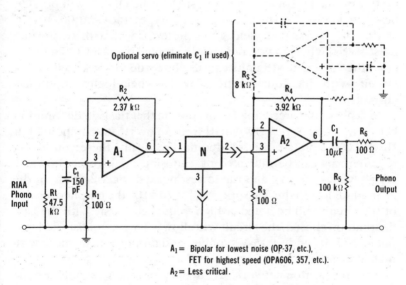

$A_1 =$ Bipolar for lowest noise (OP-37, etc.),
FET for highest speed (OPA606, 357, etc.).
$A_2 =$ Less critical.

Fig. 4-18. Passively equalized RIAA phono preamplifier.

The op-amp gain blocks, A_1 and A_2 could be identical for the purposes of simplicity, but are necessarily not so for reasons which will follow. The gain values shown yield a 1-kHz gain that is the product of the A_1-A_2 gains (24.7 times 40.2) times that of the interstage network. For a RIAA-equalized phono case, the 1-kHz gain is 0.101

times the DC gain, which yields an overall gain of 40 dB for this instance. Other gains can be realized most simply by minor increment changes to R_4. In general, the 1-kHz gain of this circuit is

$$G = 0.101 \, [1 + (R_2/R_1)] \, [1 + (R_4/R_3)]$$

A passively equalized preamplifier such as this must be carefully optimized for signal-handling capability, both from an overload standpoint and from a low-noise viewpoint. Stage A_1 is desirably chosen for a gain sufficiently high that the input-referred noise will be predominantly due to this stage (and the cartridge, when connected), but yet not so high that it will readily clip at high-level high-frequency inputs. Several amplifiers with a 10-V rms output capability will allow A_1 to accept 400-mV rms at high frequencies, as shown (with ± 18-V supplies).

Note that since A_1 operates at a relatively high gain, it need *not* be unity-gain stable. Low-noise types, such as the OP-37, will provide best signal/noise ratio here. In FET-input types, the OPA606, as well as the 357 types, will yield good performance, with reasonable noise levels. Where lowest noise can be traded off against input linearity, the 2525 and 318 units can also be made to work well in this circuit (with due consideration towards their higher input-bias currents).

In general, the preceding factors dictate that the gain distribution between A_1 and A_2 be LOW/HIGH from an overload standpoint, but HIGH/LOW from a noise standpoint. Practically, these conflicting requirements can be mitigated by choosing the highest allowable supply voltage for A_1, and the lowest noise device. Because of the near 40-dB loss in the network, "N," at 20 kHz, the output overload of the circuit will be noted at high frequencies first. With the gain distribution chosen, the circuit will allow a 3-V rms undistorted output to 20 kHz, with ± 15-V supplies, and proportionally more with higher supply voltages.

The equalization network "N," which follows A_1, should use the lowest impedance values practical from the standpoint of low noise, as the noise output at pin 2 of the network is equivalent to the input-referred noise of A_2. A practical example for this network would be the RC values of R_1-R_2-C_1-C_2 in Fig. 4-17A, scaled downward in impedance by a factor of 10 (9.76 kΩ, etc., as shown in Fig. 4-16A). As noted, scaling can be applied to either network of Fig. 4-16 for component selection, as long as the same *ratios* are maintained.

Amplifier A_2 is less critical than A_1 at low frequencies, but, still, is not negligible. A low-noise voltage-density device is very valuable to the A_1 and A_2 positions, as is a relatively low-input-current noise.

As mentioned before, a low bias current is appropriate to A_1, with the use of bipolar amplifiers. With a 100-nA, or less, bias-current device, direct coupling to a moving magnet phono cartridge is practical. For example, a 50-nA bias current will induce only an 50-μV offset at A_1 (for a typical 1-kΩ cartridge). Similarly, the bias-current induced-offset voltage of A_2, from the 10-kΩ DC resistance of "N," will be low, relative to the amplified offset of A_1. As a result, the worst-case overall-output DC offset at A_2 can be held to under 1 volt, allowing a single coupling capacitor to suffice for DC blocking purposes for the entire circuit.

This circuit also can be adapted to servo control of the output offset by the connection of a noninverting-type servo integrator around stage A_2, as shown by the dashed-line area of Fig. 4-18. The general-purpose noninverting servo described earlier in the chapter can be used, along with a low-offset FET op amp, such as the AD711 or the 34081.

Hybrid-Equalized, Differential-Input, Servo-Controlled, RIAA Phono Preamp

By using a combination of passive and active equalization, the noise/overload constraints of the totally passive equalization can be lessened. In addition, this "hybrid" equalization can be combined with a low-noise differential-input instrumentation amplifier, the AD625, for maximum noise performance in this application.[*]

Fig. 4-19 shows the hybrid-equalized phono preamp circuit, which also adds servo control for the elimination of coupling capacitors and precise DC-output offset control. A_1 is the differential-input amplifier, which accepts a balanced signal from a moving magnet cartridge. The DC and AC terminations of the cartridge are split and balanced, with an optional AC trim for best HF common-mode rejection (C_{tb}). The common-mode rejection below 100 Hz is on the order of 100 dB for A_1. To optimize the input-signal coupling, a twisted-pair signal cable is used, with an overall shield, grounded as shown.

---

[*]See Reference 26 at the end of the chapter.

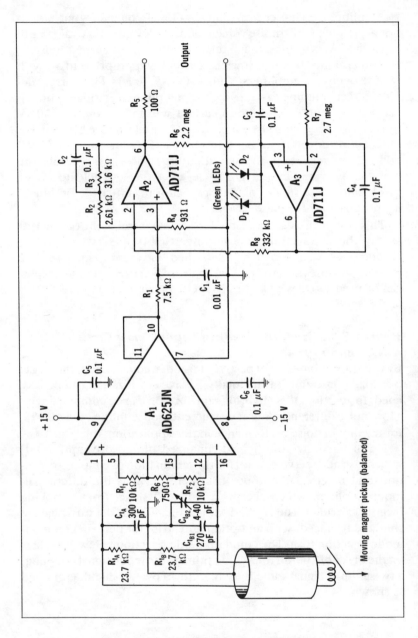

Fig. 4-19. Hybrid-equalized, differential-input, servo-controlled
RIAA phono preamp.

Practical Audio Circuits Using IC Op Amps

The gain of stage A_1 in this circuit is

$$G_{(A_1)} = (2R_F/R_G) + 1$$

where R_F and R_G are the resistances at pins 5-2, 2-15, and 15-12 of the AD625. R_{F1} and R_{F2} are nominally equal, fixed, 10-kΩ, 1% metal-film types. R_G is also a metal-film unit that is used to adjust the overall gain.

Overall, the gain of this entire circuit is the product of the A_1 and A_2 stage gains, as modified by the RIAA frequency response. At 1 kHz, the gain is

$$G_{(1 \text{ kHz})} = 0.101 \, [(2R_F/R_G) + 1] \, [(R_2 + R_3 + R_4)/(R_4) + 1]$$

With the values as shown, the gain is about 40 dB, but it can easily be adjusted up or down, via R_G. The R_2-R_4 values are preferably left alone, since they set the two lower RIAA time constants (3180 and 318 μs). The 75-μs time constant is simply set by R_1-C_1.

Amplifier A_3 is the servo stage; it uses a noninverting configuration, with a 0.22-second time constant (R_6-C_3). The DC feedback path for the servo is through the feedback input, at pin 2 on stage A_2. Diodes D_1-D_2 act as servo anti-latchup clamps around A_3, and function only in the case of an overload. They should be low-leakage types, as noted previously.

The output offset of the circuit will be essentially that of A_3, which is typically less than 1 mV. Single AD711 devices are shown for A_2-A_3, but an AD712 will function also. This circuit is capable of very high performance, with excellent signal/noise. A very careful circuit layout is warranted around the input of stage A_1, the feedback components at A_2, and the high-impedance inputs of A_3, and R_8 should be close to A_2.

The magnetic phono cartridges in popular use today consist of two basic types: moving magnet and moving coil. The moving magnet types, which are the most familiar, are suitable for the circuits thus far described. The moving coil cartridge types are higher-performance devices; they are less commonplace, but, nevertheless, still highly popular among audiophiles.

Functionally, both types of magnetic cartridges perform similarly, and both must be equalized for flat response in accordance with the RIAA characteristic. A big difference in application, however, is the fact that moving magnet types have typical sensitivities of about 1 mV of output for each cm/s of recorded velocity. In moving coil types, a sensitivity that is on the order of 0.1 mV is more common (for a similar velocity). In application then, a moving coil RIAA preamp must have more gain than a moving magnet preamp. Typical overall (1 kHz) gains are 60–70 dB for moving coils and 30–40 dB for moving magnets. Noise performance of a moving coil preamp becomes a critical performance factor, however, because of the low-output voltage and low impedance involved—typically 3 to 40 ohms.

The following circuit examples illustrate techniques that are useful to these unique requirements.

4.4.4 Moving Coil RIAA Preamplifiers

There are two general methods taken in satisfying the amplification requirement of a moving coil cartridge. These consist of two differing approaches to how the additional voltage step-up is realized, and are illustrated in Figs. 4-20 and 4-21.

In Fig. 4-20, the general conception of a standard (moving magnet compatible) RIAA preamp is shown, preceded by a step-up transformer. The step-up transformer provides a voltage-sensitivity increase, from the 0.1-mV/cm/s region up to about 1 mV/cm/s. The output of the transformer is compatible with the output as produced by a typical moving magnet pickup at this point. Thus, an unaltered (standard) RIAA preamp can be used for further processing.

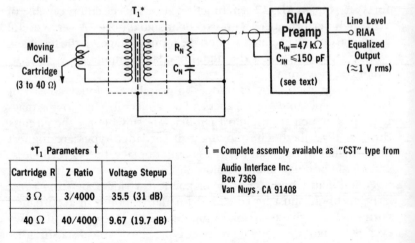

Cartridge R	Z Ratio	Voltage Stepup
3 Ω	3/4000	35.5 (31 dB)
40 Ω	40/4000	9.67 (19.7 dB)

*T_1 Parameters †

† = Complete assembly available as "CST" type from
Audio Interface Inc.
Box 7369
Van Nuys, CA 91408

Fig. 4-20. Transformer method for achieving moving coil voltage step-up.

Practical Audio Circuits Using IC Op Amps

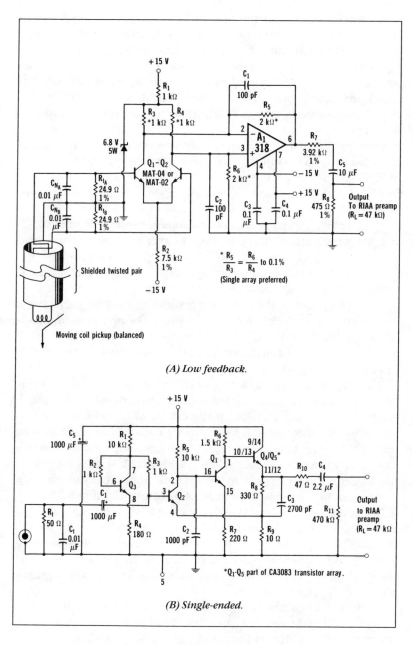

(A) Low feedback.

(B) Single-ended.

Fig. 4-21. Moving coil cartridge preamps.

Representative transformer parameters suitable for this function are listed in Fig. 4-20, and, for best results, should be used with loading networks optimum for the application. Both the input and output leads of the transformer circuit should be shielded, and the transformer should be located away from strong magnetic fields that could produce "hum" coupling. Note that there are two different transformers listed, with each optimum for a different-resistance moving coil cartridge.

In principle, any of the previously described RIAA preamp circuits can be used in conjunction with the transfomer step-up circuit of Fig. 4-20. The input impedance of the RIAA preamp is assumed to be 47 kΩ and 150 pF, and the overall gain will be that of the transformer use, plus the specific RIAA circuit's gain.

An alternate approach is to use an amplifier preceding the standard RIAA preamp, or a *pre-preamp* (sometimes called the "head amp," for its place at the head of the signal path). Two suitable preamp circuits for this use are shown in Fig. 4-21. Because of the extremely low source resistance from which this type of circuit must operate ($\cong$ 4 ohms), the feedback resistance must be very low, if used with conventional feedback. As should be appreciated, this is often not as low as desired, as, ideally, this resistor should be much less than the source (on the order of 0.5 ohm). Such a low value is usually not practical.

The circuit of Fig. 4-21A takes a different approach to lowering noise—by simply eliminating the feedback to the first stage. This allows the noise characteristic of the circuit to be essentially determined by this stage (and/or its operating current), since there is no feedback resistor to generate noise. Although output distortion will be higher without this feedback, this factor is most relevant only at the higher input levels (where the circuit is not as likely to operate).

This circuit also has the virtue of a differential input (like Fig. 4-19), as both bases of the Q_1-Q_2 pair are available for signal application. This allows a balanced twisted-pair cable, with an overall shield (grounded as shown), to be used. The cartridge's load resistance (R_t) is split into equal-value pairs, as is the capacitance, C_n. A nominal value for C_n is shown (which can be increased for greater ultrasonic filtering, if desired).

With very-low-noise transistors for Q_1-Q_2, such as the MAT-04 or MAT-02 matched pairs, the input noise (e_n) of this circuit is on the order of 1.5 nV/$\sqrt{\text{Hz}}$, at the 2-mA current level. Other transistors which can operate similarly are the LM394 and the MAT-01 (although their noise will be greater). Gain is approximately 800 times to the output of A_1; this is reduced to about 40 dB overall by the R_7-R_8 divider. Gain is best adjusted via R_8, as the balanced-bridge resistances, R_3-R_6, should not be altered for good stability. Metal-film resistors and film capacitors should be used for best results.

More conventional single-ended IC designs can also be used for the pre-preamp function, and they may be preferable for reasons of space and/or economy. These factors are brought to bear in the design of Fig. 4-21B which uses the CA3083 transistor array. The type-3083 transistors, which are higher-current units of a larger basic geometry than that of the more standard "CA"-series arrays, are superior in terms of input-noise voltage. In this circuit, the critical device, in terms of noise, is Q_2—the input stage. Here, it is operated at 1.3 mA to minimize the input-voltage noise, and at a high gain to minimize the noise of the second stage. The amplifier is a noninverting feedback type, with feedback provided from the R_8-R_9 voltage divider. R_9 is set at 10 ohms to help minimize the noise contribution of the feedback loop.

Q_2 is biased by Q_3, connected as a diode, and with a 1-kΩ base resistor (R_3). A 1.3-mA reference current is forced in Q_3 by R_1, and R_4 is selected to drop about 250 mV. This 250-mV potential (when the loop is correctly DC-biased) will be seen also at the emitter of Q_2 via DC feedback from the output. Since the output stage operates at a relatively large current of 25 mA, two of the 3083 transistors are paralleled (Q4 and Q5).

The circuit has a gain of 31 dB, as determined by the two resistors, R_8 and R_9. The equivalent input noise is on the order of 1.5 nV/$\sqrt{\text{Hz}}$. While this is a quite good performance in terms of low noise, it should be pointed out that it can only be realized with the value of coupling capacitance (C_1) noted, and with a low-noise power supply. If C_1 is not sufficiently large (at least several hundred microfarad), low-frequency noise will be produced because of its reactance. C_5 is a low-ESR electrolytic capacitor that is used as a supply bypass capacitor.

The circuit has a maximum output of 3-V rms, and distortion is below 0.03% for levels of less than 1 volt of output. Bandwidth is set by C_3 at 180 kHz, as shown. This combination of performance characteristics not only make it a good choice as a phono pre-amplifier, it is also suitable for other low-impedance (100 ohms or less) signal sources with outputs of 100 mV or less.

4.5 REFERENCES

1. Bonn, D. (Ed). *Audio Handbook.* National Semiconductor Corp., Santa Clara, CA, 1977.

2. *Analog Data Manual.* Signetics Corporation, 1977.

3. Borbely, E. "The Borbely Preamp." *The Audio Amateur,* issue 4/85, issue 1/86.

4. Gittleman, R. "Applications of the Audio Operational Amplifier to Studio Use." *JAES,* Vol. 17 #3, June 1969.

5. Hallgren, B. "On the Noise Performance of a Magnetic Phonograph Pickup." *JAES,* Vol. 23 #7, September 1975.

6. Holman, T. "Dynamic Range Requirements of Phonographic Preamplifiers." *Audio,* July 1977.

7. _____. "New Factors in Phonograph Preamplifier Design." *Journal of the AES,* Vol. 24 #4, May 1976.

8. _____. "New Tests for Preamplifiers." *Audio,* February 1977.

9. _____; Kampmann, F. "Phonograph Preamplifier Design Criteria Arising From System Measurements." Presented at 58th convention, November 1977, *preprint #1300.*

10. Jung, W. G. *IC Op-Amp Cookbook, 3rd Edition.* Howard W. Sams & Co., Indianapolis, IN, 1986.

11. _____. "Improve Op Amp Audio Circuits." *Electronic Design,* September 27, 1973.

12. _____. "The Pitfalls of the General Purpose IC Op Amp as Applied to Audio Signal Processing." *JAES,* Vol. 21 #9, November 1973.

13. _____. "Topology Considerations for RIAA Phono Preamplifiers." 67th AES Convention, November 1982, *preprint #1719.*

14. _____. "The PAT-5/WJ-1 Equalization." (Letters), *The Audio Amateur,* issue 3/1978.

15. _____; White, D. "The PAT-5/WJ-1." *The Audio Amateur,* issue 1/78.

16. _____; White, D. "The PAT-5/WJ-1A." *The Audio Amateur,* issue 3/1979.

17. _____; Marsh, R. N. "Picking Capacitors." Part I & Part II, *Audio,* February & March 1980.

18. Jenkins, A. and Bowers, D. "NPN Pairs Yield Ultra-low-noise Op Amp." *EDN,* May 3, 1984.

19. Kapoor, A. and Bowers, D. "Diverse Circuits Exploit Matching in Quad-Transistor IC." *EDN,* March 6, 1986.

20. Lipshitz. S. P. "On RIAA Equalization Networks." *JAES,* Vol. 27 #6, June 1979, pp. 458-481.

21. _____; Jung, W. "A High Accuracy Inverse RIAA Network." *The Audio Amateur,* issue 1/80.

22. Losmandy, B. J. "Operational Amplifier Applications for Audio Systems." *JAES,* Vol. 17 #1, January 1969.

23. Marsh, R. N. "A Passively Equalized Phono Preamp." *The Audio Amateur,* issue 3/80, June 1980.

24. Otala, M. "Feedback Generated Phase Non-Linearity Audio Amplifiers." London AES Convention, March 1980, *preprint #1576.*

25. Stout D. F. and Kaufman, M. *Handbook of Operational Amplifier Circuit Design.* McGraw Hill, 1976.

26. Wurcer, S. and Jung, W. "Instrumentation Amplifers Solve Unusual Design Problems." *EDN,* August 4, 1983.

27. Manufacturers' Data Sheets:

Analog Devices	{	AD711	Op amp
		AD712	Op amp
		AD625	Instrumentation Amp
Burr-Brown	{	OPA606	Op amp
		3507	Op amp
Elantec	{	EL2003	Buffer
Harris Semiconductor	{	HA2520	Op amps
		(series)	
Linear Technology	{	LTC1010	Buffer
Motorola Semiconductor	{	MC34070	Op amps
		(series)	
		MC34080	Op amps
		(series)	
National Semiconductor	{	LM318	Op amp
		LF357	Op amp
Precision Monolithics	{	MAT-02	Matched transistor dual
		MAT-04	Matched transistor quad
		OP-27	Op amp
		OP-37	Op amp

Signetics

$\left\{\begin{array}{ll} \text{NE530} & \text{Op amp} \\ \text{NE5532} & \text{Op amp} \\ \text{NE5534} & \text{Op amp} \\ \text{NE5535} & \text{Op amp} \end{array}\right.$

FIVE

Equalized Amplifiers
and Active Filters

With frequency-dependent feedback around an operational amplifier, virtually any desired gain-versus-frequency characteristic can
be synthesized, generally to an accuracy limited only by the passive
components used. Specific examples of equalized amplifiers have
been covered in the previous chapter; namely, the tape and RIAA
phono preamps. In this chapter, we will cover more general examples of equalized amplifiers that are suitable for high-level audio signal processing, as well as general-purpose active filters.

5.1 SHELVING EQUALIZERS

One very common audio-equalizer application is the *shelving* equalizer, so named because of the shape of its frequency-response characteristic, as shown in Fig. 5-1. This is a graph of both high- and
low-frequency shelving. Such a response is typical of the familiar hi-
fi "tone" controls, where the low-frequency end is controlled by the
"bass" control and the high-frequency end is controlled by the "tre-
ble" control. In general, "boost" (and "cut") capability is symmetrical, with a maximum capability of ± 20 dB or less. The frequencies
at which the equalization begins (f_{1_H} and f_{1_L}) are generally centered
within the audio spectrum so that maximum boost (or cut) is available only at the extreme ends of the frequency range, above f_{2_H}

(20 kHz) and below f_{2_L} (20 Hz). Figs. 5-2 and 5-3 illustrate two circuits that accomplish the shelving-equalizer function with simplicity, predictability, and symmetry.

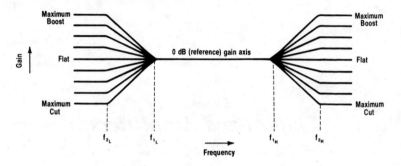

Fig. 5-1. Shelving equalizer characteristics.

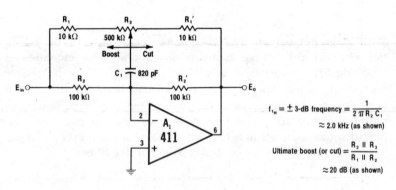

(A) Circuit.

$$f_{1_H} = \pm 3\text{-dB frequency} = \frac{1}{2\pi R_2 C_1}$$

$$\approx 2.0 \text{ kHz (as shown)}$$

$$\text{Ultimate boost (or cut)} = \frac{R_2 \parallel R_3}{R_1 \parallel R_2}$$

$$\approx 20 \text{ dB (as shown)}$$

Frequency	Probe	Value	dB
100 Hz	V:4	1.0014	0.012
200 Hz	V:4	1.00595	0.052
400 Hz	V:4	1.02398	0.206
800 Hz	V:4	1.09295	0.772
1.6 kHz	V:4	1.33166	2.488
3.2 kHz	V:4	2.00186	6.029
6.4 kHz	V:4	3.43798	10.726
12.8 kHz	V:4	5.64402	15.032
25.6 kHz	V:4	7.64329	17.666

Frequency	Probe	Value	dB
100 Hz	V:4	0.998349	−0.014
200 Hz	V:4	0.993825	−0.054
400 Hz	V:4	0.976333	−0.208
800 Hz	V:4	0.914716	−0.774
1.6 kHz	V:4	0.750698	−2.491
3.2 kHz	V:4	0.499166	−6.035
6.4 kHz	V:4	0.290175	−10.747
12.8 kHz	V:4	0.175986	−15.090
25.6 kHz	V:4	0.129158	−17.778

(B) Response for "boost"
setting of R_3.

(C) Response for "cut"
setting of R_3.

Fig. 5-2. High-frequency shelving equalizer.

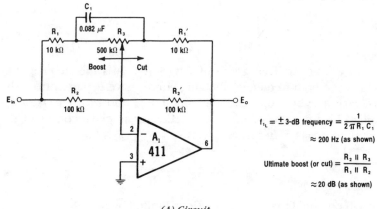

$f_{1_L} = \pm$ 3-dB frequency $= \dfrac{1}{2\pi R_1 C_1}$

$\approx$ 200 Hz (as shown)

Ultimate boost (or cut) $= \dfrac{R_2 \parallel R_3}{R_1 \parallel R_2}$

$\approx$ 20 dB (as shown)

(A) Circuit.

Frequency	Probe	Value	dB
10 Hz	V:5	0.119804	− 18.431
20 Hz	V:5	0.147718	− 16.611
40 Hz	V:5	0.224922	− 12.959
80 Hz	V:5	0.387937	− 8.225
160 Hz	V:5	0.633954	− 3.959
320 Hz	V:5	0.851644	− 1.395
640 Hz	V:5	0.954907	− 0.401
1.28 kHz	V:5	0.987316	− 0.111
2.56 kHz	V:5	0.995957	− 0.035

Frequency	Probe	Value	dB
10 Hz	V:5	8.33721	18.420
20 Hz	V:5	6.76167	16.601
40 Hz	V:5	4.44058	12.949
80 Hz	V:5	2.57434	8.213
160 Hz	V:5	1.57492	3.945
320 Hz	V:5	1.17197	1.378
640 Hz	V:5	1.04503	0.383
1.28 kHz	V:5	1.01067	0.092
2.56 kHz	V:5	1.00188	0.016

(B) Response for "boost"
setting of R_3.

(C) Response for "cut"
setting of R_3.

Fig. 5-3. Low-frequency shelving equalizer.

5.1.1 High-Frequency Shelving Equalizer

The schematic for a high-frequency shelving equalizer is shown in Fig. 5-2. It will be noted that in the absence of R_1, R_1', R_3, and C_1, this circuit is a simple unity-gain inverting stage. By building upon the basic symmetry of this inverting configuration, different types of equalizers are possible. In the circuit of Fig. 5-2A, when R_3 is at its electrical center, there will be no voltage across C_1 and thus no current flow into the summing point. When R_3 is rotated toward R_1, the input current will increase by virtue of the lowered input impedance, $R_1 + X_{C_1}$. Similarly, when R_3 is rotated toward R_1', the feedback impedance is lowered by virtue of $R_1' - X_{C_1}$. The frequency at which the shunting of R_1-C_1 and R_1'-C_1 comes into play is determined by R_2 and C_1, as

$$f_{1_H} = \frac{1}{2\pi R_2 C_1} \qquad \text{(Eq. 5-1)}$$

On the generalized graph of Fig. 5-1, this is the frequency at which the high-frequency shelving curves have departed from the flat response by 3 dB. The total amount of boost (or cut) is determined by the ratio of input and feedback impedances, as in the standard inverter. In this case, it is

$$\text{boost (or cut)} = \frac{R_2 \parallel R_3}{R_1 \parallel R_2} \qquad \text{(Eq. 5-2)}$$

It will be noted that the final ratio is limited by R_3 if R_3 is not $\gg R_2$, which is the case in this circuit.

With the values shown in Fig. 5-2, the total boost (or cut) is within a decibel of 20 dB, but is limited by the value of R_3. The value of R_3 can be increased, if desired, but this introduces a drawback in that nearly all the total change in boost (or cut) occurs in the last few degrees of control rotation. This effect is evident to some extent with the 500-kΩ value, but it is deemed desirable because it makes the "flat" setting easily repeatable. The actual value chosen for R_3 is largely a matter of user preference, but in any case, it should be a linear control.

If desired, the degree of boost (or cut) can be altered by varying the ratio of R_2 to R_1. In the circuit of Fig. 5-2, the shunting effect of C_1 introduces a slope in the response curve of ± 6 dB/octave; thus, the total dB change determines the $f_{1_H} - f_{2_H}$ frequency difference. With the values shown, $f_{1_H} = 2$ kHz, and full boost (or cut) is realized at $f_{2_H} = 20$ kHz. Equalization can be totally defeated (for flat response) by the insertion of a switch in series with C_1.

The response which results for a frequency sweep over the operating range is shown in the "boost" and "cut" tables in Fig. 5-2. While these data reflect two extreme settings for R_3, as an infinite number of similar data would be produced, for intermediate settings.

Note: The response data shown here was produced by the *ECA computer program*, a powerful circuit analysis program for IBM and MS-DOS computers. *ECA* is produced by Tatum Labs (1478 Mark

Twain Ct., Ann Arbor, MI 48103), This (or a similar) tool is a great aid for speeding circuit design and analysis, including DC annd AC performance, worst-case analysis, etc.

These two examples (Fig. 5-2, and the sister circuit to follow, Fig. 5-3) use a 411 device—a general-purpose FET op amp. For the purpose of greater power output, lower noise, etc., other more specialized units can also be used.

5.1.2 Low-Frequency Shelving Equalizer

The schematic for a low-frequency shelving equalizer is shown in Fig. 5-3. It will be noted that the only difference between this circuit and the high-frequency circuit of Fig. 5-2 is the value of C_1, and its connection to R_3. The rotation of R_3 in this circuit has the same effect as previously—a decrease in either the input impedance or the feedback impedance. In this case, however, the frequency range is at the low end. At high frequencies, the rotation of R_3 has no effect, since C_1 causes both ends of R_3 to assume the same potential. The point at which low-frequency equalization begins is given by

$$f_{1_L} = \frac{1}{2\pi R_1 C_1} \qquad \text{(Eq. 5-3)}$$

and is the frequency where the reactance of C_1 becomes equal to R_1. Below this frequency, the slope of the response curve is 6 dB/octave, as in the high-frequency circuit. Also, the total amount of boost (or cut) is determined by the ratio of R_2 to R_1, and it is limited by R_3 if R_3 is not $\gg R_2$, as previously. With the values shown in Fig. 5-3, f_{1_L} occurs at 200 Hz, and full boost (or cut) is realized at $f_{2_L} = 20$ Hz. This circuit is also defeatable by a switch, in series with the arm of R_3.

In applying either of the two shelving equalizers (Fig. 5-2 or Fig. 5-3), some general considerations are in order. First of all, the op amp chosen should have a high slewing rate that will allow full power output over the entire audio range. Also, a low input current allows high resistances to be used without serious bias-current offsets. In general, the op amp used should be compensated for unity gain. Since the greatest percentage of applications for these circuits will be in hi-fi stereo amplifiers, two of each will be required. Thus, dual or quad devices, such as the 353, 412, 347, MC34082, MC34084, etc., can be used and will perform satisfactorily, as the high slewing rate of these devices allows distortionless, high-level, high-frequency output. Both circuits require low source impedances, such as another op amp, to work properly. Also, they should be ac coupled, if possible, since this can introduce additional variables into the total response.

Note that these configurations are both *inverting;* thus, a logical step is to cascade two low- and high-frequency circuits. This yields the overall desired response, with a noninverting phase.

5.2 RESONANT EQUALIZERS

Another common equalizer application is the resonant equalizer, so named because it resonates at a certain frequency. This effect may be applied either in the form of a response peak or dip at the frequency of resonance. Conceptually, the circuit of Fig. 5-2 can be converted to a resonant equalizer simply by placing an inductor in series with the capacitor, as shown in Fig. 5-4. No other circuit elements need be changed, and this very simple circuit will peak or dip at the LC resonant frequency. In practice, however, inductors often introduce more problems than they solve. They tend to be nonlinear, bulky, expensive, sensitive to external fields, and, in general, a circuit element to be avoided whenever possible. By using op-amp techniques, however, it is possible to synthesize an inductor response without having to endure its pitfalls.

If the characteristics already described for the high-frequency and low-frequency shelving equalizers are combined in such a man-

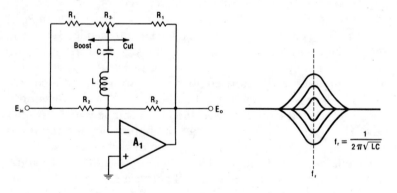

Fig. 5-4. Resonant equalizer using an LC network.

ner as to make their response slopes overlap, the composite response will be a resonance, as illustrated in Fig. 5-5. To achieve the resonance effect, f_{1_L} and f_{1_H} are placed symmetrically above and below the desired resonant frequency, f_r. The effect is as if the two individual circuits were placed in series, but it is accomplished within one circuit.

The actual circuit used in Fig. 5-5 is a combination of the two circuits of Figs. 5-2 and 5-3, and R_1, R_2, and R_3 perform similar functions. By varying the percentage of "overlap" of the two circuits, the resonance boost (or cut) can be made a percentage of the total available boost (or cut) implied by R_2/R_1. In designing this circuit, the starting point is the minimum boost (or cut) required, and the resonant frequency. With the resistances fixed as shown, both the gain and frequency are set by the capacitances C_1-C_2. Capacitors C_1 and C_2 are calculated using the modified equations given in Fig. 5-5. Their ratio sets the gain and their value, the frequency. The simplification of fixing resistances makes the design process just a two-step calculation (Steps 2 and 3). Infinite control is available for boost (or cut) by virtue of the infinite resolution of R_3. The circuit shown in Fig. 5-5A is for a 1-kHz, $\pm$ 10-dB equalizer. The response for the case of full boost is shown graphically in 5-5B.

The circuit of Fig. 5-5 can actually be called a universal equalizer, because if C_1 and C_2 are switched in and out in various combinations, any of the three equalizer responses can be achieved by the same circuit. Because of its basic simplicity and ease of adaptation, this configuration can be a very useful circuit building block.

5.3 GENERAL-PURPOSE ACTIVE FILTERS

A large number of active filter networks can be synthesized using op amps as active elements and only resistors and capacitors as passive elements. All of the standard filter functions—low-pass, high-pass, and bandpass—can be realized with cutoff slopes of up to 18 dB/octave in a single stage. In this section, we will discuss several of the more commonly used active filter designs, and show examples of their use in audio circuits.

The three basic filter response curves are shown in Fig. 5-6, along with the terms that will be used in the discussion in this section. As noted, all filters have a passband and a stopband—terms that are self-explanatory. The rolloff in the stopband of low-pass and high-pass filters is determined by the order of the filter. First-order filters, for instance, have a 6-dB/octave rolloff in the stopband. This rolloff increases by the factor "n" for increased orders, where "n" is the filter order. As can be noted, 12- and 18-dB-per-octave rolloffs result from second- and third-order filters (and so forth).

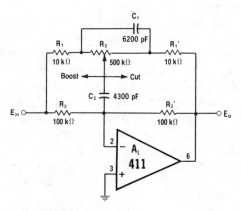

For resistances as shown,

(1) Select resonance boost or cut and f_r

$$\text{Gain} = A = \frac{C_1 + 5.1C_2}{C_1 + 0.6C_2}$$

$$f_r = \frac{1}{6.2\pi R_1} \sqrt{\frac{1}{C_1 C_2}}$$

(2) Calculate required $\dfrac{C_1}{C_2}$ ratio from expression for A.

(3) Calculate C_1 and C_2 values from expression for f_r

$$C_1 C_2 = \frac{1}{(6.2\pi R_1 f_r)^2}$$

(4) Example for $f_r = 1$ kHz, and ± 10 dB (A=3,162)

from (2) A=3.162 $\longrightarrow$ $\dfrac{C_1}{C_2} = 1.48$

from (3) f_r=1000 Hz $\longrightarrow$ C_2=4220 pF, C_1=6245 pF
(use 4300 pF, 6200 pF)

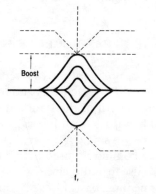

(A) Circuit. *(B) Graphic response for "boost."*

Fig. 5-5. Resonant equalizer

Equalized Amplifiers and Active Filters

A high-or low-pass filter is said to be maximally flat when its amplitude response shows a minimum of variation in the passband—that is, it neither peaks nor rolls off early. This characteristic is known as a Butterworth, and the simplest natural Butterworth filter is a single RC section. Butterworth response is achieved in a filter when the filter Q is equal to $\sqrt{2}/2$.

A Bessel, or maximally flat delay, response is obtained when the Q of the filter is equal to $1/\sqrt{3}$. Where the Butterworth response is desirable is when amplitude accuracy must be optimized over the passband; the Bessel filter is desirable when the transient response accuracy of the filter is more important than amplitude response. Compared to the Butterworth, a Bessel filter will show a more gradual rolloff in the region of cutoff.

The reader is cautioned to appreciate that the treatment of active filters in this section is only a small sampling of that which is possible. A detailed survey of active filters with possible audio uses would fill this book (and more); therefore, ample reference material is provided.

There are many approaches that can be used to arrive at a filter design, including sophisticated computer programs, the use of charts and tables, and "cookbook" design-element formulas.

For filters of modest complexity, as discussed here, the latter two approaches are sufficient and will be detailed in the following pages. In general, filter orders beyond three, and complex response shapes, separate a filter design specialist from the infrequent user. The types presented here are not complex or difficult to design, yet they are quite flexible, easy to use, and accurate in response. Given the proper attention to component quality, they will also be noise and distortion free.

Frequency	Probe	Value	dB
125 Hz	V:5	1.09314	0.773
250 Hz	V:5	1.34882	2.599
500 Hz	V:5	2.19394	6.824
1 kHz	V:5	3.41533	10.669
2 kHz	V:5	1.99412	5.995
4 kHz	V:5	1.28482	2.177
8 kHz	V:5	1.07479	0.626
16 kHz	V:5	1.01842	0.159

(C) Response for "boost" setting.

using RC networks.

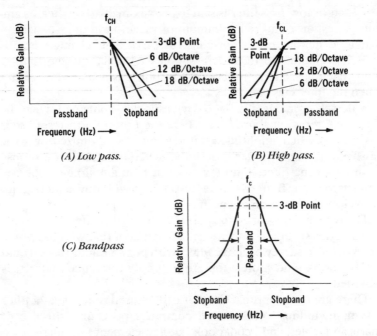

Fig. 5-6. Generalized filter responses.

5.3.1 VCVS Filters

The simplest active filter design is based on the Sallen and Key[*] voltage-controlled voltage source (VCVS) configuration, which can be either a unity-gain voltage follower or a voltage follower with gain. Described here are voltage-controlled voltage source filters of the low- and high-pass, unity-gain voltage follower types.[†] These circuits implicitly have gain of unity (within the passband), which is independent of resistor values. Thus, they can easily be used for filtering functions without any concern for passband scaling errors due to gain-setting resistors. Although Sallen and Key VCVS filters can be built with a variety of noninverting gains, the unity-gain case is illustrated here.

Fig. 5-7 illustrates the unity-gain noninverting amplifier require-

---

[*]First described in "Practical Method of Designing RC Active Filters." (See references at the end of the chapter.)

[†]See Reference 15 at the end of this chapter.

ments which are most suitable for VCVS filters. Generally, the amplifier should have a precise gain of unity, a high input impedance, and a low output impedance, as well as low DC offset. In Fig. 5-7, we show amplifier types which can fulfill these requirements, broken down into general op-amp types (Fig. 5-7B) and unity-gain video buffers (Fig. 5-7C).

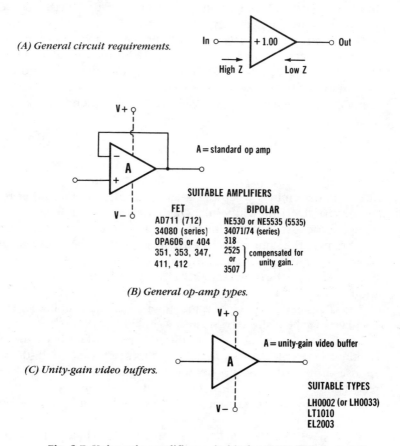

(A) General circuit requirements.

(B) General op-amp types.

(C) Unity-gain video buffers.

Fig. 5-7. Unity-gain amplifiers suitable for VCVS filters.

The use of a standard op amp will allow the lowest bias current and DC offset, and the lowest gain error, since the op amp gain is very close to unity. On the other hand, standard op amps tend to be less suitable for extremely high-amplitude, high-frequency signals (due to slew-rate problems).

Some situations may profit from the use of a dedicated unity-gain video buffer, which tends to have very high slew rates (100 V/μs to 1000 V/μs) and high output current. Although their bias currents are high (and their input impedance low), unity-gain video buffers are suitable for moderate source-resistance values ($<$ 10K). DC offset of these video buffers tend to be high (approaching 100 mV), so this may need careful consideration. Of the units listed, the last two are monolithic units; the "LH" types are hybrids.

With regard to the VCVS type of filters, the version most generally useful occurs when the response is Butterworth, or when Q = $\sqrt{2}/2$. This condition is illustrated in the examples chosen, along with the Bessel response as well.

In Fig. 5-8A, when $R_1 = R_2$, the high cutoff frequency, f_{C_H}, is

$$f_{C_H} = \frac{1}{2\pi R_1 \sqrt{C_1 C_2}} \qquad \text{(Eq. 5-4)}$$

The ratio of the capacitors, C_1-C_2, adjusts the damping or Q of the filter, and determines whether Butterworth, Bessel, or another response characteristic will result. The Butterworth and Bessel ratios of capacitance are shown in the tables with the filter. As long as these ratios remain the same, the response shape of this filter will remain constant as frequency is changed.

Frequency can be tuned smoothly by simultaneous R_1 and R_2 variation, or in steps by C_1 and C_2.

The tables in Fig. 5-8 gives values for a 1-kHz filter, and other frequencies may be realized by scaling, as noted.

The Bessell filter, since it is optimized in terms of delay response, is unique in that its "corner frequency" does not result in a 3-dB response droop—this occurs somewhat higher in frequency. The reader should appreciate this point if tables are to be used, as some references provided data arranged for the 3-dB point [*] while others are oriented in terms of delay response (as here).

You can realign a Bessell low-pass filter for 3-dB biasing by multiplying values by 1.36 (second order) or 1.75 (third order). For high-pass cases, *divide* by these factors. However, in general, don't expect sharp cutoff performance from Bessell filters—they are simply not optimized for it.

---

[*]See Reference 55 at the end of Chapter 2.

Equalized Amplifiers and Active Filters

For second-order filters, the ultimate rolloff rate is 12 dB/octave. Note that R_1-R_2 must have a dc bias return—if it is not provided by the source, a resistor, such as R_b (Fig. 5-8A), must be added. Generally, the use of FET amplifiers will allow relatively unrestricted values for R_1-R_2, and thus minimize the electrical/physical size requirements for C_1-C_2. The reader can, of course, select the R_1-R_2-C_1-C_2 types for the tolerance/accuracy most consistent to the requirements of the applications.

The high-pass filter of Fig. 5-8B is similar to the previously described low-pass circuit, but with the resistor and capacitor elements interchanged. In this circuit, when $C_1 = C_2$, the low cutoff frequency, f_{C_L}, is

$$f_{C_L} = \frac{1}{2\pi C_1 \sqrt{R_1 R_2}}$$

(Eq. 5-5)

In this circuit, the ratio of resistors controls the damping, which should be as shown for the respective types. The filter values listed in the table are for 1 kHz, and scaling is accomplished as before. Rolloff in the stopband is 12 dB/octave, ultimately.

The use of resistor, R_a, depends upon the specific amplifier used for A, and any tendencies it may have towards misbehavior (latch-up, or any other undesirable "power up" or transient-mode quirk). It is shown as a reminder (to be wary); use only as necessary. For example, it will also be advisable if the input capacitors can store appreciable charge on "switch off," so as to prevent possible amplifier failure.

For these and the remaining active filter circuits, the preceding point regarding RC component tolerances and accuracy is obvious enough. However, accuracy and predictability aside, the higher-quality metal-film resistors and polystyrene and/or polypropylene filter capacitors are recommended for freedom from the parasitic effects and nonlinearities present in low-quality parts.

A set of third-order low- and high-pass voltage-controlled voltage source filters is shown in Fig. 5-9. These circuits add an additional input RC section, providing 18-dB/octave rolloffs. The basic 1-kHz filters that are shown here may be frequency scaled, as described earlier. The same general considerations to resistances R_a and R_b apply in these cases, and amplifier selection is still as shown in Fig. 5-7.

5.3.2 Rumble Filter

A practical application of a third-order voltage-controlled voltage source filter is shown in Fig. 5-10,[*] illustrating a 30-Hz rumble filter.

The function of the rumble filter is to remove undesired high-amplitude low-frequency signals (related to turntable rumble) from a phono system, without undue alteration of higher frequencies. For this function, a 3-pole Butterworth high-pass response is chosen.

The values shown in Fig. 5-10A are scaled from Fig. 5-9B, with

---

[*] Jung, W. G. "A L.F. Garbage Filter." *The Audio Amateur,* issue 4/75. Copyright© 1975 by *The Audio Amateur* magazine, Box 576, Peterborough, NH 03458.

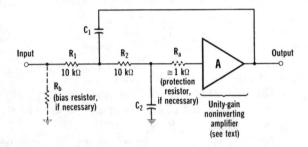

Butterworth for a 1 kHz filter	Bessel for a 1 kHz filter
$Q=\dfrac{1}{\sqrt{2}}$	$Q=\dfrac{1}{\sqrt{3}}$
$R_1=R_2 \quad C_1=2C_2$	$R_1=R_2 \quad C_1=\dfrac{4C_2}{3}$
$R_1=10\ k\Omega$ $R_2=10\ k\Omega$ $C_1=0.02251\ \mu F\ (0.022)$ $C_2=0.01125\ \mu F\ (0.011)$	$R_1=10\ k\Omega$ $R_2=10\ k\Omega$ $C_1=10610\ pF\ (11000)$ $C_2=7958\ pF\ (8200)$

To scale for other frequencies:

$f < 1$ kHz: multiply C (or R) by $\dfrac{1000}{f}$

$f > 1$ kHz: divide C (or R) by $\dfrac{1000}{f}$

(A) Low pass.

Fig. 5-8. Second-order

C_1–C_3 adjusted to a common 0.1-μF value. Note that both resistors and capacitors can be scaled (as here), as long as the correct (overall) scaling factor is used. Here, this is 1000/30, of which a factor of 4.54 is assigned to the capacitor and 7.33 to the resistor. An input buffer is used to minimize loading of the source, a procedure that is often advisable with active filters in general, and also to minimize both loading of the source and frequency-response interaction.

A more complete circuit for this function is shown in Fig. 5-10B, with a gain option indicated in the A_1 buffer. A type-34074 quad amplifier is indicated, as that allows a stereo pair of these filters to be realized. The device is adequate for levels up to 2 V. For very high source impedances, a FET-input device, such as the 34084, may be

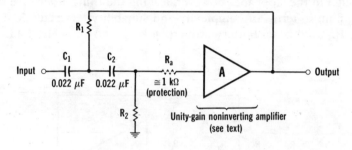

Butterworth for a 1 kHz filter	Bessel for a 1 kHz filter
$Q = \dfrac{1}{\sqrt{2}}$	$Q = \dfrac{1}{\sqrt{3}}$
$C_1 = C_2 \quad R_1 = \dfrac{R_2}{2}$	$C_1 = C_2 \quad R_1 = \dfrac{3R_2}{4}$
$C_1 = 0.022\ \mu F$ $C_2 = 0.022\ \mu F$ $R_1 = 5.115\ k\Omega\ (5.11)$ $R_2 = 10.23\ k\Omega\ (10.2)$	$C_1 = 0.022\ \mu F$ $C_2 = 0.022\ \mu F$ $R_1 = 10.85\ k\Omega\ (11)$ $R_2 = 14.47\ k\Omega\ (14.3)$

To Scale:

f < 1 kHz: multiply C (or R) by $\dfrac{1000}{f}$

f > 1 kHz: divide C (or R) by $\dfrac{1000}{f}$

(B) High pass.

unity-gain VCVS filters.

desirable. Further details on this circuit are contained in *The Audio Amateur* magazine, issue 4/75, showing how the PC layout can be used for other filtering functions.

Active Crossover Networks

Another useful application of the voltage-controlled voltage-source filter is within frequency-dividing active filters that are used as crossover networks to precede power amplifiers which are individually committed as woofer and tweeter drivers.

Previous research has shown that odd-order Butterworth networks give a minimum of phase and amplifier errors in the crossover region. A 6-dB/octave Butterworth does not attenuate sharply enough in the stopband, however, leaving the third-order case the optimum in terms of complexity and suitability. An example of a 500-Hz third-order Butterworth crossover is shown in Fig. 5-11A.

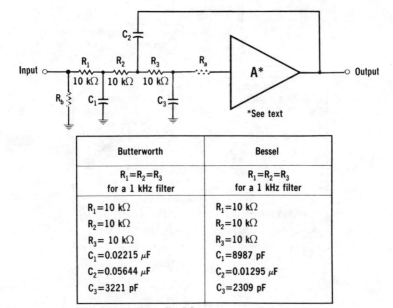

Butterworth	Bessel
$R_1=R_2=R_3$ for a 1 kHz filter	$R_1=R_2=R_3$ for a 1 kHz filter
$R_1=10$ kΩ	$R_1=10$ kΩ
$R_2=10$ kΩ	$R_2=10$ kΩ
$R_3=10$ kΩ	$R_3=10$ kΩ
$C_1=0.02215$ μF	$C_1=8987$ pF
$C_2=0.05644$ μF	$C_2=0.01295$ μF
$C_3=3221$ pF	$C_3=2309$ pF

Note: Scale similar to Fig. 5-8

(A) Low pass.

Fig. 5-9. Third-order

Equalized Amplifiers and Active Filters

As can be noted, this is simply a pair of high-pass and low-pass third-order Butterworth filters similar to those in Fig. 5-9, but scaled to a frequency of 500 Hz. Three amplifiers are required, which can be sections of a single AD711 device, plus the AD712 dual. Alternately, the universal plug-in filter arrangement shown in Fig. 5-10B can be used to physically realize this circuit as well, using a quad device. Other crossover frequencies are realized by scaling the resistor or capacitor values, as previously described. For the best results, high-quality R-C components are recommended.

Note that all cases may not require the input buffer stage, A_1. If the driving source has a low impedance, it can drive the R_1-C_1 node direct.

The response characteristics of the HI and LO outputs, respectively, are shown in Figs. 5-11B and 5-11C.

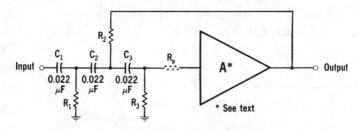

	Butterworth	Bessel
	$C_1=C_2=C_3$ for a 1 kHz filter	$C_1=C_2=C_3$ for a 1 kHz filter
	$C_1=0.022 \mu F$	$C_1=0.022 \mu F$
	$C_2=0.022 \mu F$	$C_2=0.022 \mu F$
	$C_3=0.022 \mu F$	$C_3=0.022 \mu F$
	$R_1=5.197 k\Omega$	$R_1= 12.80 k\Omega$
	$R_2=2.040 k\Omega$	$R_2=8.887 k\Omega$
	$R_3=35.74 k\Omega$	$R_3=49.89 k\Omega$

Note: Scale similar to Fig. 5-8.

(B) High pass.

unity-gain VCVS filters.

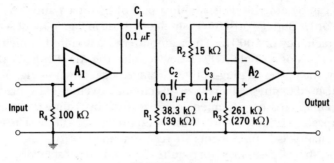

(A) 30-Hz values.

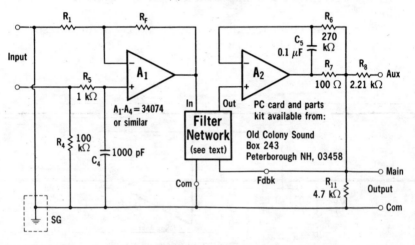

(B) The complete circuit.

Fig. 5-10. A 30-Hz rumble filter.

5.3.3 Multiple Feedback Filters

Another useful family of active filters is the "multiple feedback" type. Although not as straightforward or as easily tunable as the voltage-controlled voltage-source filters, multiple feedback filters are useful in certain situations. Since they operate in the inverting mode, they remove common-mode errors and, thus, the choice of amplifier type is less critical. The gain of these filters is not as easily controlled as the voltage-controlled voltage-source type, however, because it depends on component ratios and, sometimes, capacitor ratios. This type of circuit is best suited to fixed parameter applications; that is, constant frequency, constant Q, or constant gain. The high-pass and low-pass cutoff slopes are 12 dB/octave in the types illustrated here, which are all second-order types. Amplifier types optimum for these filters are those which perform well in the inverting mode.

The low-pass verison of the multiple feedback filter is shown in Fig. 5-12. In this circuit, R_1 and R_2 set the passband gain, H_o. The higher cutoff frequency is set by R_2-R_3 and C_1-C_2 as

$$f_{C_H} = \frac{1}{2\pi} \sqrt{\frac{1}{R_2 R_3 C_1 C_2}} \qquad \text{(Eq. 5-6)}$$

In the design of this filter, some simplifications are helpful. For the Butterworth maximally flat response, the Q will be $\sqrt{2}/2$. The ratio of C_1 to C_2 is a constant, K, which, when $K = 4Q^2(H_o + 1)$, yields simple value expressions. The design process is begun with the selection of C_1 and C_2, and then R_1, R_2, and R_3, in that order. Resistor R_4 is an optional bias resistor that is used to minimize dc output offset when necessary. Selection of the amplifier type will generally be in terms of the speed and/or noise level required, and it must be compensated for unity gain. For high-valued resistors, such as for low f_{C_H}, FET-input amplifier types, such as the AD711 and similar related units will be useful in minimizing capacitor values. Note that lowest noise will generally be realized with low resistor values, however.

The high-pass version of the multiple feedback filter is shown in Fig. 5-13. In this circuit, C_1 and C_2 set the passband gain, H_o. For maximally flat response and for $C_1 = C_3$, the lower cutoff frequency is set by C_2-C_3 and R_1-R_2 as

$$f_{C_L} = \frac{1}{2\pi} \sqrt{\frac{1}{R_1 R_2 C_2 C_3}} \qquad \text{(Eq. 5-7)}$$

The design is begun with the selection of C_1, C_2, and C_3, and then R_1 and R_2. Resistor R_3 is an optional bias resistor that is used to minimize dc output offset when necessary. Selection guidelines for the amplifier are generally the same as for the low-pass filter. Note that the input impedance of this circuit is capacitive; it should be driven from a low-impedance source.

A bandpass version of the multiple feedback filter is shown in Fig.

5-14. This circuit is generally useful with Qs up to 10, with moderate gains. The design process is begun by selecting C_1. For simplification, $C_2 = C_1$, so this also sets C_2. The center frequency of the passband is

$$f_{C_f} = \frac{1}{2\pi C_1} \sqrt{\frac{R_1 + R_2}{R_1 R_2 R_3}} \qquad \text{(Eq. 5-8)}$$

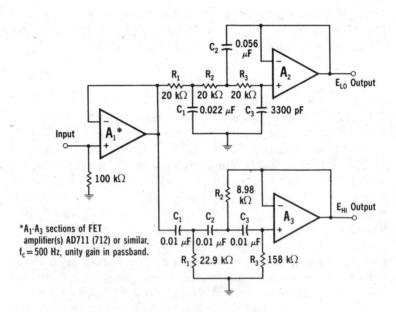

(A) Basic circuit.

Frequency	Probe	Value	dB	Phase
31.25 Hz	V:4	1.00008	0.001	172.816
62.5 Hz	V:4	1.00036	0.003	165.600
125 Hz	V:4	1.00122	0.011	150.925
250 Hz	V:4	0.995399	−0.040	119.299
500 Hz	V:4	0.697007	−3.135	43.921
1 kHz	V:4	0.121808	−18.286	−29.685
2 kHz	V:4	0.0154414	−36.226	−60.891
4 kHz	V:4	0.00193408	−54.271	−75.600
8 kHz	V:4	241.83u	−72.330	−82.949
16 kHz	V:4	30.2073u	−90.398	−87.050

(B) E_{LO} output response characteristic.

Fig. 5-11. Third-order Butterworth

Resistors R_1, R_2, and R_3 are then selected to satisfy the design requirements. Center frequency can be trimmed via R_2, if desired.

The selection guidelines for the amplifier are somewhat more restrictive in this circuit because, in addition to the general considerations for speed and noise, high Qs, frequencies, and gain will cause a loss of accuracy unless a high gain-bandwidth device is used. For example, if gains of greater than 1 with Qs approaching 10 are desired at frequencies above a few kilohertz, a high f_t device, such as the 5534 or 318, should be chosen.

10-Octave Graphic Equalizer

An interesting example of what can be done with the multiple feedback bandpass filter just described is contained in the 10-octave graphic equalizer of Figs. 5-15 through 5-19. This circuit, shown is block form in Fig. 5-15, achieves the function of "graphic" control of equalization, where a number of fixed discrete frequencies can be either boost or cut as desired. In the design described here, a 10-octave form is used with the frequencies as shown.

It is desirable that each individual bandpass response of a variable equalizer, such as this, be reciprocal in operation; that is, the shape of the bandpass must not vary between boost or cut—Q remaining constant. This is possible by placing the bandpass filters in a loop, such as was described for Fig. 5-4. Active filters, as used here, eliminate inductors and their undesirable features.

As can be noted from the block diagram, input and output buffer amplifiers are used to provide adequate drive for the multiple 10-kΩ

Frequency	Probe	Value	dB	Phase
31.25 Hz	V:4	245.958u	− 72.183	82.822
62.5 Hz	V:4	0.00196774	− 54.121	75.614
125 Hz	V:4	0.0157427	− 36.058	60.981
250 Hz	V:4	0.125052	− 18.058	29.604
500 Hz	V:4	0.710666	− 2.967	− 45.439
1 kHz	V:4	0.991721	− 0.072	− 119.990
2 kHz	V:4	0.998995	− 0.009	− 151.162
4 kHz	V:4	0.999102	− 0.008	− 165.744
8 kHz	V:4	0.999102	− 0.008	− 172.972
16 kHz	V:4	0.999097	− 0.008	− 176.659

(C) E_{HI} output response characteristic.

active crossover network.

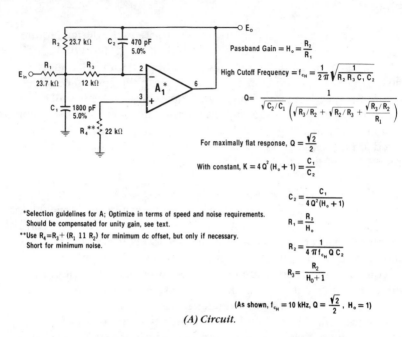

$$\text{Passband Gain} = H_o = \frac{R_2}{R_1}$$

$$\text{High Cutoff Frequency} = f_{c_H} = \frac{1}{2\pi} \sqrt{\frac{1}{R_2 R_3 C_1 C_2}}$$

$$Q = \frac{1}{\sqrt{C_2/C_1}\left(\sqrt{R_3/R_2} + \sqrt{R_2/R_3} + \frac{\sqrt{R_3/R_2}}{R_1}\right)}$$

For maximally flat response, $Q = \dfrac{\sqrt{2}}{2}$

With constant, $K = 4Q^2(H_o + 1) = \dfrac{C_1}{C_2}$

$$C_2 = \frac{C_1}{4Q^2(H_o + 1)}$$

$$R_1 = \frac{R_2}{H_o}$$

$$R_2 = \frac{1}{4\pi f_{c_H} Q C_2}$$

$$R_3 = \frac{R_2}{H_0 + 1}$$

(As shown, $f_{c_H} = 10$ kHz, $Q = \dfrac{\sqrt{2}}{2}$, $H_o = 1$)

*Selection guidelines for A; Optimize in terms of speed and noise requirements. Should be compensated for unity gain, see text.

**Use $R_4 = R_3 + (R_1 \parallel R_2)$ for minimum dc offset, but only if necessary. Short for minimum noise.

(A) Circuit.

Frequency	Probe	Value	dB	Phase
1.25 kHz	V:3	0.999258	−0.006	169.830
2.5 kHz	V:3	0.995776	−0.037	159.387
5 kHz	V:3	0.963688	−0.321	137.087
10 kHz	V:3	0.708295	−2.996	91.619
20 kHz	V:3	0.250364	−12.029	44.673
40 kHz	V:3	0.0650273	−23.738	20.960
80 kHz	V:3	0.0163236	−35.744	9.470
160 kHz	V:3	0.00408536	−47.775	2.996

(B) Response table.

Fig. 5-12. Low-pass, multiple feedback filter.

controls and filters. These two buffer circuits are inverting so that the net overall signal phase is noninverting. A DPDT bypass switch (S_1) allows A-B comparison of equalization effects. The design here allows ± 10 dB of equalization at each bandpass frequency, increasing several decibels if a number of adjacent filters are simultaneously boosted or cut, due to bandpass overlap. The Q of the bandpass filters is chosen as 1.5, to minimize overall response ripple when a

Equalized Amplifiers and Active Filters

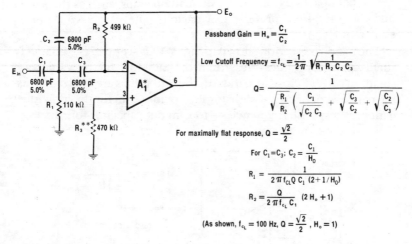

(A) Circuit.

Frequency	Probe	Value	dB	Phase
12.5 Hz	V:3	0.0156563	-36.106	-10.151
25 Hz	V:3	0.0625338	-24.078	-20.609
50 Hz	V:3	0.243453	-12.272	-43.248
100 Hz	V:3	0.710664	-2.967	-90.086
200 Hz	V:3	0.972061	-0.246	-136.856
400 Hz	V:3	0.998522	-0.013	-159.447
800 Hz	V:3	0.999967	0.000	-169.893
1.6 kHz	V:3	0.999988	0.000	-175.000

(B) Response table.

Fig. 5-13. High-pass, multiple feedback filter.

number of filters are used. In this design, the ripple over the band is less than ± 1 dB, with all filters boosted.

The individual circuit portions of the equalizer are shown in Figs. 5-16 through 5-19, and are largely self-explanatory. Within the two buffers, at input and output, a 100-mA IC output stage is used, the EL2003. This, in turn, in driven by a high-SR op amp, the 2525.

(An alternate device would be the 318, less the 20-pF capacitor.) In the 10 bandpass sections, high-SR quad op amps, such as the 34074 and the 34084 are preferred. A basic (single) stage would be as shown in Fig. 5-17.

The bandpass section shown in Fig. 5-17 is set up to use relatively small capacitor values—less than 0.1 μF. Most of the values are standard or very close to standard; the odd values are realized by using parallel connections. Resistor R_4 provides trim for the individual bandpass response frequencies—to trim out capacitor tolerances.

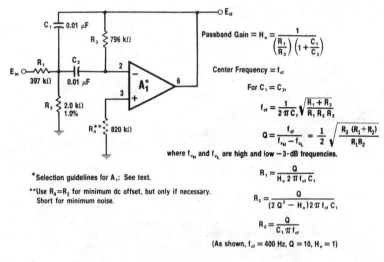

Passband Gain = $H_o = \dfrac{1}{\left(\dfrac{R_1}{R_3}\right)\left(1+\dfrac{C_1}{C_2}\right)}$

Center Frequency = f_{cf}

For $C_1 = C_2$,

$$f_{cf} = \frac{1}{2\pi C_1}\sqrt{\frac{R_1+R_2}{R_1 R_2 R_3}}$$

$$Q = \frac{f_{cf}}{f_{c_H}-f_{c_L}} = \frac{1}{2}\sqrt{\frac{R_3(R_1+R_2)}{R_1 R_2}}$$

where f_{c_H} and f_{c_L} are high and low −3-dB frequencies.

$$R_1 = \frac{Q}{H_o\, 2\pi f_{cf}\, C_1}$$

$$R_2 = \frac{Q}{(2Q^2 - H_o)2\pi f_{cf}\, C_1}$$

$$R_3 = \frac{Q}{C_1\pi f_{cf}}$$

(As shown, $f_{cf} = 400$ Hz, $Q = 10$, $H_o = 1$)

*Selection guidelines for A_1: See text.

**Use $R_4 = R_3$ for minimum dc offset, but only if necessary. Short for minimum noise.

(A) Circuit.

Frequency	Probe	Value	dB	Phase
200.000 Hz	V:3	0.0667599	−23.510	−93.829
229.740 Hz	V:3	0.085738	−21.337	−94.919
263.902 Hz	V:3	0.116584	−18.667	−96.695
303.143 Hz	V:3	0.176354	−15.072	−100.156
348.220 Hz	V:3	0.34159	−9.330	−109.968
400.000 Hz	V:3	1.00021	0.002	178.534
459.479 Hz	V:3	0.336034	−9.472	109.618
527.803 Hz	V:3	0.174749	−15.152	100.051
606.287 Hz	V:3	0.115841	−18.723	96.640
696.440 Hz	V:3	0.0853082	−21.380	94.881
800.000 Hz	V:3	0.0664779	−23.546	93.798

(B) Response table.

Fig. 5-14. Bandpass, multiple feedback filter.

Equalized Amplifiers and Active Filters

Although this circuit performs a specific function as described, it can also be modified for other characteristics, if desired. Equalization boost/cut limit can be increased or decreased by adjustment of the 2.49-kΩ resistor in Fig. 5-19. Overall (nonequalized) gain can be raised above unity by increasing the 10-kΩ feedback resistor in Fig. 5-16. Quad ICs of the types mentioned will, of course, allow greater packaging density of the bandpass circuits. Linear-motion slide potentiometers are most suitable for the individual bandpass controls, as is commonly seen in graphic equalizers.

5.3.4 The Biquad and State Variable Filters

There is a class of filters that is comprised of three or more op amps, connected as integrators and summing amplifiers, which synthesize filter characteristics. These filters simultaneously provide high-pass, low-pass, and bandpass outputs, and are relatively insensitive to Q

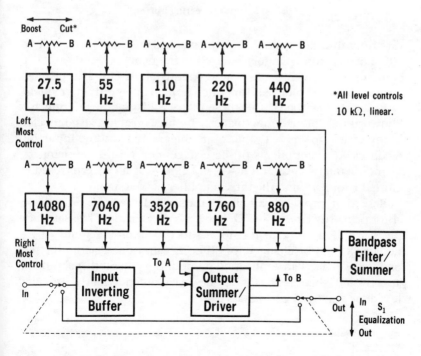

Fig. 5-15. Block diagram of 10-octave graphic equalizer.

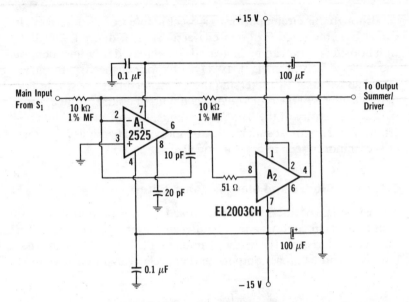

Fig. 5-16. Input inverting buffer.

variations due change in their elements, and are capable of Qs up to 100. Furthermore, parameters, such as frequency, Q, and gain, can be independently variable. These circuits are useful as a general-purpose building block and are often termed universal active filters.

In Fig. 5-20,[*] the first of these filters is diagrammed. Popularly known as the "biquad," it is made up of three op amps, all connected as inverters. Op amps A_2 and A_3 are integrators, and the input and feedback RC components of these stages control the resonant frequency, namely R_1-C_1 and R_2-C_2. Op amp A_1 is an inverter used to close the loop around the three amplifiers as a system.

Resistor R_3 provides damping of the second integrator, A_3. This resistor primarily determines Q, but it affects gain also. The signal input is applied via gain resistor R_4 to the summing point of A_3. Resistor R_4 may be changed for differing gain values, without effect on f_c or Q. This is an application point of the biquad that should be appreciated—bandpass gain may be varied independently, provided it is done via R_4. The bandpass gain is

---

[*]See Reference 16 at the end of the chapter for a discussion of this filter family.

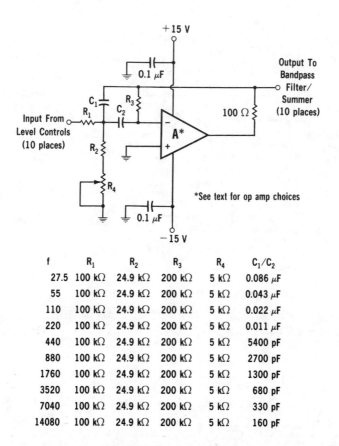

f	R₁	R₂	R₃	R₄	C₁/C₂
27.5	100 kΩ	24.9 kΩ	200 kΩ	5 kΩ	0.086 µF
55	100 kΩ	24.9 kΩ	200 kΩ	5 kΩ	0.043 µF
110	100 kΩ	24.9 kΩ	200 kΩ	5 kΩ	0.022 µF
220	100 kΩ	24.9 kΩ	200 kΩ	5 kΩ	0.011 µF
440	100 kΩ	24.9 kΩ	200 kΩ	5 kΩ	5400 pF
880	100 kΩ	24.9 kΩ	200 kΩ	5 kΩ	2700 pF
1760	100 kΩ	24.9 kΩ	200 kΩ	5 kΩ	1300 pF
3520	100 kΩ	24.9 kΩ	200 kΩ	5 kΩ	680 pF
7040	100 kΩ	24.9 kΩ	200 kΩ	5 kΩ	330 pF
14080	100 kΩ	24.9 kΩ	200 kΩ	5 kΩ	160 pF

Fig. 5-17. Bandpass filter.

$$H_{O_{BP}} = \frac{R_3}{R_4} \qquad \text{(Eq. 5-9)}$$

Q of the circuit is expressed as

$$Q = \frac{R_3}{R_2} \qquad \text{(Eq. 5-10)}$$

Since R_3 appears in both Q and gain expressions, a change in Q (via R_3) also affects gain.

Tuning may be accomplished via both the resistors or the capacitors, but there are other effects that should be understood. First of

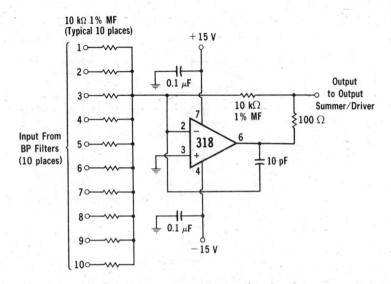

Fig. 5-18. Bandpass filter summer.

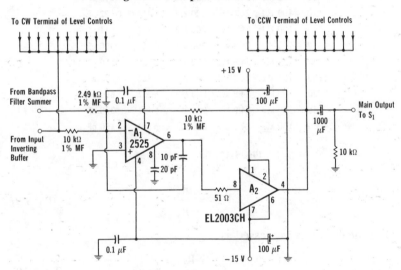

Fig. 5-19. Output summer/driver.

all, for frequency to vary inversely with R_1 (or C_1), both R (or C) elements must be varied simultaneously. A ganged tracking control (or switch selected pair) can be used for R_1-R_2 or switch selected C_1-C_2. Also, there is another important practical point to be considered.

Equalized Amplifiers and Active Filters

From Equation 5-10, it can noted that Q varies inversely with the value of R_2. As a result, variation of R_1-R_2 for tuning will vary Q as a natural consequence. If it is desired that Q be independent of frequency as it is varied, this may be accomplished by using C_1-C_2 to control frequency, rather than R_1-R_2.

It should be noted that the net effect of the change in Q, with R_1-R_2 tuning, is to maintain the bandwidth constant.

The biquad is most useful as a resonator or bandpass filter, and the bandpass response can be taken from either A_1 or A_3, with a choice of phase, as noted. In addition, a low-pass output is available from A_2.

One of the most attractive features of the biquad is its relatively high stability with regard to its passive components. Without this important stability factor, it would not be usable at very high Qs. The biquad is, in fact, capable of achieving Qs of several hundred, and high gain also. Best predictability of Q of high values, at frequencies of 1 kHz and up, is with high gain-bandwidth-product op amps, i.e., 3 to 4 MHz or more. A biquad design begins with the given values for f_c, H_o, and Q. Then, the designer selects C_1, which also fixes C_2. Next, R_1 (and R_2) are calculated from the f_c expression.

Note that with modern FET-input op amps, R_1 is not restricted due to bias current, and may range up to several megohms if desired. A practical limit for R, however, is set by the ratio to R_3, or Q. High Q values (such as in the example) may directly affect the R_1-R_2 values and/or C_1-C_2, because of the lack of abundance of good stable resistors above a few megohms. The design is complete with the selection of R_4.

It should be noted that attention to component quality is quite important in this circuit, otherwise some of its inherently high capability can be sacrificed. All resistors used in the circuit should be stable types, such as the low-temperature-coefficient metal-film types; the capacitors should be low-leakage, high-Q types, such as polystyrene or polypropylene types.

Multiple amplifier types, such as the dual and quad units, obviously make this filter attractive, and not really excessive in cost when the relative performance is considered. In the example shown in Fig. 5-20, a 34074 or similar op amp is suitable because of relatively low impedance and frequency. High frequencies and/or high Qs, particularly at high levels, will be better satisfied by higher-SR and/or GBP units, such as the 34084 or the OPA404.

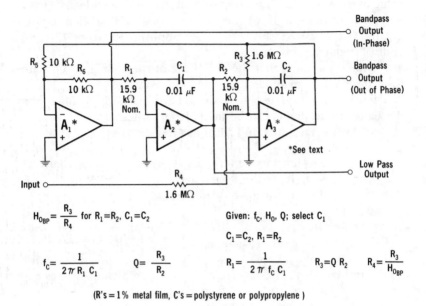

$$H_{O_{BP}} = \frac{R_3}{R_4} \text{ for } R_1 = R_2, C_1 = C_2$$

Given: f_c, H_0, Q; select C_1

$$C_1 = C_2, R_1 = R_2$$

$$f_c = \frac{1}{2\pi R_1 C_1} \qquad Q = \frac{R_3}{R_2} \qquad R_1 = \frac{1}{2\pi f_c C_1} \qquad R_3 = Q R_2 \qquad R_4 = \frac{R_3}{H_{O_{BP}}}$$

(R's = 1% metal film, C's = polystyrene or polypropylene)

Example parameters: $H_0 = 1$

$f_c = 1000$

$Q = 100$

Fig. 5-20. Biquad filter.

A more complete and flexible filter, that is closely related to the biquad, is the state variable filter (SVF) shown in Fig. 5-21. Actually, both filter circuits can be realized with the same amplifiers and basic circuit configurations, with but minor differences. There is a big difference in *flexibility* provided by the state variable type, however, as it simultaneously provides all three outputs. In addition, it can be manipulated for complete independence of the three design parameters: frequency, Q, and gain.

Simplification is also helpful in reducing this filter to an easily used form. If $R_1 = R_2$, $R_5 = R_6$, and $C_1 = C_2$, it becomes easily tunable and adjustable. The center frequency is then determined as

$$f_{cf} = \frac{1}{2\pi R_1 C_1} \qquad \text{(Eq. 5-11)}$$

The Q is set by R_3 and R_4 as

$$Q = \frac{R_3 + R_4}{2R_3}$$ (Eq. 5-12)

The passband gain equations for the three outputs differ only slightly. For the bandpass output,

$$H_{O_{BP}} = \frac{R_4}{R_3}$$ (Eq. 5-13)

For the low-pass output,

$$H_{O_{LP}} = \frac{2R_4}{R_3 + R_4}$$ (Eq. 5-14)

For the high-pass output,

$$H_{O_{HP}} = \frac{2R_4}{R_3 + R_4}$$ (Eq. 5-15)

This circuit (as does the biquad) offers a second-order response for the low-pass and high-pass outputs, but it should be noted that maximally flat response cannot be realized with a high Q, such as will often be desired from the bandpass output. If desired, a fourth output, in the form of a notch at the center frequency, may be obtained by summing the low-pass and high-pass outputs through equal value resistors, R_L and R_H. The input/output phase relations are noted in the figure (as in the biquad). Otherwise, the same general amplifier considerations apply to the state variable filter.

All three op amps used in this circuit must be unity-gain stable, but only A_1 must respond to differential signals. Tuning is accomplished by the simultaneous variation of C_1-C_2 or R_1-R_2, as in the biquad. There is no interaction with Q, however.

In the circuit shown in Fig. 5-21, operation is tailored for the bandpass response, yielding a Q of 50 at a frequency of 60 Hz and with a gain of 100. Resistors R_1 and R_2 are made variable by a small percentage to allow for the initial tolerance of C_1 and C_2. This allows tuning the filter exactly to the described frequency, which is a virtual necessity with a high-Q circuit.

As can be noted from the basic performance equations, Q and gain are independent of frequency, but are not independent of one another. Some useful options can be used with the Form A state variable filter, which allow further freedom in terms of these parameters and is shown in Fig. 5-22.*

In Fig. 5-22A, a method to minimize and control gain is shown, with high Q operation. Resistors R_A and R_B form an input attenuator, with R_B much less than R_3, so as to not alter Q. Resistor R_A can then adjust gain independent of Q. An alternate modification of this circuit is shown in Fig. 5-22B, for situations where Q must vary independent of gain. Both R_C and series resistor R_3 control Q, with R_3 adjusting gain. Note that this configuration can be relatively limited, in that variation of R_3 will still alter Q. This may or may not be significant, depending upon the relative gain and Q desired.

The scheme of Fig. 5-22C allows complete and unrestricted independence of gain and Q, albeit at the expense of an extra op amp and a ganged control. By tracking R_4 and R_7, Q is varied; while R_8 adjusts gain. Note that both parameters can range to low levels with this type of circuit, and still be independent.

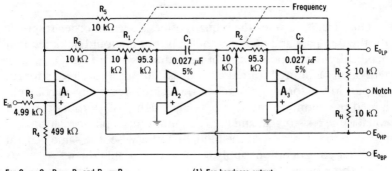

For $C_1 = C_2$, $R_1 = R_2$ and $R_5 = R_6$

$$f_{cf} = \frac{1}{2\pi R_1 C_1}$$

$$Q = \frac{R_3 + R_4}{2R_3}$$

$$R_4 = R_3 (2Q\text{-}1)$$

Tune by adjusting R_1-R_2 (or C_1-C_2) simultaneously (as shown, $f_{cf} = 60$Hz, $Q = 50$, $H_0 = 1000$).

(1) For bandpass output:
Passband Gain = $H_{0BP} = \frac{R_4}{R_3}$; Phase = $-180°$ @ f_c

(2) For low-pass output:
Passband Gain = $H_{0LP} = \frac{2 R_4}{R_3 + R_4}$;
Phase = $-90°$ @ f_c, in phase in passband.

(3) For high-pass output:
Passband Gain = $H_{0HP} = \frac{2 R_4}{R_3 + R_4}$;
Phase = $+90°$ @ f_c, in phase in passband.

Fig. 5-21. State variable filter, Form A.

---

*Jung, W. G. "Active Filters, Part III." *The Audio Amateur,* issue 2/76. Copyright© 1976 by *The Audio Amateur* magazine, Box 576, Peterborough, NH 03458.

Equalized Amplifiers and Active Filters

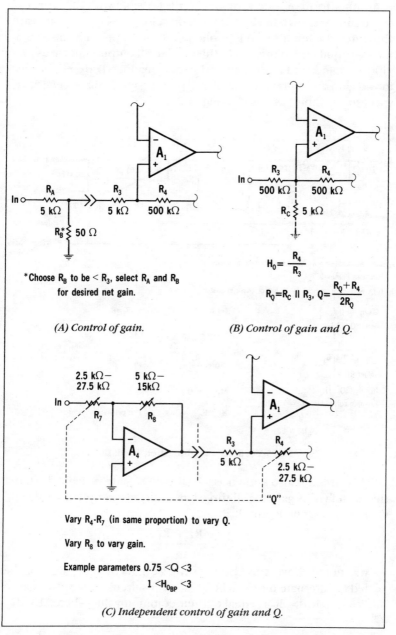

$*$Choose R_B to be $< R_3$, select R_A and R_B
for desired net gain.

(A) Control of gain.

$$H_0 = \frac{R_4}{R_3}$$

$$R_Q = R_C \parallel R_3, \quad Q = \frac{R_Q + R_4}{2R_Q}$$

(B) Control of gain and Q.

Vary R_4-R_7 (in same proportion) to vary Q.

Vary R_8 to vary gain.

Example parameters $0.75 < Q < 3$

$1 < H_{0BP} < 3$

(C) Independent control of gain and Q.

Fig. 5-22. Modifications to basic Form A state variable filter.

Another form of state variable filter is possible with the same basic circuit, as shown in Fig. 5-23.[*] In this circuit, a Form B state variable filter, the input signal is applied to the (–) input of A_1 instead of the (+) input (as in Form A). In this circuit, all outputs appear as previously stated, and it is tuned in the same manner. Differences exist in the gain and Q relations and the output signal phase(s) with respect to the input, as noted in Fig. 5-23.

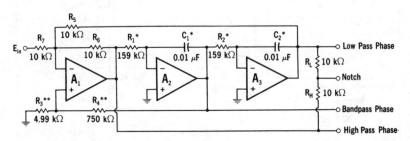

Low Pass Phase=+90°@f_c, out of phase in passband.
Bandpass Phase=0°@f_c.
High Pass Phase=−90°@ f_c, out of phase in passband.

Given: f_c, Q

Select C_1 (C_2)

$$R_1 = \frac{1}{2\pi f_c C_1}$$

Select R_3

$R_4 = R_3 (3Q-1)$

Example parameters: $f_c = 100$ Hz

$Q = 50$

$H_0 = 50$

For $R_1=R_2$, $C_1=C_2$, and $R_5=R_6=R_7$

$$*f_c = \frac{1}{2\pi R_1 C_1}$$

$$**Q = \frac{R_3+R_4}{3R_3}$$

$**H_{0BP} = Q$

H_{0HP}, $H_{0LP} = Q$ @ $f_c = 1$ in passband

Fig. 5-23. State variable filter, Form B.

This circuit is also known as a "gain of Q" state variable filter, for that is in fact its gain for all three basic outputs, simply the value of Q. The Q is set by R_3 and R_4.

$$Q = \frac{R_3 + R_4}{3R_3} \qquad \text{(Eq. 5-16)}$$

As was noted above, this also fixes the gain. As before, gain must be scaled by alternate means when using this circuit. Note also that in addition to R_5-R_6, R_7 is equal to their common value—here, 10 kΩ.

---

[*] Jung, W. G. "Active Filters, Part III." *The Audio Amateur,* issue 2/76. Copyright© 1976 by *The Audio Amateur* magazine, Box 576, Peterborough, NH 03458.

The Form B state variable filter has both advantages and disadvantages in performance over the Form A state variable filter. One of the advantages is that the gain equations for all three outputs are the same, or Q. However, gain and Q cannot be manipulated independently, at least in the basic Form B circuit.

The modified state variable Form B filter circuit of Fig. 5-24* allows Q to be adjusted independently of gain, by using a fourth op amp that enables all amplifiers to be true summers. The Q is varied here by R_4, and will still vary gain also. However, gain is varied by R_7 and will not affect Q in this circuit. If complete independence of Q and gain are desired, the circuit of Fig. 5-22B or C is the best choice.

State variable filter and biquad circuits are extremely powerful forms of active filters and, if desired, one can theoretically implement any desired filter response by the appropriate combination of stages and individual design parameters. As mentioned previously, the circuit is termed a universal one and many manufacturers offer hybrid forms in dual inline packages. An example is the National Semiconductor AFT-100, as well as units manufactured by Burr-Brown.

Infinitely Variable Equalizer

A unique application example which capitalizes on the performance features of the state variable filter is shown in Fig. 5-25. This circuit is an equalizer that is infinitely variable in terms of all control parameters: namely, frequency, Q, and gain.

The basic circuit that forms the heart of this equalizer is shown in Fig. 5-25. A state variable bandpass filter is placed within the input/feedback loop with op amp A_1. The state variable filter is a modified Form A type, and has an independently variable frequency and Q. The bandpass response can be spotted in frequency, with Q adjusted for the desired bandwidth. The level control allows reciprocal boost or cut. All controls are continuously variable, thus the term "infinitely variable" equalizer (also known as "parametric" equalization).

A block diagram of the circuit is shown in Fig. 5-26. As can be noted, it uses three state variable filter bandpass sections arranged for low-, mid-, and high-frequency bands. Op amp A_1 provides input

---

*Jung, W. G. "Active Filters, Part III." *The Audio Amateur,* issue 2/76. Copyright © 1976 by *The Audio Amateur* magazine, Box 176, Peterborough, NH 03458.

buffing and an overall noninverting signal phase. A 2525-type op amp is used for high gain-bandwidth-product and high output drive. An alternate for lower noise would be a pair of 5534 devices.

The details of the state variable filter bandpass sections are shown in Fig. 5-27. Here, A_1-A_3 form a state variable filter Form A circuit, with A_4 providing gain and an overall noninverting phase. The connection of R_c provides a wide-range variable Q characteristic (as described with the circuits of Fig. 5-22B). Resistors R_1-R_2 provide a 10/1 tuning range, and the C_1-C_2 values determine the operating range (see table in Fig. 5-27). In the experimental version of this circuit, 4136-type op amps were used, as they are generally suitable for output levels of 2 V or less. However, FET op-amp types, such as the 34084, are better suited, particularly for higher operating levels.

5.3.5 Twin-T Notch Filter

A well-known frequency rejection filter is the twin-T configuration of Fig. 5-28. Theoretically, this circuit is capable of infinite rejection at its frequency, f_o, if the components are well matched and if the

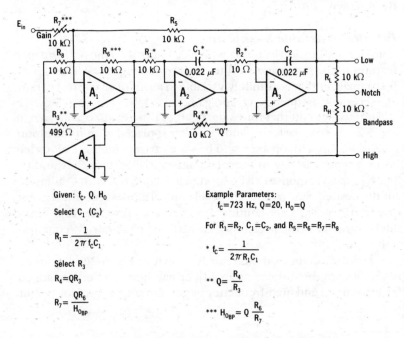

Given: f_c, Q, H_0

Select C_1 (C_2)

$$R_1 = \frac{1}{2\pi f_c C_1}$$

Select R_3

$R_4 = QR_3$

$$R_7 = \frac{QR_6}{H_{0BP}}$$

Example Parameters:
$f_c = 723$ Hz, Q=20, H_0=Q

For $R_1 = R_2$, $C_1 = C_2$, and $R_5 = R_6 = R_7 = R_8$

* $f_c = \dfrac{1}{2\pi R_1 C_1}$

** $Q = \dfrac{R_4}{R_3}$

*** $H_{0BP} = Q\dfrac{R_6}{R_7}$

Fig. 5-24. Modification to Form B state variable filter for control of gain.

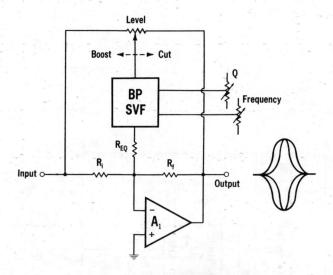

Fig. 5-25. Basic equalizer circuit.

source impedance is low and the load impedance is high. Buffering the output with a voltage follower will satisfy the requirement for high load impedance, and driving the input from an op-amp output will normally satisfy the requirement for low source impedance.

In terms of Q, or notch width, the response of the basic twin-T network can be enhanced appreciably by bootstrapping the normally grounded node of R_2-C_2 from the follower output, as shown in Fig. 5-29. This allows extremely narrow bandwidth notches to be realized even at low frequencies, with Q values of up to 50. Such a characteristic is very useful in removing 60-Hz hum components, for example, with a minimum of degradation to the bordering frequency response. If a variable-Q characteristic is desired, the loop can be broken at "X" and the A_2 circuit inserted, as shown in Fig. 5-29. The Q control (R_3) serves to continuously vary the effective performance between the normal and the bootstrapped condition. In either case, the R_2-C_2 node of the twin-T network should see a low source impedance in order to minimize null depth or frequency variations.

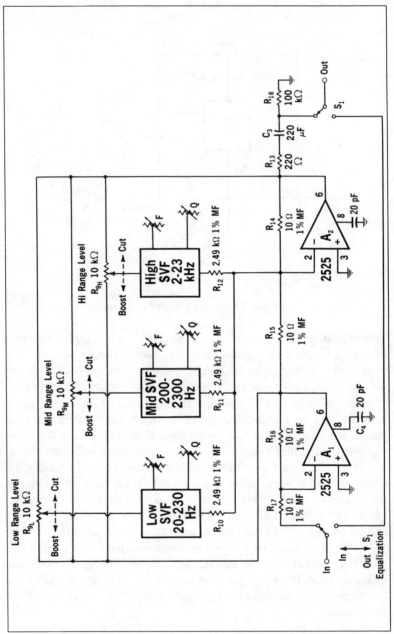

Fig. 5-26. Block diagram of an infinitely variable equalizer circuit.

Equalized Amplifiers and Active Filters

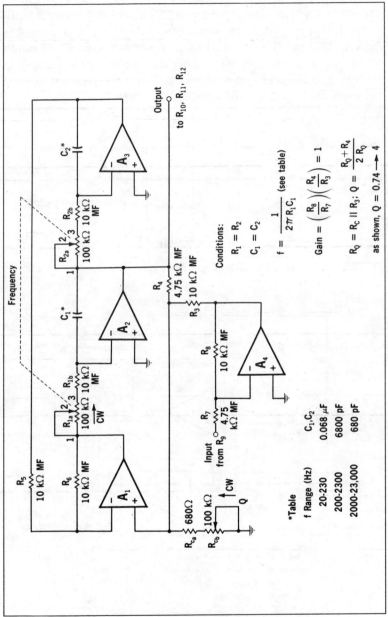

**Fig. 5-27. Independent and infinitely variable
state variable filter circuit.**

Equalized Amplifiers and Active Filters

The depth of the notch provided by the twin-T network can be effectively varied by connecting a potentiometer (R_4) from the input to the output and taking the output from the arm of the control as shown. This provides a continuously variable control of notch depth, and it can be used with either the normal or the variable-Q version. A 412 dual FET-input device is shown; if A_2 is not utilized, a 411 (or similar) device will operate just as well.

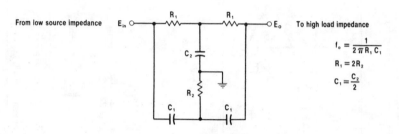

Fig. 5-28. Basic twin-T filter configuration.

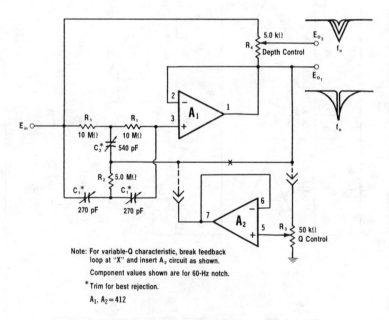

Note: For variable-Q characteristic, break feedback loop at "X" and insert A_2 circuit as shown.

Component values shown are for 60-Hz notch.

*Trim for best rejection.

$A_1, A_2 = 412$

Fig. 5-29. High-Q, twin-T filter with buffered output and variable-Q option.

Equalized Amplifiers and Active Filters

5.3.6 Easily Tuned Notch filter

Although the twin-T filter provides excellent rejection at a specific frequency, it is not readily adapted to the requirements of tuning. The circuit of Fig. 5-30, however, allows tuning by varying either a single capacitor or a resistor. The circuit is actually a bridge consisting of R_4-R_5, and R_3 plus the C_1-R_1-R_2 network. Components A_2, C_2, and R_1-R_2 form an equivalent circuit inductance, which at some frequency resonates with C_1, forming a notch in the response. The notch frequency, f_o, is

$$f_o = \frac{1}{2\pi\sqrt{R_1\ R_2\ C_1\ C_2}} \qquad \text{(Eq. 5-17)}$$

Thus, either R_1, R_2, C_1, or C_2 can be used to tune the circuit. It is convenient to make C_2 a large fixed value and use C_1 as a trimmer, as shown in the schematic. An alternate method is to use a potentiometer for R_1-R_2 that is equal in value to R_3 and trim the circuit in this manner. The close tolerances indicated for the resistances are necessary for best notch depth. These resistances can be realized either by using high-quality precision resistors or by trimming.

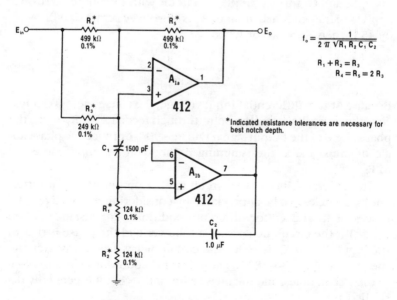

Fig. 5-30. Easily tuned notch filter.

When the dual 412 device is used for A_1, the circuit of Fig. 5-30 is suited for high-performance applications at frequencies up to 20 kHz. For higher-frequency use, a 318 device can be substituted for the two amplifiers, with a general lowering of resistances values. Both amplifiers should have good common-mode rejection. For less critical applications, a dual device, such as the 4558, can be used for both A_1 and A_2. In such cases, it is best to keep R_3 in the range of 100 kΩ or less and the signal levels at 2 V rms or less.

5.3.7 All-Pass Circuits

Using op-amp techniques, it is possible to alter the phase/frequency and amplitude characteristics of audio signals in a very precise and predictable manner. Phase-shifted and controlled stages are very useful tools when used in combination with other op-amp circuits. A class of active filters called *all-pass filters,* are useful for this and they exhibit a constant amplitude versus frequency characteristic.

Two circuits that exemplify the simplicity of op-amp techniques in phase manipulation are shown in Fig. 5-31. These circuits are identical except for the positions of R_3 and C_1, which determine the lag or lead characteristics. The circuit of Fig. 5-31A operates as follows; R_3 and C_1 form a simple lag circuit with the output across C_1 applied to the reference input of A_1. The voltage across C_1 will lag E_{in} by $45°$ when $X_{c_1} = R_3$, or when

$$f = \frac{1}{2\pi R_3 C_1} \qquad \text{(Eq. 5-18)}$$

Because of zero differential-input voltage, the voltage across C_1 must also appear at the summing point through feedback. If $R_1 = R_2$, the phase angle of the output signal will be $-90°$, or twice the phase angle of the signal at the summing point, with an amplitude equal to E_{in}.

The general ability of the circuit to alter output phase for different frequencies can be appreciated by considering the relative reactances of R_3 and C_1 for different conditions. For instance, when $X_{c_1} \gg R_3$, the circuit behaves as a follower and the phase is that of the input. When X_{c_1} is $\ll R_3$, the circuit behaves as an inverter and the output phase is $-180°$. These general conditions are described in the circuit notes, and the phase shift of the circuit is generally described as

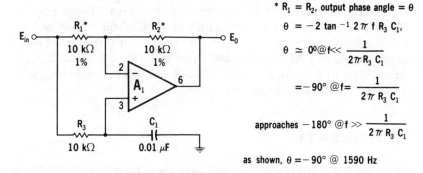

(A) Constant-amplitude lag circuit.

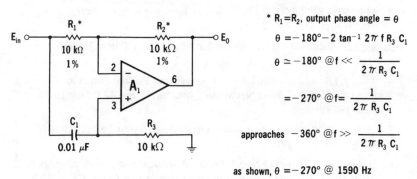

(B) Constant-amplitude lead circuit.

Fig. 5-31. Constant-amplitude, phase lead/lag circuits.

$$\theta = -2 \tan^{-1} 2\pi f R_3 C_1 \qquad \text{(Eq. 5-19)}$$

The companion circuit of Fig. 5-31B is achieved by interchanging C_1 and R_3. This circuit has the same amplitude properties as the circuit of Fig. 5-31A but, in this case, the phase shift is described as

$$\theta = -180° - 2 \tan^{-1} 2\pi f R_3 C_1 \qquad \text{(Eq. 5-20)}$$

As can be seen from the notes, this circuit behaves as an inverter at low frequencies and as a follower at very high frequencies, again due the relative reactances of C_1 and R_3.

Perhaps the most useful function for these circuits is the generation of 90° leading or lagging signals for phase detectors and similar circuits. The networks are easily adjustable by varying either R_3 or C_1, and the constant amplitude output can be a great convenience. Op amps compensated for unity gain will work in this circuit, but a low input-current, high input-resistance type, such as the 34081 (or other similar FET-input unit), will allow the widest range of R_3/C_1 values. The R_1-R_2 values are not critical but should be matched, so 10-kΩ, 1% values are suggested.

5.4 REFERENCES

1. Allen, P. E. "Practical Considerations of Active Filter Design." *Journal of the AES,* Vol. 22 #10, December 1974.

2. Al-Nassar, F. "Tables Shorten Design Time for Active Filters." *Electronics,* October 23, 1972.

3. _____. "Tables Speed Design of Low-Pass Active Filters." *EDN,* March 15, 1971.

4. Ashley, J R. and Kaminsky, A. L. "Active and Passive Filters as Loudspeaker Crossover Networks." *Journal of the AES,* Vol. 19 #6, June 1971.

5. Brokaw, A. P. "Simplify 3-Pole Active Filter Design." *EDN,* December 15, 1970.

6. Dobkin, R C. "High Q Notch Filter." *National Semiconductor LB-5,* April 1967, National Semiconductor Corp., Santa Clara, CA.

7. Doyle, N. P. "Swift, Sure Design of Active Bandpass Filters." *EDN,* January 15, 1970.

8. *Data Sheet AF100,* "Universal Active Filter." National Semiconductor Corp., 1976.

9. Estep, G. J. "The State Variable Filter Handbook."

10. _____. "Universal Active Filter Theory and Applications." Kinetic Technology, Santa Clara, CA, 1971.

11. Geffe, P. R. "Designer's Guide to Active Bandpass Filters, Parts 1–5." *EDN,* Febuary 5, 1974; March 5, 1974; April 5, 1974; May 5, 1974; June 5, 1974.

12. Hilburn, J. L. and Johnson, D. E. *Manual of Active Filter Design.* McGraw Hill, NY, 1973.

13. *IEEE Transactions on Circuits and System*—"A continuing dialogue on active filter realizations." (IEEE, New York).

14. Johnson, D. E. and Hilburn, J. L. *Rapid Practical Design of Active Filters*. Wiley, NY, 1975.

15. Jung, W. G. "Active Filters Part I." *The Audio Amateur,* issue 1/75.

16. _____. "Active Filters, Part II." *The Audio Amateur,* issue 2/75.

17. _____. "Active Filters, Part III." *The Audio Amateur,* issue 2/76.

18. _____. *IC Op-Amp Cookbook, 3rd Edition,* Howard W. Sams & Co., Indianapolis, IN, 1986.

19. Kerwin, W. J., Huelsman, L. P., and Newcomb, R.W. "State Variable Synthesis for Insensitive Integrated Circuit Transfer Functions." *IEEE JSSC,* Vol. SC-2, September 1967.

20. Kincaid, R. "RC Filter Design by the Numbers." *The Electronic Engineer,* October 1968.

21. Lancaster, D. *Active Filter Cookbook.* Howard W. Sams & Co., Indianapolis, IN, 1975.

22. Mitra, S. K. *Active Inductorless Filters.* IEEE Press, NY, 1971.

23. Patterson, M. "Designer's Guide to Active Filters, Parts 1–3." *EDN,* August 20, 1974; September 20, 1974; October 20, 1974.

24. Sallen, R. P. and Key, E. L. "Practical Method of Designing RC Active Filters." *IRE Transactions,* Vol. CT-2, 1955.

25. Shepard, R. R. "Active Filters Part 12, Short Cuts to Network Design." *Electronics,* August 18, 1969.

26. Tobey, G. E., Graeme, J. G., and Huelsaman, L. P. *Operational Amplifiers Design and Applications.* McGraw Hill, NY, 1971.

27. Williams, A B. *Active Filter Design.* Artech House, Dedham, MA, 1975.

28. _____. *Electronic Filter Design Handbook.* McGraw Hill, NY, 1981.

29. Manufacturers' Data Sheets.

Analog Devices	AD711	Op Amp
	AD712	Op Amp
Burr-Brown	OPA404	Op Amp
	3507	Op Amp
Elantec	EL2003	Buffer
Harris Semiconductor	HA2525 (series)	Op Amps
Linear Technology, Inc.	LTC1010	Buffer

Motorola Semiconductor Products Inc.	MC34070 (series)	Op Amps
	MC34080 (series)	Op Amps
National Semiconductor Corp.	LH0002	Buffer
	LH0033	Buffer
	LM318	Op Amp
Signetics	NE530	Op Amp
	NE5535	Op Amp
Tatum Labs	ECA software package.	

SIX

Miscellaneous Audio Circuits

In this final chapter of the book, we will discuss a variety of more special-purpose audio circuits that do not fit directly into any of the other distinct categories discussed in the preceding chapters.

6.1 SUMMING AMPLIFIER

A standard audio-signal processing function is the linear combination of a number of individual signals into a common output without crosstalk or loss. This function is well suited for the summing amplifier (inverter), which is often referred to as an *active combining network*. A 10-input summing inverter configured for unity signal gain in each channel is shown in Fig. 6-1. This circuit uses 10-kΩ input resistances and a 10-kΩ feedback resistance. Either a 318 or a 2525 (unity-gain compensated) op amp is used because of their high gain-bandwidth product, very high linearity, and fast slewing rate. An alternate type is the 5534, useful for low-noise requirements, or high-power outputs.

Channel isolation is an important performance parameter in a summing amplifier because it is undesirable for any signals to be coupled between adjacent channels. In general, for maximum isolation, the input resistances (R_i) should be high and the source impedances (R_s) low. Also, the feedback resistance (R_f) should be high,

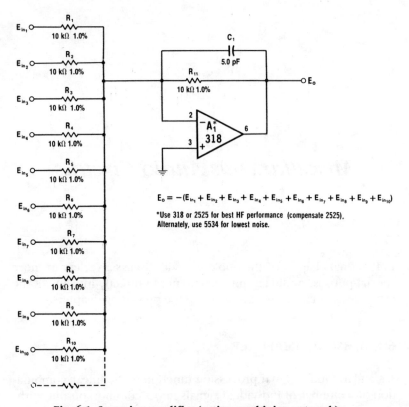

$$E_o = -(E_{in_1} + E_{in_2} + E_{in_3} + E_{in_4} + E_{in_5} + E_{in_6} + E_{in_7} + E_{in_8} + E_{in_9} + E_{in_{10}})$$

*Use 318 or 2525 for best HF performance (compensate 2525),
Alternately, use 5534 for lowest noise.

Fig. 6-1. Summing amplifier (active combining network).

with high loop gain ($A_{vo}\beta$). In practice, summing amplifiers are often
made unity gain where each individual input resistance equals the
feedback resistance, so channel isolation must be optimized by con-
trolling the source impedances or the loop gain.

The primary determinant of interchannel isolation is the nonzero
summing-bus impedance presented by the virtual ground of the inverter and, to a lesser extent, by the source impedances at the inputs.
Fig. 6-2 illustrates the method of calculating interchannel isolation.
There are two attenuations that a signal must undergo in order to
leak from one channel to an adjacent channel. The first attenuation
consists of R_i and R_{in}; the second consists of R_i and R_s. A typical example is calculated in Fig. 6-2.

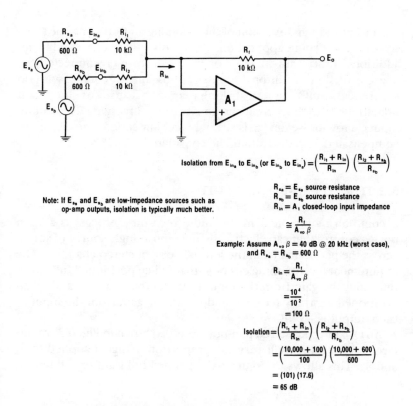

Isolation from E_{in_a} to E_{in_b} (or E_{in_b} to E_{in_a}) $= \left(\dfrac{R_{i_1} + R_{in}}{R_{in}}\right)\left(\dfrac{R_{i_2} + R_{s_b}}{R_{s_b}}\right)$

Note: If E_{s_a} and E_{s_b} are low-impedance sources such as op-amp outputs, isolation is typically much better.

$R_{s_a} = E_{s_a}$ source resistance
$R_{s_b} = E_{s_b}$ source resistance
$R_{in} = A_1$ closed-loop input impedance

$$\cong \frac{R_f}{A_{vo}\,\beta}$$

Example: Assume $A_{vo}\,\beta = 40$ dB @ 20 kHz (worst case), and $R_{s_a} = R_{s_b} = 600\ \Omega$

$$R_{in} = \frac{R_f}{A_{vo}\,\beta}$$

$$= \frac{10^4}{10^2}$$

$$= 100\ \Omega$$

$$\text{Isolation} = \left(\frac{R_{i_1} + R_{in}}{R_{in}}\right)\left(\frac{R_{i_2} + R_{s_b}}{R_{s_b}}\right)$$

$$= \left(\frac{10{,}000 + 100}{100}\right)\left(\frac{10{,}000 + 600}{600}\right)$$

$$= (101)\,(17.6)$$

$$= 65\ \text{dB}$$

**Fig. 6-2. Method of calculating interchannel isolation
for summing amplifier.**

The loop gain of the amplifier used will limit the attenuation due to a rise in R_{in} at the higher audio frequencies where the loop gain is lower. For a noise gain of 20 dB, such as in the 10-input summing amplifier of Fig. 6-1, a gain-bandwidth product of 20 MHz is required for 40 dB of loop gain at 20 kHz. In the example calculation in Fig. 6-2, the resulting crosstalk is −65 dB at 20 kHz, which is quite reasonable.

It can be seen from this example calculation that if R_s is low, crosstalk decreases. Therefore, by operating from low-impedance sources, such as op-amp outputs, R_s is controlled and crosstalk is reduced. In any case, the figures quoted are worst case, and crosstalk decreases in proportion to the increase in loop gain at the lower frequencies. For this reason, a high gain-bandwidth product amplifier is useful for summing-amplifier use.

The natural sign inversion of the summing amplifier may be a disadvantage for some applications. If so, this can be cancelled by an additional unity-gain inverter or by a transformer connected for phase inversion. Additional inputs are possible, of course, with no theoretical limit. Practical limits arise because of loop-gain limitations at high frequencies. In situations involving 20 or more inputs, a low-noise device is strongly recommended, and a custom-compensated amplifier should be considered.

6.2 STEREO PAN-POT CIRCUIT

A common requirement in the audio recording process is a "pan pot," a control that can electrically position a single source of sound across the panorama from the left to the right stereo channels. The requirement for a panning circuit is that, when positioned full left or full right, the gain from the input to the output is unity, and when positioned centrally (control midpoint), the gain from the input to each output is −3 dB.

An Orban-type[*] stereo pan-pot circuit is shown in Fig. 6-3. In this circuit, control R_2 will vary the proportion of signal applied to R_4 and R_6. This allows the signal to be panned full right or full left. At

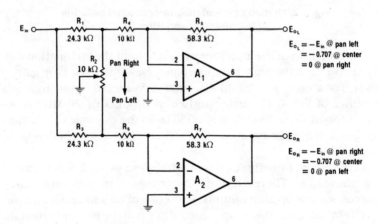

Fig. 6-3. Stereo pan-pot circuit.

[*]See Reference 19 at the end of the chapter.

the midpoint of rotation of R_2, the output from each amplifier is 0.707 (–3 dB) relative to a full pan right. Inverters A_1 and A_2 can also be summing amplifiers when additional panning circuits are wired into their summing points. The selection guidelines for A_1 and A_2 are the same as for the summing amplifier of Fig. 6-1.

6.3 IMPEDANCE-MATCHING TECHNIQUES

In Chapter 4, Section 4.2, on increased power output circuits using op amps, little attention was paid to matching the op-amp output impedance to the load. Usually, the extremely low characteristic output impedance of an op amp with heavy feedback is not a detriment, but rather a great asset, because it makes the output voltage quite independent of loading. There are, however, situations that require matched or controlled source impedances. The best examples of these are circuits that feed telephone distribution lines, and circuits that work into passive filters or equalizers designed for specific source impedances. In these situations, it is mandatory to provide a matched source of impedance, typically 500 or 600 ohms.

The simplest method of impedance matching is the "brute-force" technique of a "build out" series resistance equal to the load impedance, as illustrated in Fig. 6-4A. In this circuit, A_1 and its associated components can be any type of op-amp feedback circuit; the only assumption made is that the output impedance of the op amp is much less than R_s and R_L, which, for typical load values, is reasonable. Resistor R_s is simply a dummy resistance that is equal in value to the load impedance, R_L. For complete isolation, an output transformer is used together with a coupling capacitor, C_o, to eliminate dc from the transformer primary. If a DC servo is used with A_1, C_o is not necessary, of course.

The obvious disadvantage of this technique is that power is wasted in R_s, since R_s drops half the output voltage from A_1. This is not serious in terms of gain (which can be made up), but it is serious in terms of overload margin and dynamic range. A modification of this technique is illustrated in the circuit of Fig. 6-4B, which drives the transformer differentially, thereby recovering the dynamic range lost due to the source termination.

In this circuit, A_1 is a voltage follower with a gain of $(R_2 + R_3)/R_3$; thus, its output, E_{o_1}, is

$$E_{o_1} = E_{in} \left(\frac{R_2 + R_3}{R_3} \right) \qquad \text{(Eq. 6-1)}$$

A_2 is an inverter that inverts the output of A_1, developing an output E_{o_2}, which is

$$E_{o_2} = -E_{in} \left(\frac{R_2 + R_3}{R_3} \right) \left(\frac{R_5}{R_4} \right) \qquad \text{(Eq. 6-2)}$$

The signal applied to R_s, then, is the difference between E_{o_1} and E_{o_2}, or

$$\begin{aligned} E_{o_d} &= E_{o_1} - E_{o_2} \\ &= E_{in} \left(\frac{R_2 + R_3}{R_3} \right) \left(1 + \frac{R_5}{R_4} \right) \end{aligned} \qquad \text{(Eq. 6-3)}$$

The output voltage, E_o, is the voltage seen after the termination, or across R_L (assuming T_1 is a 1:1 transfer).

$$E_o = E_{in} \left(\frac{R_2 + R_3}{R_3} \right) \left(1 + \frac{R_5}{R_4} \right) \left(\frac{R_L}{R_s + R_L} \right) \qquad \text{(Eq. 6-4)}$$

Both stages in the circuit of Fig. 6-4B are operated with similar noise gains, but this is not essential. The gain of A_1 can be used to vary the composite circuit gain without altering the balance between the two outputs. The absolute power-output capability of this circuit is limited by the 5534 op amps, but it can easily develop outputs of + 15 dBm or more with negligible distortion (which is more than can be applied to a telephone line). In practice, the theoretical value of $R_s = R_L$ may need a slight downward adjustment if T_1 does not have negligible series resistance. Other op amps can be used, of course, for reasons of size and/or economy. For example, a 34082 (dual) amp will fair well in this circuit.

The preceding two methods of impedance matching are actually the same basic technique—the insertion of a fixed resistance in series with a low-impedance source to define the source impedance. A third method, shown in Fig. 6-4C, accomplishes impedance matching with considerably more finesse, using a combination of current and voltage feedback to improve efficiency. This circuit uses current feedback that is developed across a small resistance (R_1), which is in series with the load. This current feedback is combined with voltage feedback from R_2–R_3 in such a manner as to cause the circuit to act as an impedance equal to R_L, thus satisfying the matching requirement.

Since the resistance (R_1) in series with the load can be low in value and "transformed" upward by feedback, this technique is most efficient, and capable of delivering nearly the full output swing of the amplifier to the load.

The operation of this circuit is based on the fact that in any amplifier, when $R_s = R_L$, the loaded voltage gain is one half that of the unloaded voltage gain. In Fig. 6-4C, the voltage feedback from R_2–R_3 defines the unloaded voltage gain; then an equal gain ratio, provided by $(R_1 + R_L)/R_1$, is made to reduce this gain by a factor of two, thus satisfying the requirement of matched impedance. The circuit is most efficient at higher gains where $R_1 \ll R_L$. Also, $R_2 + R_s$ should be $\gg R_L$ for minimum power loss. The relationships given are approximate and if exact figures for gain and source impedance are required, some trimming of R_1 may be necessary. The values shown yield a closed-loop gain of 34 dB matched to the 600-ohm line. Power output, of course, depends on the amplifier, and losses due to R_1 will be almost negligible at closed-loop gains of 20 dB or greater. Although any op amp can be used in this circuit, the 2525 device offers a good choice of bandwidth (with single-capacitor compensation required). If an appreciably higher power output is required, either a 5534 device or a booster amp can be used (Chapter 4).

6.4 A TRANSFORMERLESS, BALANCED TRANSMISSION SYSTEM

Standard audio interconnection techniques employ transformer coupling at both the input and output, and use balanced transmission lines for common-mode noise immunity. This system works very well, but for high-quality use, the transformer cost is appreciable. Fig. 6-5 illustrates a system that electronically performs the functions of output and input transformers, and also retains the noise-rejection property of balanced signal-line transmission.

The circuit of Fig. 6-5A forms the transmission end of the system and employs two 5534 amps as a follower with gain and an inverter, respectively. Op amp A_1 amplifies (by a factor of 1.5) the input signal, E_{in}, which appears in low-impedance form at E_{o_1}, to drive one side of the balanced line. Simultaneously, A_2 inverts E_{o_1}, creating E_{o_2}, which is a mirror image of E_{in}. Output voltage E_{o_2} is applied to the opposite side of the balanced line. The total voltage across the line is then the difference of E_{o_1} and E_{o_2}, or $E_{o_1} - E_{o_2}$, which equals 3 E_{in}.

The 5534 amp was chosen for this application primarily because of its high-output capability. Resistors R_6 and R_7 are necessary to stabilize A_1 and A_2 in the presence of long high-capacitance lines. This stage can apply over ± 20 V across the twisted pair with negligible distortion, even up to a capability of + 24 dBm into a 600-ohm load. Among the dual-type amplifiers which will also work well (with less output) are the 34082 and TL072 units. Note that while it is not absolutely essential, resistors R_1–R_5 can be "made up" from a standard "8 × 2K" array, such as that specified.

At the opposite end of the transmission line, the signal is received

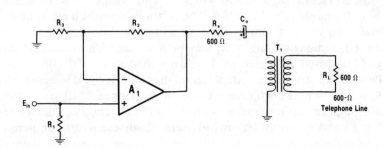

(A) Series resistance.

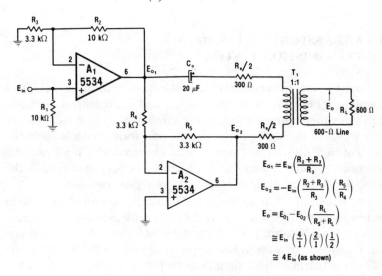

$$E_{o_1} = E_{in}\left(\frac{R_2 + R_3}{R_3}\right)$$

$$E_{o_2} = -E_{in}\left(\frac{R_2 + R_3}{R_3}\right)\left(\frac{R_5}{R_4}\right)$$

$$E_o = E_{o_1} - E_{o_2}\left(\frac{R_L}{R_s + R_L}\right)$$

$$\cong E_{in}\left(\frac{4}{1}\right)\left(\frac{2}{1}\right)\left(\frac{1}{2}\right)$$

$$\cong 4\,E_{in}\text{ (as shown)}$$

(B) Series resistance with differential drive.

Fig. 6-4. Impedance-

by the circuit of Fig. 6-5B. This circuit is a differential amplifier optimized for audio-frequency use. It converts the balanced line signal back to single-ended form, restored to its original level.

One of the drawbacks of the basic differential amplifier is the low input impedance, which causes common-mode errors when source impedances are unequal. In this case, however, the source impedance is quite low (and balanced), being essentially the dc resistance of the transmission line. Therefore, additional buffering is not required.

A 318 op amp was chosen for this application because of its excellent common-mode rejection at the higher audio frequencies, its high gain-bandwidth product, and its internal compensation. In order to realize a high common-mode rejection ratio at the higher frequencies, the bridge resistances must be kept low enough to negate the effects of capacitive imbalance at the input terminals of A_1. Equal

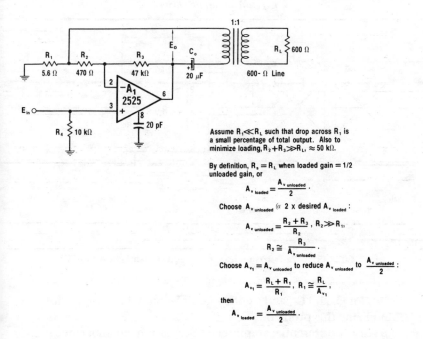

Assume $R_1 \ll R_L$ such that drop across R_1 is a small percentage of total output. Also to minimize loading, $R_2 + R_3 \gg R_L$, $\approx 50\ k\Omega$.

By definition, $R_s = R_L$ when loaded gain $= 1/2$ unloaded gain, or

$$A_{v\ loaded} = \frac{A_{v\ unloaded}}{2}.$$

Choose $A_{v\ unloaded}$ ($= 2 \times$ desired $A_{v\ loaded}$:

$$A_{v\ unloaded} = \frac{R_2 + R_3}{R_2},\ R_2 \gg R_1,$$

$$R_2 \cong \frac{R_3}{A_{v\ unloaded}}.$$

Choose $A_{v_1} = A_{v\ unloaded}$ to reduce $A_{v\ unloaded}$ to $\frac{A_{v\ unloaded}}{2}$:

$$A_{v_1} = \frac{R_L + R_1}{R_1},\ R_1 \cong \frac{R_L}{A_{v_1}},$$

then

$$A_{v\ loaded} = \frac{A_{v\ unloaded}}{2}.$$

(C) Impedance transformation.

matching techniques.

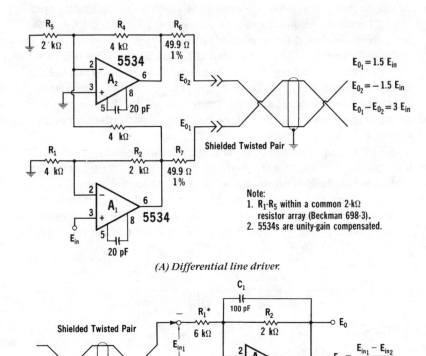

(A) Differential line driver.

(B) Differential line amplifier.

Fig. 6-5. A transformerless, balanced transmission system.

values for C_1 and C_2, and a good circuit layout will also be helpful in minimizing this problem.

As in any differential amplifier configuration, an imbalance in the bridge components will ruin the common-mode rejection ratio, and the situation is even worse in low-gain configurations. In the circuit of Fig. 6-5B, if any one of the resistors is off by 0.1%, the common-mode rejection ratio will be 60 dB. With well-matched components, this circuit will have a common-mode rejection ratio of 80 dB or better over the entire audio range. Thus, a common resistor array in strongly suggested for R_1–R_4 for best all-around results.

With regard to performance, this system can meet or exceed the performance of any system using the best available transformers. Frequency response is far in excess of transformer capability, as is linearity. Noise rejection should be as good as, or better than, a transformer system since the lines are held at a very low impedance by the line-driver circuit (Fig. 6-5A), which minimizes electrostatic coupling. Finally, the cost of the components for this system is below that of a high-quality transformer.

6.5 PRECISION VU-METER AMPLIFIER

The almost universal method of monitoring audio-signal levels is by means of a VU meter—a specialized voltmeter calibrated to read power in a 600-ohm circuit. Standard VU meters will read 0 VU when connected across a 600-ohm line at a level of 1 mW (0 dBm), which is an industry standard reference level. A VU meter is a specially designed meter with defined ballistic characteristics that are valid only when the meter is connected through its specified source impedance of 3600 ohms. It has an internal rectifier and, with the external resistor, is used as a passive device to monitor the level of 600-ohm lines. The total impedance of such a metering circuit is 7500 ohms which, although generally termed a bridging circuit, does introduce a small loss of a fraction of a decibel, in addition to a slight distortion of the signal, in a 600-ohm circuit.

The bridging error and distortion, due to the meter impedance in shunt with the signal line, can be virtually eliminated by the voltage-follower buffer circuit shown in Fig. 6-6. This circuit uses a 351 or TL071 FET-input op amp because of its low bias current, which allows it to work from megohm source resistances with low output offset. A 1-megohm bias resistor (R_1) is used, which essentially constitutes the input impedance of the circuit. The only real need for R_1 is to prevent off-scale meter deflection in the absence of an input connection, such as is encountered in portable use. If the circuit is used as an integral part of a piece of equipment, R_1 can be eliminated.

Since the VU meter is actually a voltmeter calibrated to read power in a 600-ohm circuit, its use at other line impedances will necessitate recalibration. This is a relatively simple matter because most standard impedances are lower than 600 Ω. It involves rescaling the voltage for 1 mW at the lower impedance, up to the 600-ohm voltage for 1 mW. In practice, this is done by adding a feedback network to provide the A_1 stage with a gain higher than unity, and does not compromise the input impedance to any significant extent. As noted in Fig. 6-6, the difference in voltage levels between the impedances is equal to the square root of the impedance ratio, and this defines the gain of the stage. Since this circuit is a measuring device, the scaling factor provided by R_3 and R_4 should be accurate; therefore, precision components should be used.

The 351 device has a quiescent power-supply current of less than 2 mA, and works well at lower supply voltages; thus, operation from a pair of 9-volt batteries is quite feasible. With this circuit, the accuracy of the indicated audio-signal levels will be entirely a function of the quality of the VU meter used.

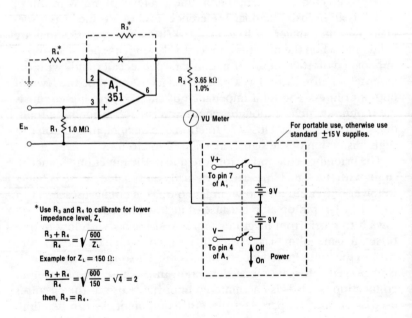

Fig. 6-6. Precision VU-meter amplifier.

6.6 LINEAR-FEEDBACK, GAIN-CONTROLLED STAGES

A very useful feature of the op-amp feedback configuration is the fact that the feedback current is independent of the resistance through which it flows. This factor can be used to advantage to build precision gain-controlled stages, with the gain adjusted by means of a single resistance, as illustrated in Fig. 6-7.

Fig. 6-7A is an inverting configuration in which feedback resistor R_2 is used to vary the gain. With R_1 and C_1 fixed in this circuit, the input current to the summing point will remain constant, as will the low-frequency −3-dB rolloff point. Resistor R_2 permits adjustment of the inverting gain from zero, when $R_2 = 0$, up to a maximum gain of R_2/R_1, when R_2 is at maximum resistance. Tabular values are given for maximum gains of 1 and 10.

The amplifier must be compensated for the lowest gain condition, where $R_2 = 0$ and feedback is 100%; therefore, unity-gain compensation is necessary. If maximum gains much higher than unity are required, A_1 should be a wide-bandwidth, fast-slewing type, such as a 5534, a 318, or a 2525 compensated for unity gain. This circuit can serve as a precision attenuator if R_2 is made a calibrated control, with the gain varying linearly with the total resistance of R_2.

A similar gain-controlled stage is possible with the noninverting configuration, as shown in Fig. 6-7B. Feedback resistor R_2 is also used in this circuit to vary the gain. A basic difference in this circuit is its minimum gain, which is unity when $R_2 = 0$. The circuit must also be compensated for unity gain due to 100% feedback when $R_2 = 0$. For this reason, a wide-bandwidth, fast-slewing device is preferred for A_1, as in the inverting circuit. Also, as in the inverting circuit, gain adjustment does not affect the frequency response or the input impedance (within the limits of gain noted). The gain of this circuit will vary linearly with R_2 from a minimum of unity when $R_2 = 0$, up to a maximum gain of $(R_1 + R_2)/R_1$ when R_2 is at maximum resistance.

In both of these circuits, remote adjustment of gain is possible if feedback resistor R_2 is electronically adjustable. For example, if R_2 is a light-dependent resistor or other voltage- or current-dependent resistance, such possible uses as agc amplifiers, compression amplifiers, etc., are suggested.

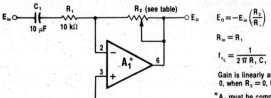

$$E_o = -E_{in}\left(\frac{R_2}{R_1}\right)$$

$$R_{in} = R_1$$

$$f_{c_L} = \frac{1}{2\pi R_1 C_1}$$

Gain is linearly and continuously variable from 0, when $R_2 = 0$, to R_2/R_1, when $R_2 =$ maximum.

*A_1 must be compensated for unity gain; therefore, it should be a high f_t type if $R_{2(max)} / R_1 > 1$.

$R_{2(max)} / R_1$	R_2 (linear)	A_1 (suggested)
1	10 kΩ	5534, 318, 2525
10	100 kΩ	5534, 2625, 357

(A) Inverting amplifier.

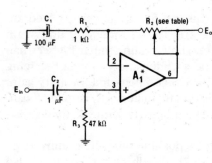

$$E_o = E_{in}\left(\frac{R_1 + R_2}{R_1}\right)$$

$$R_{in} = R_3$$

$$f_{c_L} = \frac{1}{2\pi R_1 C_1}$$

Gain is linearly and continuously variable from 1, when $R_2 = 0$, to $(R_1 + R_2)/R_1$, when $R_2 =$ maximum.

*A_1 must be compensated for unity gain; therefore, it should be a high f_t type if $R_{2(max)} / R_1 > 1$.

$R_{2(max)} / R_1$	R_2 (linear)	A_1 (suggested)
2	1.0 kΩ	5534, 318, 2525
11	10 kΩ	5534, 2625, 357

(B) Noninverting amplifier.

Fig. 6-7. Linear-feedback, gain-controlled stages.

6.7 SINUSOIDAL OSCILLATORS

The most familiar waveform in electronics is the sine wave, and sine-wave signals of different frequencies are as fundamental to audio-circuit work as dc supply potentials. Generating a sine wave is not hard in concept, as we have already seen by the ready tendency of op amps to oscillate when amplification is really the prime intent. This section concerns itself with the controlled form of sine-wave oscillator, having a defined and predictable frequency, amplitude, and, in some cases, phase.

Miscellaneous Audio Circuits

6.7.1 Wien-Bridge Oscillators

One of the most familiar types of sine-wave generators is the Wien-bridge circuit shown in Fig. 6-8. This circuit is a classic one in electronics and has been used since the days when it was realized in vacuum-tube verisons. The Wien network, composed of R_1–C_1 and R_2–C_2, provides a positive feedback path around A_1, while R_3 and L_1 provide negative feedback. At some fundamental frequency, f_o, the overall phase shift is zero and transmission at this frequency is maximum in relation to all others. Positive feedback causes the circuit to oscillate at f_o, where

$$f_o = \frac{1}{2\pi R_1 C_1} \qquad \text{(Eq. 6-5)}$$

and $R_1 = R_2$, $C_1 = C_2$.

The attenuation of the Wien network at the frequency of oscillation is equal to 3. If the attenuation in the negative feedback path (R_3–L_1) is also 3, the bridge will be in balance and the differential input to A_1 will be small. It is this condition that must be maintained because, if the positive feedback is greater, oscillations will quickly build up until amplifier saturation is reached. On the other hand, if the negative feedback is greater, the oscillations die out. In a practical Wien-bridge oscillator, it is therefore necessary to provide some means of automatically balancing the feedback so that the amplitude of the oscillation can be regulated. In this state, the purity of the output waveform will be at a maximum, as will the frequency stability. Another requisite is that the amplifier gain be large at the frequency of oscillation—the input error will then be small, which guarantees that the Wien network operates close to its natural frequency and is stable.

Any means of stablizing the amplitude of a Wien-bridge oscillator must involve adjustment of the negative feedback divider to maintain the attenuation at a value of 3. Typically, this can take the form of nonlinear elements: thermal types (such as lamps or thermistors), nonlinear resistors, diode clippers, zener diodes, and so on. In Fig. 6-9, the nonlinear resistance of a lamp (L_1) is used to regulate the amount of negative feedback. Lamp L_1 responds to the average (not instantaneous) output level of A_1, adjusting its terminal resistance in inverse proportion. If the output level of A_1 rises, L_1 increases resistance, counteracting the rise. Similarly, a reduction in output results in a decrease of lamp resistance, stabilizing the oscillation level.

Lamp and thermistor stabilization schemes are popular ones, due mainly to their simplicity. They have several drawbacks, however, such an inherent thermal time constant that limits usefulness to the lower frequencies.

The circuit of Fig. 6-8 is quite useful as a general-purpose Wien oscillator; with the appropriate amplifier, it can be used over a wide range of frequencies. Resistors R_3-R_4 trim the negative feedback to accommodate lamp tolerances. If precise amplitude control or optimum stability for individual lamps is not necessary, let $R_3 + R_4 = 750\ \Omega$. For frequency-turnable generators, either R_1-R_2 or C_1-C_2 can be ganged as a pair (with good tracking characteristics). If C_1-C_2 are selected as the tunable elements, large values for R_1-R_2 are required to cover the lower frequencies, which raises the network impedance. In such cases, C_1-C_2 should be in a shielded enclosure and stray capacitances to ground should be minimized for best results.

The amplifier type should be a high-slew-rate unit for high-frequency, high-level outputs, such as a 318, 5534, OP-27 or OP-37, or one of the FET types. FET types also work well with high-value resistances.

6.7.2 FET-Stabilized Wien Oscillator

Another popular method of achieving amplitude control is by using the variable channel resistance of a field-effect transistor. By sam-

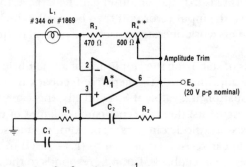

Set $R_1 = R_2$, $C_1 = C_2$; then $f_o = \dfrac{1}{2\pi R_1 C_1}$

*Select A_1 according to operating frequency and value of R_1; see text.
* *Use R_4 to correct for lamp tolerance and set output level, or fix $R_3 + R_4$ at 750 Ω.

Fig. 6-8. Wien-bridge oscillator.

Miscellaneous Audio Circuits

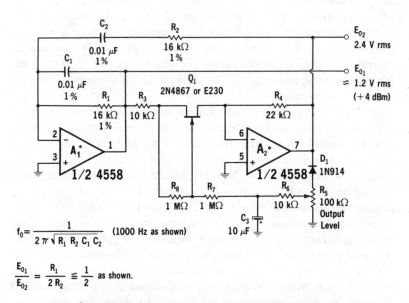

$$f_0 = \frac{1}{2\pi\sqrt{R_1 R_2 C_1 C_2}} \quad \text{(1000 Hz as shown)}$$

$$\frac{E_{01}}{E_{02}} = \frac{R_1}{2R_2} \cong \frac{1}{2} \quad \text{as shown.}$$

Fig. 6-9. Wien-bridge oscillator with FET stabilization.

pling and rectifying the output voltage, a dc signal proportional to the output amplitude can be made to control the resistance of a FET. This technique works well within limits, but the channel resistance of the FET itself is nonlinear at high signal levels, and appreciable distortion can occur.

Fig. 6-9 is a Wien-bridge oscillator rearranged to effectively utilize the FET channel resistance as a gain control. In this circuit, R_1-R_2 and C_1-C_2 again compromise the Wien network, but with the impedance of the legs scaled so that R_1-C_1 sees a voltage lower than R_2-C_2. This allows the voltage level at R_1-C_1 to be of lower amplitude. The circuit uses two amplifiers in the inverting mode; gain control is accomplished by FET Q_1, which is placed at the summing point of A_2 (a point of minimum voltage). Field-effect transistor Q_1 can then operate at a level low enough to make its distortion negligible. Op-amp A_2 provides a nominal gain of 2, which is trimmed by R_5 so that Q_1 is operating in the most linear portion of its characteristic curve.

The circuit has dual outputs available with two amplifiers; level differences are determined by the Wien network (R_1-R_2). Output voltage E_{0_1} will have less residual distortion than E_{0_2} because it operates at a lower level and is filtered by the Wien network prior to being controlled by Q_1. The high output level of A_2 is sampled by R_5, which derives the bias to control Q_1. This resistor can be used as an output-level control to adjust the output level linearly. Resistor R_4 can be trimmed for lowest distortion, which is necessary due to differences among individual FETs, if distortion is to be at the lowest level.

The amplifiers used should follow the guidelines set down for Fig. 6-8. For general-purpose use, dual devices are obviously attractive. It should be noted that the equation for operating frequency is the general form, due to the difference in R_1-R_2 and C_1-C_2. The ratio used in the bridge may be altered from that shown, if desired, but it should be appreciated that as R_2 increases above R_1, stage A_2 must supply additional gain, thus making its distortion contribution more significant, particularly at high frequencies. The ratio shown provides a good compromise between the low-level operation of Q_1 and minimal gain for the A_2 stage. When property trimmed, the oscillator has less than 0.05% distortion at both outputs with A_2 levels up to $\pm$ 10 V p-p. When the oscillator is operated over a wide range of frequencies, some adjustment of C_3 may be necessary at low frequencies. Note that dual-FET op amps, such as the high-slew-rate 34082, will be very effective in this circuit.

6.7.3 Oscillators Using Gain-Control ICs

From the two circuits that have already been described, it is obvious that two of the fundamental elements of a low-distortion sine-wave oscillator are the amplifier and the agc system. Very efficient circuitry can result if these two ingredients can be realized in a single IC. The oscillator circuit of Fig. 6-10 uses this principle, employing the Signetics NE570 or NE571, ICs specifically designed for gain-control use, which includes (two) op amp, rectifier, and gain-control circuits. Each section of these devices (A and B) may be used separately. The NE570 and NE571 are designed to be used with single-supply systems, and the circuit of Fig. 6-10 operates from + 15 V.

A Wien-type oscillator is shown in Fig. 6-10; it can use either the 570 or 571 IC. The two internal op amps of the device operate in the inverting mode, and the gain control of section B provides the necessary agc to stabilize oscillations. Resistor R_6 sets the output level, which is either 1.5 V, as shown, or 3 V if taken from pin 10.

Resistors R_1, R_2 and capacitors C_1, and C_2 are the frequency-determining components, and the frequency expression is the same as in the previous Wien circuits. Operating range is 10 Hz to 10 kHz, and distortion is generally below 0.1%. C_{rect} serves as the rectifier filter capacitor, and may require optimizing for frequencies other than the 400-Hz example illustrated.

The circuit, as shown, is a simple and useful source of spot frequencies. In addition, phase shift oscillators can also be constructed. Further information on the 571 and related circuits can be found in the references at the end of the chapter.

6.7.4 Oscillators Based on the State Variable Filter (SVF)

Some very interesting, useful, and very-high-performance oscillators can be realized by using the state variable frequency as the frequency-determining element of a sine-wave oscillator. Two examples of this technique are shown in Fig. 6-11.

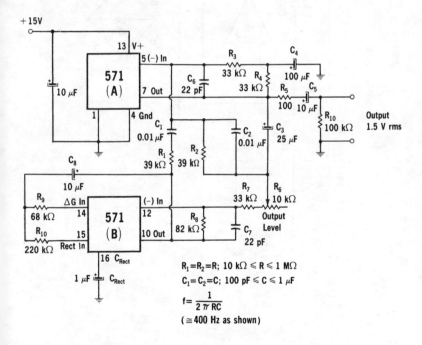

Fig. 6-10. Wien oscillator using a 571 (or 570) gain-control IC.

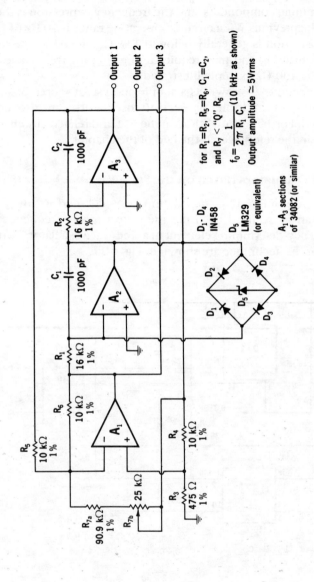

for $R_1 = R_2$, $R_5 = R_6$, $C_1 = C_2$,
and $R_7 < $ "Q" R_6

$$f_0 = \frac{1}{2\pi\, R_1\, C_1} \text{ (10 kHz as shown)}$$

Output amplitude $\simeq$ 5Vrms

$D_1 \cdot D_4$
1N458

D_5
LM329
(or equivalent)

A_1-A_3 sections
of 34082 (or similar)

(A) Amplitude limit stabilization.

Fig. 6-11. Oscillators

In Fig. 6-11A, a state variable frequency oscillator is shown which is amplitude stablized by the zener diode clamping one of the integrators, A_2. This has the effect of rigidly defining the peak amplitude swing of this stage and, in turn, defines the output amplitude of all outputs. At resonance, all three outputs are of equal amplitude, but differ in phase. The frequency is simply;

$$f = \frac{1}{2\pi R_1 C_1}$$ (Eq. 6-6)

(Note that R_1, R_2, C_1, and C_2 should be precision types.)

Aside from the zener amplitude limiter, the other salient difference of this state variable frequency beyond the basic form-A type is resistor R_7. This resistor provides the necessary positive feedback to initiate and sustain oscillation. The selection of R_7 is somewhat critical, if maximum performance is to be realized. If R_7 is too large, in-

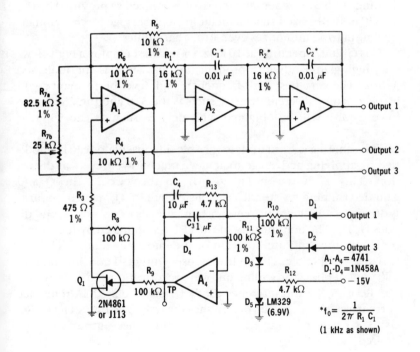

(B) Active FET agc.

based on the SVF.

sufficient positive feedback is attained and oscillation will not start. If too small, the excessive positive feedback drives D_5 into hard conduction and creates excessive distortion.

Trimmer R_7 is selected to provide a gain that is just in excess of the Q, as defined by $(R_3 + R_4)/2R_3$. Here the Q is 11, which indicates R_7 should be 10 kΩ $\times$ 11 = 110 kΩ. To guarantee self-starting, R_7 is purposely made several percent lower, or 90.9 kΩ.

For a given set of operating conditions, R_7 can be optimized by observing the distortion present at Output 2. With D_5 being driven into a moderate degree of conduction, the total harmonic distortion will be on the order of 0.3%, and R_{7_b} can be trimmed to provide this.

Due to the natural low-pass filter action of the A_3 integrator, Output 1 will be approximately 10 dB cleaner in distortion than Output 2, or on the order of 0.1% (for 0.3% at Output 2).

One of the advantages of zener-limiting stabilization in a scheme such as this is that it is fast and has no time constant. To optimize the limiting, a "hard" zener characteristic is utilized as provided by the LM329 (a synthesized zener). Including it in a bridge forces symmetric limiting and minimizes even-order harmonics.

This circuit, operating at 10 kHz, should best employ a high-slew-rate, high-gain-bandwidth-product op amp, such as the indicated 34082. The very best high-frequency, high-level performance will be obtained by discrete devices, such as the 318 and the 2525. The lowest noise will be obtained with devices such as the 5534 or the OP-27.

This same basic form of state variable filter oscillator can be modified by applying active agc to achieve much lower levels of distortion. This is shown in Fig. 6-11B. In this circuit, the Q and gain-determining resistor, R_3, is adjusted by FET Q_1, which, in turn, is driven by an integrator/rectifier that consists of op amp A_4 and diodes D_1,D_2. The nonlinearity of the FET is minimized by local feedback, and the "infinite" dc gain of the integrator renders FET V_{GS} variations negligible. The rectifier senses Outputs 1 and 3, which are 180° out of phase, providing full-wave rectification and easier filtering. Resistor R_{11} and reference diode D_5 provide a 70-μA reference current (set by R_{11}), which determines the stabilized output level. Resistor R_{11} can, of course, be adjusted for other output levels, if desired.

Distortion in this oscillator is extremely low, due to the linear method of stabilization. Output 2 distortion will be 0.005% or less when operating properly, and Output 1 distortion will be 0.002% or less. Setting time for frequency changes, or at "switch on," is 5 seconds or less, and is determined by the feedback network of the integrator, C_3 and C_4-R_{14}. These components may require adjustment for frequencies largely separated from 1 kHz.

Distortion is, of course, lowest at Output 1, but the extremely low levels quoted should be preserved by the use of a buffer amplifier, as described in Chapter 4. At the (1 kHz) example frequency, the 4741 or 348 quad op amps will work well. The circuit will operate with any FET as specified, but distortion can be optimized to match the exact characteristics by trimming R_7. As R_7 is increased above 82 kΩ, distortion lowers toward 0.002% (Output 2). The dc bias at the test point should be –1 V to –2 V, an indication of linear operation.

6.8 FUNCTION GENERATORS

One of the most useful op-amp oscillator circuits is the triangle/square-wave function generator of Fig. 6-12A. This circuit, comprised of an "ideal" integrator (A_2) and a comparator with hysteresis (A_1), simultaneously generates ultralinear triangle waveforms and symmetrical square waves. Operation over an extremely wide range of frequencies is possible using appropriate devices, from ultralow frequencies with periods measured in hours up to hundreds of kilohertz.

The circuit is best understood by regarding the timing diagram in Fig. 6-12B. Assume that the output of the type-311 comparator, A_1, has just switched to the high state, and that E_{o_2} is at $+V_z$ (breakdown voltage of D_1–D_5). The input to the integrator is then $+V_z$, which means output E_{o_1} will integrate at a rate

$$\frac{E_{in}}{RC} = \frac{V_z}{R_t C_t} \text{ V/s.} \qquad \text{(Eq. 6-7)}$$

The sum of the voltages E_{o_1} and E_{o_2} are compared by A_1 against the ground reference on its (–) input. As E_{o_1} ramps negative, the junction of R_1-R_2 decreases toward zero (t_1). When E_{o_1} crosses $-V_z$ (or when E_{o_1} is equal and opposite to E_{o_2}), the voltage at the (+) input of A_1 crosses zero and A_1 changes state rapidly, aided by positive feedback. Output voltage E_{o_2} is now at $-V_z$, and A_2 begins to integrate positive toward $+V_z$ (t_2). When E_{o_1} crosses $+V_z$, A_1 changes back the high state and the cycle repeats.

The output voltage of A_1 is clamped at $\pm V_z$, which determines the output amplitudes. The positive and negative ramp slopes are determined by $\pm V_z$, R_t, and C_t, and are equal if the zener voltage is symmetrical, as provided here by the balanced bridge.

The unclamped direct output from A_1 (E_{o_3}) is available for external use. This output can be used to feed A_2 (in lieu of the clamping network), but it will introduce side effects. First, the frequency will vary as the saturation voltages or supply voltages of A_1 change. Second, if A_1 is used to feed A_2 directly, R_1 must always be greater than R_2 to set $E_{o_1} < E_{o_3}$. Op amp A_2 cannot be allowed to saturate, which would happen if $R_2 = R_1$ ($E_{o_1} = E_{o_3}$). This modification may be useful for noncritical applications, however, as it does eliminate R_3 and D_1–D_4.

Since the circuit is actually a linear ramp generator made to oscillate between two voltage limits, an expression for the operating period (or frequency) must include both slopes of the ramp and the voltage limits. The pertinent timing data is shown in Fig. 6-12B, where t_1 and t_2 are the half periods and T is the period of a single cycle.

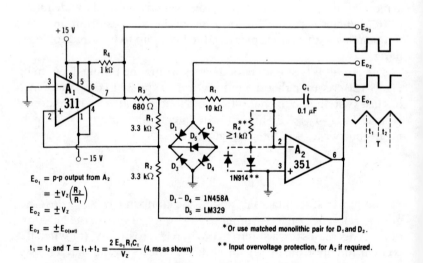

E_{o_1} = p-p output from A_2

$\quad = \pm V_z \left(\dfrac{R_2}{R_1} \right)$

$E_{o_2} = \pm V_z$

$E_{o_3} = \pm E_{o(sat)}$

$t_1 = t_2$ and $T = t_1 + t_2 = \dfrac{2 E_{o_1} R_1 C_1}{V_z}$ (4. ms as shown)

$D_1 - D_4 = $ 1N458A
$D_5 = $ LM329

* Or use matched monolithic pair for D_1 and D_2.

** Input overvoltage protection, for A_2 if required.

(A) Circuit.

Fig. 6-12. Function

The time for the first half-cycle is

$$t_1 = \frac{E_o\, t}{\Delta E_o} \qquad \text{(Eq. 6-8)}$$

Since

$$\frac{\Delta E_o}{t} = \frac{E_{in}}{RC} \qquad \text{(Eq. 6-9)}$$

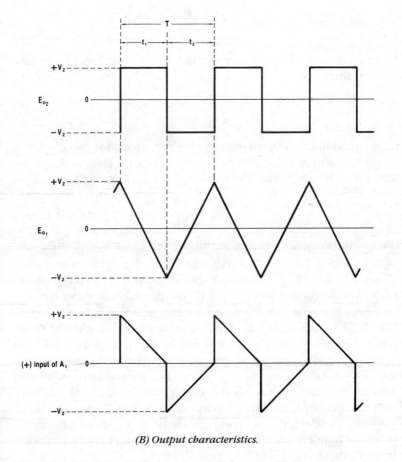

(B) Output characteristics.

generator.

then

$$t_1 = \frac{E_0 RC}{E_{in}}$$ (Eq. 6-10)

or

$$t_1 = \frac{E_{0_1} R_t C_t}{V_Z}$$ (Eq. 6-11)

where E_{0_1} is the desired peak-to-peak amplitude from A_2. Similarly, for the second half-cycle,

$$t_2 = \frac{E_{0_1} R_t C_t}{V_Z}$$

Since the zener voltage (hence the times) are symmetrical, the period T is then

$$T = \frac{2E_{0_1} R_t C_t}{V_Z}$$ (Eq. 6-12)

This equation can be used in designing the circuit for specific times of specific output voltages. The output voltage (E_{0_1}) is scaled to V_Z by a factor of 2:1; therefore, the relationship used to select R_1 and R_2 is

$$E_{0_1} = 2 V_Z \left(\frac{R_2}{R_1} \right)$$ (Eq. 6-13)

These points may be further illustrated in the example shown, which uses a 6.9-V zener (LM329) in series with two diodes (V_Z ± 8 V). In Fig. 6-12A, $R_1 = R_2$, so the output is 16 volts peak-to-peak. The frequency is then $1/4R_t C_t$, or approximately 250 Hz.

Frequency can be varied without amplitude change by varying either R_t or C_t. Resistance R_t variation allows frequency change over many decades—limited at the low end by the bias current of A_2 and at the high end by the output current of A_2, or by its slew rate. Capacitance C_t is most conveniently changed in decade steps, with low maximum values for reasons of economy. Obviously, as the stability of the frequency is directly proportional to R_t and C_t, they should be low-TC, close-tolerance types. Similarly, R_1-R_2 should be stable types for frequency and amplitude stability. Diodes D_1–D_5 provide a low-TC, due to the low TC of the LM329.

As always, amplifier selection plays an important role in performance. Since A_1 operates as a comparator, the use of a general-purpose "true" comparator, such as the LM311, is suggested. If an op amp is used, it should be an uncompensated, or high slew-rate type. Op amp A_2 must be internally compensated and have a high slew rate for high-frequency operation; thus, the 351 amp is a good choice here. At ultralow frequencies where the integration current becomes very small, the low bias current of FETs is quite attractive. If extension of the low-frequency range is achieved by large C_t values, input protection precautions should be taken for A_2, if the amplifier is unprotected. Dual and quad FET types are excellent general-purpose choices, but will sacrifice some speed in the A_1 stage. One good example would be the use of a 34082 or 712 dual amp for A_1 and A_2.

6.8.1 Modifications to the Basic Function Generator

The function generator of Fig. 6-12A not only is a versatile circuit in its own right, but it adapts readily to many extremely useful variations.

As discussed previously, the frequency of the function generator is controlled by varying either R_t or C_t. Variation of R_t is the simplest means of frequency change, but there is an alternate method that is attractive for other reasons. This circuit (Fig. 6-13) introduces a divider network, β, composed of R_5 and R_6, and placed between the clamping diodes and R_t. Divider network R_5 and R_6 vary the fraction of $\pm V_Z$ that is fed to R_t; thus, the input to the integrator in this circuit is $\pm \beta V_Z$. If the term βV_Z is substituted in the expression for t_1 and t_2, the new timing equation for T is

$$t_1 = t_2 = \frac{E_{o_1} R_t C_t}{\beta V_Z} \qquad \text{(Eq. 6-14)}$$

and

$$T = t_1 + t_2 = \frac{2E_{o_1} R_t C_t}{\beta V_Z} \qquad \text{(Eq. 6-15)}$$

The use of R_5-R_6 represents a reduction in input current to A_2, the fraction being equal to β. Thus, similar to large values of R_t, it places a limitation on A_2 (in terms of input current) for very low frequencies. Dynamic range of frequency is optimized by selecting R_t such that, when β is minimum, the input current is still much greater than the bias current of A_2. Frequency variations of 1000:1 are relatively easy to achieve, and ratios of 10,000:1 are possible.

The reason behind the β voltage divider may already be obvious—the control of gain from unity to some fraction of the input can then be provided by an analog multiplier. Thus, if β ($R_5 + R_6$) is replaced by a two-quadrant multilplier (VCA), the frequency may be made electronically variable, with a dynamic range proportional to the resistance range of the multiplier.

In the example shown, the dynamic range is 3 decades; R_t and C_t are chosen for an upper frequency limit of 20 kHz, and the oscillator can be adjusted from 20 Hz to 20 kHz using R_5.

For the integrator A_2, an OPA606 or other low-offset 356-type is suggested for best high-frequency operation and low input current. With both these amplifiers, 20 kHz is not the upper limit of operation—they may be used up to 100 kHz or more. At such frequencies, A_1 should also be very fast, hence the use of a 357 device for this amplifier. Op amp A_2 should be (preferably) a low-offset unit. Alternately, it can be offset nulled by adjusting for best symmetry at the lowest frequency of operation. If the frequency range is scaled downward, general-purpose types can be used for both A_1 and A_2, but nulling is still necessary if a 1000:1 frequency range is retained. Another op amp useful for A_2 is the OP-27, which will eliminate the need for nulling (with slightly reduced frequency range).

6.8.2 Triangle to Sine-Wave Converter

The formation of sine waves in a function generator is normally a conversion process—one that synthesizes approximate sine curves from a triangular input wave. Many sine-wave generators used biased diodes to "round" and shape the peaks of triangle waves. The circuit of Fig. 6-14 is much simpler in concept, yet produces excellent results. It can be used with any triangle wave having constant amplitude and a 50% duty cycle, such as the sources just described.

The circuit uses a differential amplifier (A_1) and a matched transistor pair (Q_1-Q_2) with a controlled amount of emitter coupling. An undegenerated emitter-coupled amplifier is linear only for small signal levels; however, if operation is held to a region of controlled nonlinearity, an emitter-coupled pair can convert a linear input voltage, such as a triangle wave, into a good approximation of a sine-wave

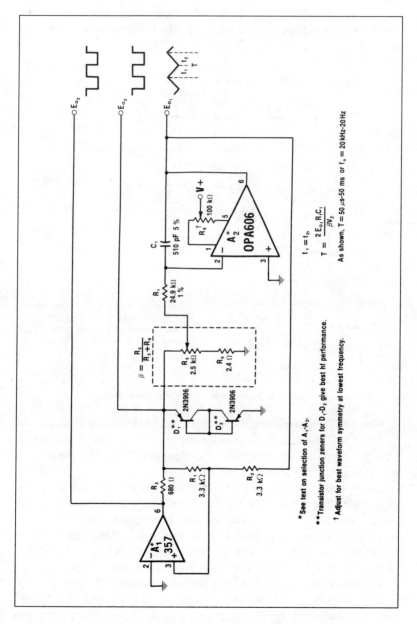

Fig. 6-13. Variable-frequency function generator (20 Hz to 20 kHz).

output. This is what Q_1-Q_2 of Fig. 6-14 accomplish, and A_1 converts the sinusoidal output current of Q_1-Q_2 to a buffered sine-wave output voltage.

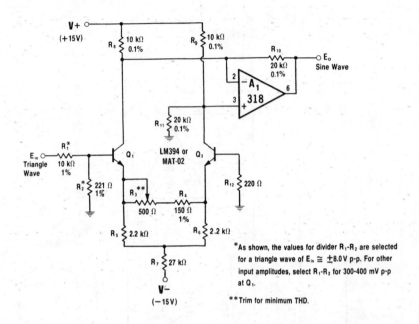

Fig. 6-14. Triangle to sine-wave converter.

Since this scheme involves precise control over the conduction of Q_1 and Q_2, it is critically dependent upon both the input amplitude and the degree of emitter coupling. Resistors R_1 and R_2 are chosen for approximately 300- to 400-mV p-p drive at Q_1. With levels in this range, R_3 can be set for a point of minimum output distortion. This is best done with a distortion analyzer, but an oscilloscope can also be used. Once R_3 is set, the input level must not change, or the distortion in the output will climb rapidly. For this reason, high-stability components are preferred for R_1–R_4; R_3 should preferably be a high-resolution trimmer, such as a 10-turn potentiometer.

Distortion is also affected to a smaller degree by the match of Q_1 and Q_2. A matched transistor pair can be used without nulling and distortion will still be reasonably low ($\leq 1\%$). However, optimum performance (total harmonic distortion $\cong 0.3\%$) is obtained by offset nulling or selection of a tightly controlled offset-voltage pair

(V_{io} < 0.5 mV). Resistors R_{10} and R_{11} may be used to scale the sine-wave output level. The values used in this example yield levels comparable to those of the triangular input waveforms. The op amp should be consistent with required speeds—a type-318 device yields optimum performance in this regard. Note that this amp could be one from a quad device, such as the TL074, etc. The LM394 and MAT-01/02 types are tightly controlled (50 μV) offset devices, eliminating the null requirement.

6.9 VOLTAGE-CONTROLLED AMPLIFIER (VCA)

Fig. 6-15 is a highly developed form of voltage-controlled amplifier that incorporates a number of features to lend it great precision, optimum for audio use. The gain TC of a transconductance amplifier can be compensated by introducing an equal and opposite TC into the signal path. Another method is the generation of a linear transfer function by using an element within a feedback loop. Fig. 6-15 is an example of the latter approach.

The diode bridge, consisting of matched diodes D_1–D_4, is biased at a current value nominally equal to $I_{ABC(max)}$. With one side of the bridge (pin 6) grounded, the impedance looking into the opposite side (pin 2) is very low—essentially the diode dynamic impedance. If a linear current is fed into the bridge at this junction, the voltage developed will be the current/voltage characteristic of the bridge— identical to the differential-input voltage required for linear output current. A current source to drive the bridge is very closely approximated by R_1, which converts the input voltage to a current that is absorbed in the bridge. The resultant voltage is applied to A_1 as an input voltage, automatically adjusting the drive as temperature varies.

With the values shown, the input and output signal-handling range is ± 10 V. Even at these output levels, the distortion remains well below 1%, and at lower levels, it falls to 0.1% or less. Trimmer R_8 is a trim for unity gain at $I_{ABC(max)}$; R_4 is used to trim the input offset of A_1 for optimum linearity. The currents in R_5 and R_6 must be balanced for minimum voltage offset of the bridge—if this is not done, additional distortion will be generated due to the unbalanced transfer characteristic. Thus, R_5 and R_6 should have close tolerances and V + and V– should track together.

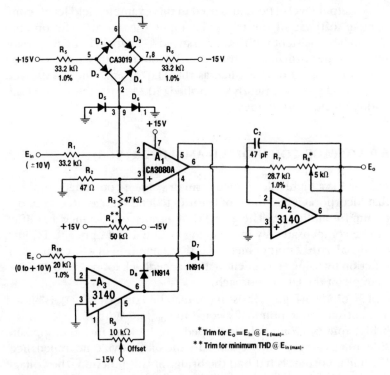

Fig. 6-15. High-performance VCA.

The control current for A_1 is generated by a precision VCCS (A_3), which forces I_{ABC} to be linearly proportional to E_c. If other than a low offset type is used for A_3, it should be offset trimmed for calibration with E_c at + 10 mV, or three decades below maximum. Operation over four decades or more is possible using a 3080A device for A_1, but for I_{ABC} levels below 100 nA, A_3 should be a low-offset (or trimmed) FET type, such as the 3140 shown, to provide best tracking. The output amplifier here is also a 3140; the pair could be replaced by a single 3240 unit, if desired.

Another desirable form of I_{ABC} control is one that is exponentially related to the input control voltage, E_c. An antilog generator can be adapted to this purpose, giving an attenuation that changes by a factor of 10 for each volt of change in E_c, or 20 dB/V. This arrangement offers a distinct advantage in audio mixers, for instance, where the attenuators are calibrated in dB units.

6.10 COMPACT DISC AUDIO CIRCUITS

The most recent major development in audio has been the appearance of the compact disc (CD). The CD furnishes a playback-only function that is functionally similar to the phonograph record (in general). However, the information on the CD is recorded in a digital format, offering far greater noise immunity and longevity, as well as increased dynamic range and fidelity. While a complete rundown of CD circuits is beyond the scope of this book, some of the analog portions typically used is in context and warrants discussion.

CD players are very sophisticated, performing such functions as programmed track selection/playback, dropout correction, etc. However, these functions are performed mostly while the signal is still in digital form. Very often, the analog processing circuits can be easily improved.

Fig. 6-16 illustrates an analog processing section typical of those based on the European approach, an approach used by Philips. This system uses two current-output D/A converters (or converter sections) for the two stereo channels, with each of these followed by a linear-phase low-pass filter. While the basic compact disc recording format samples at a rate of 44.1 kHz, the Philips playback scheme samples at 4 times this rate, or 176.4 kHz. This is done to shift the bulk of the sampling frequency by-products upwards in the frequency spectrum, where they can be low-pass filtered by relatively simple means.

Thus, a D/A conversion circuit and a low-pass filter for this system is relatively simple. In Fig. 6-16, A_1 is a 14-bit current-output D/A device, a TDA1540, which drives A_{2A}, an op-amp current-to-voltage converter. A_{2A} converts the varying currents from A_1 into a corresponding voltage, as well as providing some filtering (by virtue of C_1).

The second op amp adds two more stages of filtering, as well as a low impedance output. The three filter sections, together, form a linear phase alignment, designed to allow minimal audio degradation to the signal. The more recent 16-bit version of this system operates similarly, but uses the TDA1541, a dual 16-bit D/A IC.

The recovered audio signal in AC-coupled to the output by a polypropylene film capacitor, C_4. The mating relay (K_1), used to suppress transients and between-track noise, is used in a shunt configuration.

Although a variety of op-amp types have been used to perform

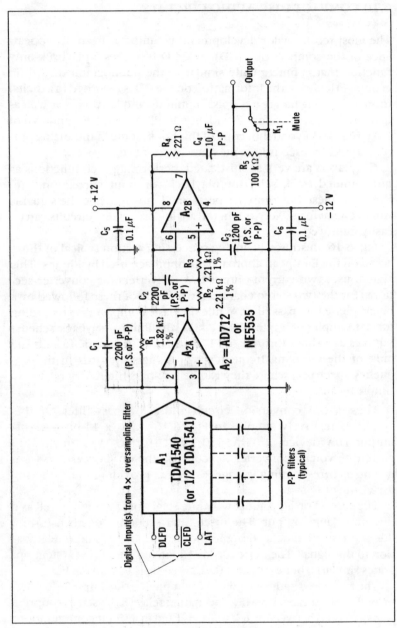

Fig. 6-16. "European" compact disc D/A converter and low-pass filter circuit.

this filtering function, linear high-V_{th}, high-slew-rate devices perform very well and are preferred. Among these are many FET types; the AD712 (dual) device shown performs well in this circuit, as does the bipolar 5535. For the low-pass filter components, metal film resistors are suggested, and either polystyrene or polypropylene capacitors. The supplies to the op amps should be well regulated, and bypassed local to the op amps.

6.10.1 CD Player Output Stage with Servo Control

Like the more general audio signal-handling stages described in Chapter 4, a CD player's audio stage can be enhanced by the addition of DC servo control amplifiers. This permits complete DC coupling—from the D/A converter outward.

A sample CD output stage that is adapted for servo control is shown in Fig. 6-17. This circuit uses a 3507 or 2525 high-speed inverting op-amp stage, with a noninverting servo in the feedback path. The servo uses a single 34081 FET-input op amp (for each channel). The overall servo time constant is set at 1 second, for minimal low-frequency rolloff. The components used around the servo should be of high quality (following the guidelines of Chapter 4 on servos). The MUTE function is accomplished in this example by a cascade of two shunt switches, using general-purpose NPN transistors. (This is functionally similar to the MUTE relay of Fig. 6-16.)

Overall, this circuit has an AC gain of 1.5 and very low distortion characteristics. The op amp used for A_1 must be compensated for unity gain; thus the addition of C_2 with the use of the 3507 device. Internally compensated units, such as the 318, the AD711, or the AD712 (dual) will also work well for A_1.

6.10.2 Single D/A 2 × Oversampled Converter

Another approach used in the CD player audio reconstruction process is the employment of a single D/A converter, which carries the information for both left and right channels in sequential time slots. The information is demultiplexed into discrete L and R channels, after D/A conversion. Such a system is used by Yamaha in their CD players.

A high-performance circuit for this type of converter is shown in Fig. 6-18. For the highest possible speed in the conversion process, a

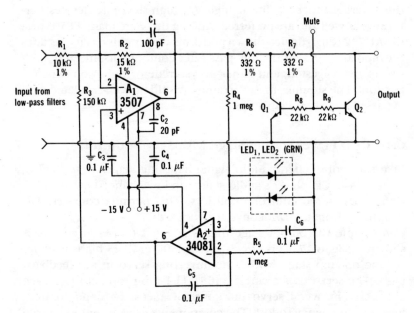

Fig. 6-17. CD output stage with servo control.

current-output form of D/A converter is used, in conjunction with a high-speed external op amp. A_1 is the 16-bit D/A converter, a Burr-Brown PCM53JP-I device. The high-speed op amp is A_2, a 3507 unit, which settles in less than 1 μs. Overall, this combination is functionally equivalent to the popular voltage-output model of this converter (the PCM53JP-V). In this case, however, the settling time is lessened appreciably, a factor important to oversampled converters.

To demultiplex the output of amplifier stage, A_2, a high-speed "HC series" CMOS switch is used at A_5. Driven by the L and R outputs of the LSI control section, this switch performs a current-steering control function. For the respective "on states," the switch outputs are steered to an op-amp summing point. For the "off states," the current is diverted to ground.

Op amps A_3 and A_4 act as sample/hold amplifiers, in conjunction with switch A_5 and storage capacitors C_6 and C_7. These capacitors store the L and R information between respective samples, reconstructing the signal into two discrete channels. After the L and R sample/hold functions, the signal is then further processed with more stages of low-pass filters. Frequency compensation for A_3 and A_4 is provided by C_8 and C_9 (when the 3507 or 2525 types are used).

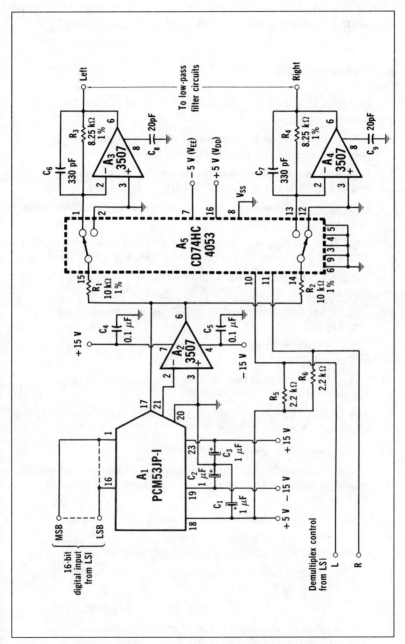

Fig. 6-18. Single D/A, 2 × oversampled converter.

The system, as described, can be used with 2-times (88.2 kHz) oversampling digital domain filters, with excellent results.

6.11 REFERENCES

1. Childress, H. "Modifying the Yamaha CD-2." *The Audio Amateur,* issue 3/1986.

2. Gilbert, B. "A Precise Four-Quadrant Multiplier With Sub-Nanosecond Response." *IEEE JSSC,* December 1968.

3. Gittleman, R. "Applications of the Audio Operational Amplifier to Studio Use." *Journal of the AES,* Vol. 17 #3, June 1969.

4. Grebene, A. B. "Monolithic Waveform Generation." *IEEE Spectrum,* April 1972.

5. Jung, W. G. "Application of the Two-Quadrant Amplifier Multiplier in Audio Signal Processing." *Journal of the AES,* Vol. 23 #3, April 1975.

6. _____. "Gain Control IC for Audio Processing." *Ham Radio,* Vol. 10 #7, July 1977.

7. _____. "Get Gain Control of 80 to 100 dB." *Electronic Design,* June 21, 1974.

8. _____. *IC Timer Cookbook, 2nd Edition,* Howard W. Sams & Co., Indianapolis, IN, 1983.

9. _____. "LED's Do Dual Duty in Sine Wave Oscillator." *EDN,* August 20, 1976.

10. _____. "Low Distortion Oscillator Uses State Variable Filter." *Electronics,* February 5, 1976.

11. _____. "Sine Wave Oscillators." *db,* July 1976.

12. _____. "The Pitfalls of the General Purpose IC Operational Amplifier as Applied to Audio Signal Processing." *Journal of the AES,* Vol. 21 #9, November 1973.

13. _____. "The Signal Path: Function Generators." *db,* December 1975.

14. _____; Todd, C. C. "Operation and Uses for the 570/571 IC Compandor Chip." *The Audio Amateur,* issue 4/76.

15. _____. "IC Op-Amp Cookbook, 3rd Edition." Howard W. Sams & Co., Indianapolis, IN, 1986.

16. _____. "Op Amp Meets CD." *The Audio Amateur,* issue 3/1986.

17. Losmandy, B. J. "Operational Amplifier Applications for Audio Systems." *Journal of the AES,* Vol. 17 #1, January 1969.

18. Matull, J. "IC's for Compact Disc Decoders." *Signetics Application Note AN200,* September 1985.

19. Orban, R. "Notes on Pan-Pots." *Journal of the AES,* Vol. 19 #11, December 1971.

20. Sheingold, D. (Ed). *Non Linear Circuits Handbook.* Analog Devices, Norwood, MA, 1974.

21. Todd, C. "A Monolithic Analog Compandor." *IEEE JSSC* Vol. SC-11 #6, December 1976.

22. _____. "The Monolithic Compandor—A High Performance Gain Control IC." *AES preprint #1100,* May 1976.

23. Van de Plassche, R. J. and Goedhart, D. "A Monolithic 14-bit D/A Converter." *IEEE JSSC,* Vol. SC-14 #3, June 1979.

24. Van de Plassche, R. J. "Dynamic Element Matching for High-Accuracy Monolithic D/A Converters." *IEEE JSSC,* Vol. SC-11 #6, December 1976.

25. Wittlinger, H. A. "Applications of the CA3080 and CA3080A High Performance Operational Transconductance Amplifiers." *RCA ICAN 6668,* September 1971, RCA, Somerville, NJ.

26. Manufacturers' Data Sheets.

Burr-Brown	PCM53	16-bit D/A converter.
Signetics	TDA1540	14-bit D/A converter.
	TDA1541	Dual 16-bit D/A converter.

Device Data Sheets

Within this section, the data sheets of several op-amp devices, suitable for higher-performance audio applications, are given. They are reproduced through the courtesy of their respective manufacturers.

In many cases, related or "family" devices are also available. More complete and/or timely information can be requested directly from the manufacturer in question (addresses are listed in Appendix B). When writing in regard to these devices, it will be helpful to mention this book.

**ANALOG
DEVICES**

Precision Low Cost
High-Speed BIFET Op Amp

FEATURES
Improved Replacement for LF411, TL071
AC PERFORMANCE:
  Settles to ±0.01% in 1μs
  16V/μs min Slew Rate (AD711J)
  3MHz min Unity Gain Bandwidth (AD711J)
DC PERFORMANCE:
  0.25mV max Offset Voltage: (AD711C)
  3μV/°C max Drift: (AD711C)
  200V/mV min Open Loop Gain (AD711K)
  4μV p-p max Noise, 0.1Hz to 10Hz (AD711C)
**Available In Plastic, Hermetic CERDIP, and Hermetic
Metal Can Packages**
MIL-STD-883B Parts Available
Dual Version Available: AD712
Pricing in 100s: AD711JN – $0.80
               AD711KN – $1.90
               AD711CQ – $4.90

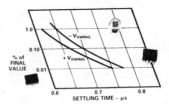

PRODUCT DESCRIPTION

The AD711 is a high-speed, precision monolithic operational amplifier offering high performance at very modest prices. Its very low offset voltage and offset voltage drift are the results of advanced laser wafer trimming technology. These performance benefits allow the user to easily upgrade existing designs that use older precision BIFETs and, in many cases, bipolar op amps.

The superior ac and dc performance of this op amp makes it suitable for active filter applications. With a slew rate of 16V/μs and a settling time of 1μs to ±0.01%, the AD711 is ideal as a buffer for 12-bit D/A and A/D Converters and as a high-speed integrator. The settling time is unmatched by any similar IC amplifier.

The combination of excellent noise performance and low input current also make the AD711 useful for photo diode preamps. Common-mode rejection of 88dB and open loop gain of 400V/mV ensure 12-bit performance even in high-speed unity gain buffer circuits.

The AD711 is pinned out in a standard op amp configuration and is available in seven performance grades. The AD711J and AD711K are rated over the commercial temperature range of 0 to +70°C. The AD711A, AD711B and AD711C are rated over the industrial temperature range of −40°C to +85°C. The AD711S and AD711T are rated over the military temperature range of −55°C to +125°C and are available processed to MIL-STD-883B, Rev. C.

Extended reliability PLUS screening is available, specified over the commercial and industrial temperature ranges. PLUS screening

includes 168-hour burn-in, as well as other environmental and physical tests.

The AD711 is available in an 8-Pin Plastic Mini-DIP, CERDIP, or TO-99 metal can.

PRODUCT HIGHLIGHTS

1. The AD711 offers excellent overall performance at very competitive prices. It may be used as an upgrade or alternate source for all grades of the LF411, LF356 and in most applications, the TL071.

2. Analog Devices' advanced processing technology and with 100% testing guarantees a low input offset voltage (0.25mV max, C grade, 2mV max, J grade). Input offset voltage is specified in the warmed-up condition. Analog Devices' laser wafer drift trimming process reduces input offset voltage drifts to 3μV/°C max on the AD711C.

3. Along with precision dc performance, the AD711 offers excellent dynamic response. It settles to ±0.01% in 1μs and has a 100% tested minimum slew rate of 16V/μs. Thus this device is ideal for applications such as DAC and ADC buffers which require a combination of superior ac and dc performance.

4. The AD711 has a guaranteed and tested maximum voltage noise of 4μV p-p, 0.1 to 10Hz (AD711C).

5. Analog Devices' well-matched, ion-implanted JFETs ensure a guaranteed input bias current (at either input) of 25pA max (AD711C) and an input offset current of 10pA max (AD711C). Both input bias current and input offset current are guaranteed in the warmed-up condition.

One Technology Way; P. O. Box 9106; Norwood, MA 02062-9106
Tel: 617/329-4700   TWX: 710/394-6577
West Coast   **Mid-West**   **Texas**
714/641-9391   312/350-9399   214/231-5094

Courtesy Analog Devices, Inc.

SPECIFICATIONS (@ + 25°C and V_S = ± 15V dc, unless otherwise noted)

Model	AD711J/A/S			AD711K/B/T			AD711C			Units
	Min	Typ	Max	Min	Typ	Max	Min	Typ	Max	
INPUT OFFSET VOLTAGE[1]										
Initial Offset		1/0.3/0.3	2/1/1		0.25	0.5		0.10	0.25	mV
T_{min} to T_{max}			3/2/2			1.0			0.45	mV
vs. Temp.		12	20/20/20		5	10		2	3	μV/°C
vs. Supply	76	95		80	100		86	110		dB
vs. Supply, T_{min} to T_{max}	76			80			86			dB
Long Term Offset Stability		15			15			15		μV/month
INPUT BIAS CURRENT[2]										
Either Input, V_{CM} = 0		15	50		15	50		15	25	pA
Either Input at T_{max}.			1.1/4.5/51			1.1/4.5/51			2.3	nA
V_{CM} = 0 (70°C/85°C/125°C)										
Either Input, V_{CM} = + 10V		20	100		20	100		20	50	pA
Offset Current, V_{CM} = 0		10	25		5	25		5	10	pA
Offset Current at T_{max}			0.57/2.3/26			0.57/2.3/26			0.25/1.0	nA
(70°C/85°C/125°C)										
FREQUENCY RESPONSE										
Unity Gain, Small Signal	3.0	4		3.4	4		3.4	4		MHz
Full Power Response		200			200			200		kHz
Slew Rate, Unity Gain	16	20		18	20		18	20		V/μs
Settling Time to 0.01%[3]		1	1.8		1	1.8		1	1.8	μs
Total Harmonic Distortion										
f = 1kHz										
$R_L \geq 2k\Omega$, V_O = 3V RMS		0.0003			0.0003			0.0003		%
INPUT IMPEDANCE										
Differential		$3 \times 10^{12} \| 5.5$			$3 \times 10^{12} \| 5.5$			$3 \times 10^{12} \| 5.5$		$\Omega \| pF$
Common Mode		$3 \times 10^{12} \| 5.5$			$3 \times 10^{12} \| 5.5$			$3 \times 10^{12} \| 5.5$		$\Omega \| pF$
INPUT VOLTAGE RANGE										
Differential[4]		± 20			± 20			± 20		V
Common Mode Voltage		+ 14.5, − 11.5			+ 14.5, − 11.5			+ 14.5, − 11.5		V
Over Max Operating Range[5]	$-V_S + 4V$		$+V_S - 2V$	$-V_S + 4V$		$+V_S - 2V$	$-V_S + 4V$		$+V_S - 2V$	V
Common Mode Rejection Ratio										
V_{CM} = ± 10V	76	88		80	88		86	94		dB
T_{min} to T_{max}	76	84		80	84		86	90		dB
V_{CM} = ± 11V	70	84		76	84		76	90		dB
T_{min} to T_{max}	70	80		74	80		74	84		dB
INPUT VOLTAGE NOISE										
Voltage 0.1Hz to 10Hz		2			2			2	4.0	μV p-p
f = 10Hz		45			45			45		nV/√Hz
f = 100Hz		22			22			22		nV/√Hz
f = 1kHz		18			18			18		nV/√Hz
f = 10kHz		16			16			16		nV/√Hz
INPUT CURRENT NOISE										
f = 1kHz		0.01			0.01			0.01		pA/√Hz
OPEN LOOP GAIN[6]										
V_O = ± 10V, $R_L \geq 2k\Omega$	150	400		200	400		200	400		V/mV
V_O = ± 10V, $R_L \geq 2k\Omega$,	100			100			100			V/mV
T_{min} to T_{max}										
OUTPUT CHARACTERISTICS										
Voltage @ $R_L \geq 2k\Omega$	+13, −12.5	+13.9, −13.3		+13, −12.5	+13.9, −13.3		+13, −12.5	+13.9, −13.3		V
Voltage @ $R_L \geq 2k\Omega$,										
T_{min} to T_{max}	±12	+13.8, −13.1		±12	+13.8, −13.1		±12	+13.8, −13.1		V
Short Circuit Current		25			25			25		mA
POWER SUPPLY										
Rated Performance		± 15			± 15			± 15		V
Operating Range	±4.5		±18	±4.5		±18	±4.5		±18	V
Quiescent Current		2.5	3.4		2.5	3.0		2.5	2.8	mA
TEMPERATURE RANGE										
Operating, Rated Performance										
Commercial (0 to + 70°C)		AD711J			AD711K					
Industrial (− 40°C to + 85°C)		AD711A			AD711B			AD711C		
Military (− 55°C to + 125°C)		AD711S			AD711T					
PACKAGE OPTIONS										
Plastic (N)		AD711JN			AD711KN					
Cerdip (Q)		AD711AQ, AD711SQ			AD711BQ, AD711TQ			AD711CQ		
Metal Can (H)		AD711AH, AD711SH			AD711BH, AD711TH			AD711CH		

-2-

NOTES

[1]Input Offset Voltage specifications are guaranteed after 5 minutes of operation at $T_A = +25°C$.
[2]Bias Current specifications are guaranteed maximum at either input after 5 minutes of operation at $T_A = +25°C$.
For higher temperature, the current doubles every 10°C.
[3]Refer to Figure 29.
[4]Defined as voltage between inputs, such that neither exceeds ±10V from ground.
[5]Typically exceeding −14.1V negative common-mode voltage on either input results in an output phase reversal.
[6]Open Loop Gain is specified with V_{OS} both nulled and unnulled.

Specifications subject to change without notice.

Specifications in boldface are tested on all production units at final electrical test. Results from those tests are used to calculate outgoing quality levels. All min and max specifications are guaranteed, although only those shown in boldface are tested on all production units.

ABSOLUTE MAXIMUM RATINGS[1]

Supply Voltage . . . . ±18V
Internal Power Dissipation 500mW
Input Voltage . . . . ±18V
Output Short Circuit Duration . . . . Indefinite
Differential Input Voltage . . . . +V_S and −V_S
Storage Temperature Range Q, H . . . . . −65°C to +150°C
Storage Temperature Range N . . . . −65°C to +125°C
Operating Temperature Range
   AD711J/K . . . . 0 to +70°C
   AD711A/B/C . . . . −40°C to +85°C
   AD711S/T . . . . −55°C to +125°C
Lead Temperature Range (Soldering 60 seconds) . . . . 300°C

NOTES

[1]Stresses above those listed under "Absolute Maximum Ratings" may cause permanent damage to the device. This is a stress rating only and functional operation of the device at these or any other conditions above those indicated in the operational section of this specification is not implied. Exposure to absolute maximum rating conditions for extended periods may affect device reliability.
[2]For supply voltages less than ±18V, the absolute maximum input voltage is equal to the supply voltage.

ORDERING GUIDE

Model No.	Price $(100s)	Model No.	Price $(100s)
AD711JN	0.80	AD711SQ	3.65
AD711KN	1.90	AD711SQ/883B	5.75
AD711AQ	1.45	AD711SH	3.80
AD711BQ	2.45	AD711SH/883B	5.90
AD711CQ	4.90	AD711TQ	6.70
AD711AH	1.45	AD711TQ/883B	9.35
AD711BH	2.60	AD711TH	6.85
AD711CH	4.90	AD711TH/883B	9.50

CONNECTION DIAGRAMS
(Top View)

TO-99
(H) Package

Plastic MINI-DIP (N) Package
and
CERDIP (Q) Package

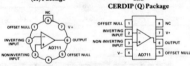

V_{OS} TRIM

OUTLINE DIMENSIONS
Dimensions shown in inches and (mm).

TO-99 (H) Package

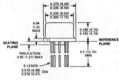

MINI-DIP (N) Package

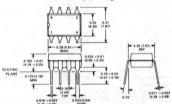

CERDIP (Q) Package

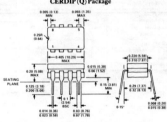

-3-

Courtesy Analog Devices, Inc.

Typical Characteristics

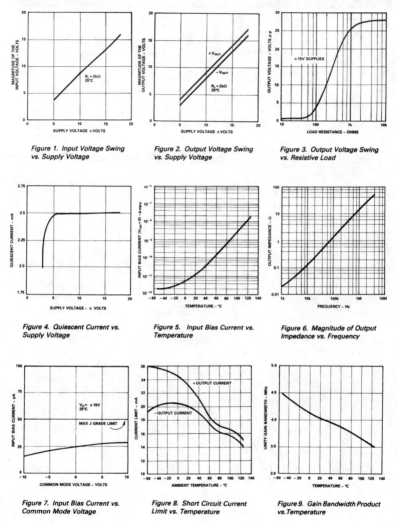

Figure 1. Input Voltage Swing vs. Supply Voltage

Figure 2. Output Voltage Swing vs. Supply Voltage

Figure 3. Output Voltage Swing vs. Resistive Load

Figure 4. Quiescent Current vs. Supply Voltage

Figure 5. Input Bias Current vs. Temperature

Figure 6. Magnitude of Output Impedance vs. Frequency

Figure 7. Input Bias Current vs. Common Mode Voltage

Figure 8. Short Circuit Current Limit vs. Temperature

Figure 9. Gain Bandwidth Product vs. Temperature

–4–

Courtesy Analog Devices, Inc.

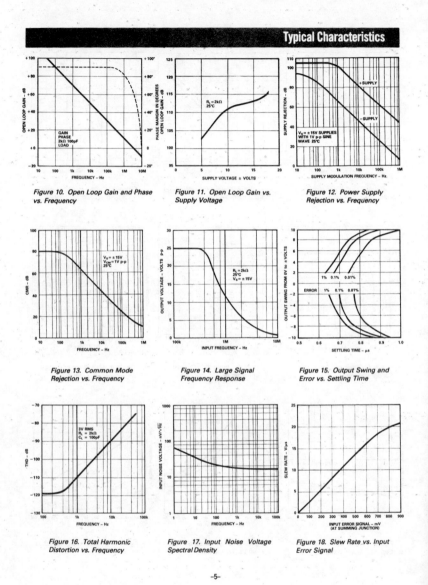

Figure 10. Open Loop Gain and Phase vs. Frequency

Figure 11. Open Loop Gain vs. Supply Voltage

Figure 12. Power Supply Rejection vs. Frequency

Figure 13. Common Mode Rejection vs. Frequency

Figure 14. Large Signal Frequency Response

Figure 15. Output Swing and Error vs. Settling Time

Figure 16. Total Harmonic Distortion vs. Frequency

Figure 17. Input Noise Voltage Spectral Density

Figure 18. Slew Rate vs. Input Error Signal

–5–

Courtesy Analog Devices, Inc.

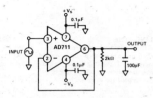

Figure 20. T.H.D. Test Circuit

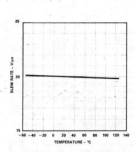

Figure 19. Slew Rate vs. Temperature

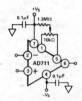

Figure 21. Offset Null Configurations

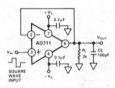

Figure 22a. Unity Gain Follower

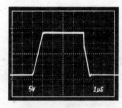

Figure 22b. Unity Gain Follower
Pulse Response (Large Signal)

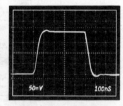

Figure 22c. Unity Gain Follower
Pulse Response (Small Signal)

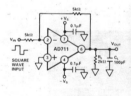

Figure 23a. Unity Gain Inverter

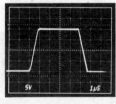

Figure 23b. Unity Gain Inverter
Pulse Response (Large Signal)

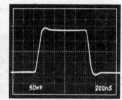

Figure 23c. Unity Gain Inverter
Pulse Response (Small Signal)

–6–

Courtesy Analog Devices, Inc.

OPTIMIZING SETTLING TIME

Most bipolar high-speed D/A converters have curent outputs; therefore, for most applications, an external op-amp is required for current-to-voltage conversion. The settling time of the converter/op-amp combination depends on the settling time of the DAC and output amplifier. A good approximation is:

$$t_s \text{ Total} = \sqrt{(t_s \text{ DAC})^2 + (t_s \text{ AMP})^2}$$

The settling time of an op amp DAC buffer will vary with the noise gain of the circuit, the DAC output capacitance, and with the amount of external compensation capacitance across the DAC output scaling resistor.

Settling time for a bipolar DAC is typically 100 to 500ns. Previously, conventional op-amps have required much longer settling times than have typical state-of-the-art DACs; therefore, the amplifier settling time has been the major limitation to a high-speed voltage-output D-to-A function. The introduction of the AD711/712 family of op amps with their 1µs (to ±0.01% of final value) settling time now permits the full high-speed capabilities of most modern DACs to be realized.

In addition to a significant improvement in settling time, the low offset voltage, low offset voltage drift, and high open-loop gain of the AD711 family assures 12-bit accuracy over the full operating temperature range.

The excellent high-speed performance of the AD711 is shown in the oscilloscope photos of Figure 25. Measurements were taken using a low input capacitance amplifier connected directly to the summing junction of the AD711 – both photos show the worst case situation: a full-scale input transition. The DAC's 4kΩ [10kΩ‖8kΩ=4.4kΩ] output impedence together with a 10kΩ feedback resistor produce an op-amp noise gain of 3.25. The current output from the DAC produces a 10V step at the op-amp output (0 to −10V Figure 25a, −10V to 0V Figure 25b.)

Therefore, with an ideal op-amp, settling to ±1/2LSB (±0.01%) requires that 375µV or less appears at the summing junction. This means that the error between the input and output (that voltage which appears at the AD711 summing junction) must be less than 375µV. As shown in Figure 25, the total settling time for the AD711/AD565 combination is 1.2 microseconds.

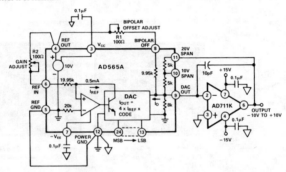

Figure 24. ±10V Voltage Output Bipolar DAC

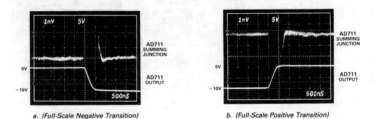

a. (Full-Scale Negative Transition)

b. (Full-Scale Positive Transition)

Figure 25. Settling Characteristics for AD711 with AD565A

–7–

OP-AMP SETTLING TIME – A MATHEMATICAL MODEL

The design of the AD711 gives careful attention to optimizing individual circuit components; in addition, a careful tradeoff was made: the gain bandwidth product (4MHz) and slew rate (20V/μs) were chosen to be high enough to provide very fast settling time but not too high to cause a significant reduction in phase margin (and therefore stability). Thus designed, the AD711 settles to ±0.01%, with a 10V output step, in under 1μs, while retaining the ability to drive a 250pF load capacitance when operating as a unity gain follower.

If an op-amp is modeled as an ideal integrator with a unity gain crossover frequency of $\omega_O/2\pi$, Equation 1 will accurately describe the small signal behavior of the circuit of Figure 26a, consisting of an op-amp connected as an I-to-V converter at the output of a bipolar or CMOS DAC. This equation would completely describe the output of the system if not for the op-amp's finite slew rate and other nonlinear effects.

Equation 1.

$$\frac{V_O}{I_{IN}} = \frac{-R}{\frac{R(C_f + C_X)}{\omega_o} S^2 + \left(\frac{G_N}{\omega_o} + RC_f\right) S + 1}$$

where $\frac{\omega_o}{2\pi}$ = op amp's unity gain frequency

G_N = "noise" gain of circuit $\left(1 + \frac{R}{R_O}\right)$

This equation may then be solved for C_f:

Equation 2.

$$C_f = \frac{2 - G_N}{R\omega_o} + \frac{2\sqrt{RC_X\omega_o + (1 - G_N)}}{R\omega_o}$$

In these equations, capacitor C_X is the total capacitance appearing at the inverting terminal of the op-amp. When modeling a DAC buffer application, the Norton equivalent circuit of Figure 26a can be used directly; capacitance C_X is the total capacitance of the output of the DAC plus the input capacitance of the op-amp (since the two are in parallel).

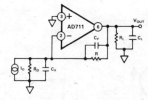

Figure 26a. Simplified Model of the AD711 Used as a Current-Out DAC Buffer

When R_O and I_O are replaced with their Thevenin V_{IN} and R_{IN} equivalents, the general purpose inverting amplifier of Figure 26b is created. Note that when using this general model, capacitance C_X is EITHER the input capacitance of the op-amp if a simple inverting op-amp is being simulated OR it is the combined capacitance of the DAC output and the op-amp input if the DAC buffer is being modeled.

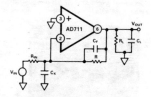

Figure 26b. Simplified Model of the AD711 Used as an Inverter

In either case, the capacitance C_X causes the system to go from a one-pole to a two-pole response; this additional pole increases settling time by introducing peaking or ringing in the op-amp output. Since the value of C_X can be estimated with reasonable accuracy, Equation 2 can be used to choose a small capacitor, C_F, to cancel the input pole and optimize amplifier response. Figure 27 is a graphical solution of Equation 2 for the AD711 with $R = 4k\Omega$.

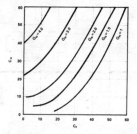

Figure 27. Value of Capacitor C_F vs. Value of C_X

-8-

Courtesy Analog Devices, Inc.

The photos of Figures 28a and 28b show the dynamic response of the AD711 in the settling test circuit of Figure 29.

The input of the settling time fixture is driven by a flat-top pulse generator. The error signal output from the false summing node of A1 is clamped, amplified by A2 and then clamped again. The error signal is thus clamped twice: once to prevent overloading amplifier A2 and then a second time to avoid overloading the oscilloscope preamp. The Tektronix oscilloscope preamp type 7A26 was carefully chosen because it does not overload with these input levels. Amplifier A2 needs to be a very high speed FET-input op-amp; it provides a gain of 10, amplifying the error signal output of A1.

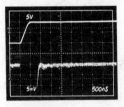

Figure 28a. Settling Characteristics 0 to +10V Step
Upper Trace: Output of AD711 Under Test (5V/Div)
Lower Trace: Amplified Error Voltage (0.01%/Div)

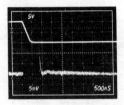

Figure 28b. Settling Characteristics 0 to −10V Step
Upper Trace: Output of AD711 Under Test (5V/Div)
Lower Trace: Amplified Error Voltage (0.01%/Div)

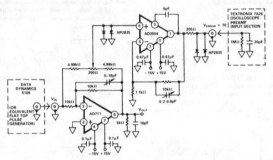

Figure 29. Settling Time Test Circuit

GUARDING

The low input bias current (15pA) and low noise characteristics of the AD711 BIFET op amp make it suitable for electrometer applications such as photo diode preamplifiers and picoampere current-to-voltage converters. The use of a guarding technique such as that shown in Figure 30, in printed circuit board layout and construction is critical to minimize leakage currents. The guard ring is connected to a low impedance potential at the same level as the inputs. High impedance signal lines should not be extended for any unnecessary length on the printed circuit board.

TO-99 (H) PACKAGE

PLASTIC (N) AND CERDIP (Q) PACKAGE

Figure 30. Board Layout for Guarding Inputs

–9–

D/A CONVERTER APPLICATIONS

The AD711 is an excellent output amplifier for CMOS DACs. It can be used to perform both 2 quadrant and 4 quadrant operation. The output impedance of a DAC using an inverted R-2R ladder approaches R for codes containing many 1s, 3R for codes containing a single 1, and for codes containing all zero, the output impedance is infinite.

For example, the output resistance of the AD7545 will modulate between 11kΩ and 33kΩ. Therefore, with the DAC's internal feedback resistance of 11kΩ, the noise gain will vary from 2 to 4/3. This changing noise gain modulates the effect of the input offset voltage of the amplifier, resulting in nonlinear DAC-amplifier performance.

The AD711K with guaranteed 500μV offset voltage minimizes this effect to achieve 12-bit performance.

Figures 31 and 32 show the AD711 and AD7545 (12-bit CMOS DAC) configured for unipolar binary (2 quadrant multiplication) or bipolar (4 quadrant multiplication) operation. Capacitor C1 provides phase compensation to reduce overshoot and ringing.

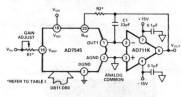

*REFER TO TABLE I

Figure 31. Unipolar Binary Operation

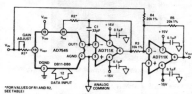

*FOR VALUES OF R1 AND R2, SEE TABLE I

Figure 32. Bipolar Operation

R1 and R2 calibrate the zero offset and gain error of the DAC. Specific values for these resistors depend upon the grade of AD7545 and are shown below.

TRIM

RESISTOR	JN/AQ/SD	KN/BQ/TD	LN/CQ/UD	GLN/GCQ/GUD
R1	500Ω	200Ω	100Ω	20Ω
R2	150Ω	68Ω	33Ω	6.8Ω

Table I. Recommended Trim Resistor Values vs. Grades of the AD7545 for $V_{DD} = +5V$

Figures 33a and 33b show the settling time characteristics of the AD711 when used as a DAC output buffer for the AD7545.

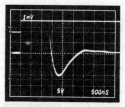

a. Full-Scale Positive Transition

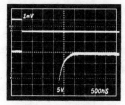

b. Full-Scale Negative Transition

Figure 33. Settling Characteristics for AD711 with AD7545

NOISE CHARACTERISTICS

The random nature of noise, particularly in the I/F region, makes it difficult to specify in practical terms. At the same time, designers of precision instrumentation require certain guaranteed maximum noise levels to realize the full accuracy of their equipment.

The AD711C grade is specified at a maximum level of 4.0μV p-p, in a 0.1 to 10Hz bandwidth. Each AD711C receives a 100% noise test for two 10-second intervals; devices with any excursion in excess of 4.0μV are rejected. The screened lot is then submitted to Quality Control for verification on an AQL basis.

All other grades of the AD711 are sample-tested on an AQL basis to a limit of 6μV p-p, 0.1 to 10Hz.

–10–

DRIVING THE ANALOG INPUT OF AN A/D CONVERTER

An op amp driving the analog input of an A/D converter, such as that shown in Figure 34, must be capable of maintaining a constant output voltage under dynamically-changing load conditions. In successive-approximation converters, the input current is compared to a series of switched trial currents. The comparison point is diode clamped but may deviate several hundred millivolts resulting in high frequency modulation of A/D input current. The output impedance of a feedback amplifier is made artificially low by the loop gain. At high frequencies, where the loop gain is low, the amplifier output impedance can approach its open loop value. Most IC amplifiers exhibit a minimum open loop output impedance of 25Ω due to current limiting resistors. A few hundred microamps reflected from the change in converter

loading can introduce errors in instantaneous input voltage. If the A/D conversion speed is not excessive and the bandwidth of the amplifier is sufficient, the amplifier's output will return to the nominal value before the converter makes its comparison. However, many amplifiers have relatively narrow bandwidth yielding slow recovery from output transients. The AD711 is ideally suited to drive high speed A/D converters since it offers both wide bandwidth and high open-loop gain.

DRIVING A LARGE CAPACITIVE LOAD

The circuit in Figure 36 employs a 100Ω isolation resistor which enables the amplifier to drive capacitive loads exceeding 1500pF; the resistor effectively isolates the high frequency feedback from the load and stabilizes the circuit. Low frequency feedback is returned to the amplifier summing junction via the low pass filter formed by the 100Ω series resistor and the load capacitance, C_L. Figure 37 shows a typical transient response for this connection.

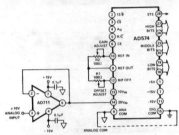

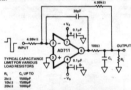

Figure 36. Circuit for Driving a Large Capacitive Load

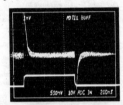

a. Source Current = 2mA

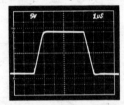

Figure 37. Transient Response $R_L = 2k\Omega$, $C_L = 500pF$

ACTIVE FILTER APPLICATIONS

In active filter applications using op amps, the d.c. accuracy of the amplifier is critical to optimal filter performance. The amplifier's offset voltage and bias current contribute to output error. Offset voltage will be passed by the filter and may be amplified to produce excessive output offset. For low frequency applications requiring large value input resistors, bias currents flowing through these resistors will also generate an offset voltage.

In addition, at higher frequencies, an op-amp's dynamics must be carefully considered. Here, slew rate, bandwidth, and open-loop gain play a major role in op-amp selection. The slew rate must be fast as well as symmetrical to minimize distortion. The amplifier's bandwidth in conjunction with the filter's gain will dictate the frequency response of the filter.

The use of a high performance amplifier such as the AD711 will minimize both dc and ac errors in all active filter applications.

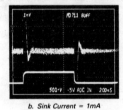

b. Sink Current = 1mA

Figure 35. ADC Input Unity Gain Buffer Recovery Times

Figure 34. AD711 as ADC Unity Gain Buffer

-11-

Courtesy Analog Devices, Inc.

SECOND ORDER LOW PASS FILTER

Figure 38 depicts the AD711 configured as a second order Butterworth low pass filter. With the values as shown, the corner frequency will be 20kHz; however, the wide bandwidth of the AD711 permits a corner frequency as high as several hundred kilohertz. Equations for component selection are shown below.

$R1 = R2$ = user selected (typical values: $10k\Omega - 100k\Omega$)

$$C1 = \frac{1.414F}{(2\pi)\,(f_{cutoff})\,(R1)} \quad C2 = \frac{0.707F}{(2\pi)\,(f_{cutoff})\,(R1)}$$

An important property of filters is their out-of-band rejection. The simple 20kHz low pass filter shown in Figure 38, might be used to condition a signal contaminated with clock pulses or sampling glitches which have considerable energy content at high frequencies.

The low output impedance and high bandwidth of the AD711 minimize high frequency feedthrough as shown in Figure 39.

The upper trace is that of another low cost BiFET op-amp showing 17dB more feedthrough at 5MHz.

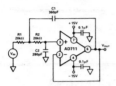

Figure 38. Second Order Low Pass Filter

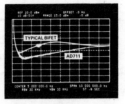

Figure 39.

9 POLE CHEBYCHEV FILTER

Figure 40 shows the AD711 and its dual counterpart, the AD712, as a 9 pole Chebychev filter using active frequency dependent negative resistors (FDNR). With a cutoff frequency of 50kHz and better than 90dB rejection, it may be used as an anti-aliasing filter for a 12-bit Data Acquisition System with 100kHz throughput.

As shown in Figure 40, the filter is comprised of four FDNRs

(A, B, C, D) having values of 4.9395×10^{-15} and 5.9276×10^{-15} farad-seconds. Each FDNR active network provides a two-pole response; for a total of 8 poles. The 9th pole consists of a $0.001\mu F$ capacitor and a $124k\Omega$ resistor at Pin 3 of amplifier A2. Figure 41 depicts the circuits for each FDNR with the proper selection of R. To achieve optimal performance, the $0.001\mu F$ capacitors must be selected for 1% or better matching and all resistors should have 1% or better tolerance.

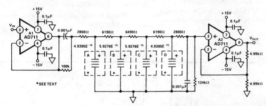

Figure 40. 9 Pole Chebychev Filter

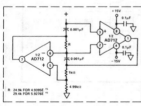

Figure 41. FDNR for 9 Pole Chebychev Filter

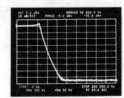

Figure 42. High Frequency Response for 9 Pole Chebychev Filter

-12-

OPA606

Wide-Bandwidth *Difet*™
OPERATIONAL AMPLIFIER

FEATURES
- WIDE BANDWIDTH, 13MHz typ
- HIGH SLEW RATE, 35V/μsec typ
- LOW BIAS CURRENT, 10pA max at $T_A = +25°C$
- LOW OFFSET VOLTAGE, 500μV max
- LOW DISTORTION, 0.0035% typ at 10kHz

APPLICATIONS
- OPTOELECTRONICS
- DATA ACQUISITION
- TEST EQUIPMENT
- AUDIO AMPLIFIERS

DESCRIPTION

The OPA606 is a wide-bandwidth monolithic dielectrically-isolated FET (*Difet*™) operational amplifier featuring a wider bandwidth and lower bias current than BIFET® LF156A amplifiers. Bias current is specified under warmed-up and operating conditions, not at a JUNCTION temperature of +25°C.

Laser-trimmed thin-film resistors offer improved offset voltage and noise performance.

The OPA606 is internally compensated for unity-gain stability.

Difet™ Burr-Brown Corp., Bifet® National Semiconductor Corp.

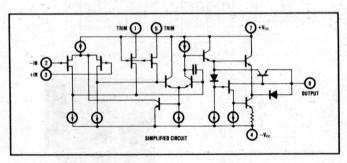

SIMPLIFIED CIRCUIT

International Airport Industrial Park - P.O. Box 11400 - Tucson, Arizona 85734 - Tel. (602) 746-1111 - Twx: 910-952-1111 - Cable: BBRCORP - Telex: 66-6491

SPECIFICATIONS

ELECTRICAL

At $V_{CC} = \pm 15VDC$ and $T_A = +25°C$ unless otherwise specified.

PARAMETER	CONDITIONS	OPA606KM/SM MIN	OPA606KM/SM TYP	OPA606KM/SM MAX	OPA606LM MIN	OPA606LM TYP	OPA606LM MAX	OPA606KP MIN	OPA606KP TYP	OPA606KP MAX	UNITS
FREQUENCY RESPONSE											
Gain Bandwidth	Small signal	10	12.5		11	13		9	12		MHz
Full Power Response	20V p-p, $R_L = 2k\Omega$		515			550			470		kHz
Slew Rate	$V_O = \pm 10V$, $R_L = 2k\Omega$	22	33		25	35		20	30		V/μsec
Settling Time[1]: 0.1%	Gain = −1, $R_L = 2k\Omega$		1.0			1.0			1.0		μsec
0.01%	10V step		2.1			2.1			2.1		μsec
Total Harmonic Distortion	G = +1, 20V p-p $R_L = 2k\Omega$, f = 10kHz		0.0035			0.0035			0.0035		%
INPUT											
OFFSET VOLTAGE[2]											
Input Offset Voltage	$V_{CM} = 0VDC$		±180	±1.5mV		±100	±500		±300	±3mV	μV
Average Drift	$T_A = T_{MIN}$ to T_{MAX}		±5			±3	±5		±10		μV/°C
Supply Rejection	$V_{CC} = \pm 10V$ to ±18V	82	100		90	104		80	90		dB
			±10	±79		±6	±32		±32	±100	μV/V
BIAS CURRENT[2]											
Input Bias Current	$V_{CM} = 0VDC$		±7	±15		±5	±10		±8	±25	pA
OFFSET CURRENT[2]											
Input Offset Current	$V_{CM} = 0VDC$		±0.6	±10		±0.4	±5		±1	±15	pA
NOISE											
Voltage, $f_O = 10Hz$	100% tested (L)		37			30	40		37		nV/$\sqrt{Hz}$
100Hz	100% tested (L)		21			20	28		21		nV/$\sqrt{Hz}$
1kHz	100% tested (L)		14			13	16		14		nV/$\sqrt{Hz}$
10kHz	[3]		12			11	13		12		nV/$\sqrt{Hz}$
20kHz	[3]		11			10.5	13		11		nV/$\sqrt{Hz}$
$f_B = 10Hz$ to 10kHz	[3]		1.3			1.2	1.5		1.3		μV rms
Current, $f_O = 0.1Hz$ thru 20kHz	[3]		1.5			1.3	2		1.7		fA/$\sqrt{Hz}$
IMPEDANCE											
Differential			$10^{13} \| 1$			$10^{13} \| 1$			$10^{13} \| 1$		$\Omega \| pF$
Common-Mode			$10^{14} \| 3$			$10^{14} \| 3$			$10^{14} \| 3$		$\Omega \| pF$
VOLTAGE RANGE											
Common-Mode Input Range		±10.5	±11.5		±11	±11.6		±10.2	±11		V
Common-Mode Rejection	$V_{IN} = \pm 10VDC$	80	95		85	96		78	90		dB
OPEN-LOOP GAIN, DC											
Open-Loop Voltage Gain	$R_L \geq 2k\Omega$	95	115		100	118		90	110		dB
RATED OUTPUT											
Voltage Output	$R_L = 2k\Omega$	±11	±12.2		±12	±12.6		±11	±12		V
Current Output	$V_O = \pm 10VDC$	±5	±10		±5	±10		±5	±10		mA
Output Resistance	DC, open loop		40			40			40		Ω
Load Capacitance Stability	Gain = +1		1000			1000			1000		pF
Short-Circuit Current		10	20		10	20		10	20		mA
POWER SUPPLY											
Rated Voltage			±15			±15			±15		VDC
Voltage Range, Derated Performance		±5		±18	±5		±18	±5		±18	VDC
Current, Quiescent	$I_O = 0mADC$		6.5	9.5		6.2	9		6.5	10	mA
TEMPERATURE RANGE											
Specification	Ambient temp.										
KM, KP, LM		0		+70	0		+70	0		+70	°C
SM		−55		+125							°C
Operating	Ambient Temp.	−55		+125	−55		+125	−25		+85	°C
θ Junction-Ambient			200			200			155		°C/W

NOTES: (1) See settling time test circuit in Figure 2. (2) Offset voltage, offset current, and bias current are measured with the units fully warmed up. (3) Sample tested—this parameter is guaranteed on L grade only.

2

® 1985 Burr-Brown Corp. Reproduced with permission.

ELECTRICAL (FULL TEMPERATURE RANGE SPECIFICATIONS)

At $V_{CC} = \pm15VDC$ and $T_A = T_{MIN}$ to T_{MAX} unless otherwise noted.

PARAMETER	CONDITIONS		OPA606KM/SM MIN	TYP	MAX	OPA606LM MIN	TYP	MAX	OPA606KP MIN	TYP	MAX	UNITS
TEMPERATURE RANGE												
Specification Range	Ambient temp.	KM	0		+70	0		+70	0		+70	°C
		SM	−55		+125							°C
INPUT												
OFFSET VOLTAGE[1]												
Input Offset Voltage	$V_{CM} = 0VDC$	KM		±400	±2mV		±335	±750		±750	±3.5mV	μV
		SM		±680	±3mV							μV
Average Drift				±5			±3	±5		±10		μV/°C
Supply Rejection	$V_{cc} = \pm10V$ to $\pm18V$		80	98		85	100		78	95		dB
				±13	±100		±10	±56		±18	±126	μV/V
BIAS CURRENT[1]												
Input Bias Current	$V_{CM} = 0VDC$	KM		±158	±339		±113	±226		±181	±566	pA
		SM		±7.2	±15.4							nA
OFFSET CURRENT[1]												
Input Offset Current	$V_{CM} = 0VDC$	KM		±14	±226		±9	±113		±23	±339	pA
		SM		±614	±10.2nA							pA
VOLTAGE RANGE												
Common-Mode Input Range			±10.4	±11.4		±10.9	±11.5		±10	±10.9		V
Common-Mode Rejection	$V_{IN} = \pm10VDC$		78	92		82	95		75	88		dB
OPEN-LOOP GAIN, DC												
Open-Loop Voltage Gain	$R_L \geq 2k\Omega$		90	106		95	112		88	104		dB
RATED OUTPUT												
Voltage Output	$R_L = 2k\Omega$		±10.5	±12		±11.5	±12.4		±10.4	±11.8		V
Current Output	$V_O = \pm10VDC$		±5	±10		±5	±10		±5	±10		mA
POWER SUPPLY												
Current, Quiescent	$I = 0mADC$			6.6	10		6.4	9.5		6.6	10.5	mA

NOTES: (1) Offset voltage, offset current, and bias current are measured with the units fully warmed up.

PRICES

QUANTITY	OPA606KP	OPA606KM	OPA606LM	OPA606SM
1–24	$3.75	$5.70	$13.85	$14.25
25–99	2.85	4.35	9.95	10.25
100+	2.30	3.50	8.25	8.50

ORDERING INFORMATION

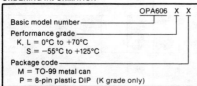

OPA606 X X

Basic model number
Performance grade
K, L = 0°C to +70°C
S = −55°C to +125°C
Package code
M = TO-99 metal can
P = 8-pin plastic DIP (K grade only)

ABSOLUTE MAXIMUM RATINGS

Supply	±18VDC
Internal Power Dissipation[1]	500mW
Differential Input Voltage	±36VDC
Input Voltage Range[2]	±18VDC
Storage Temperature Range	M = −65°C to +150°C, P = −40°C to +85°C
Operating Temperature Range	M = −55°C to +125°C, P = −40°C to +85°C
Lead Temperature (soldering, 10 seconds)	+300°C
Output Short Circuit Duration[3]	Continuous
Junction Temperature	+175°C

NOTES: (1) Packages must be derated based on $\theta_{JC} = 15°C/W$ or θ_{JA}. (2) For supply voltages less than ±18VDC, the absolute maximum input voltage is equal to the negative supply voltage. (3) Short circuit may be to power supply common only. Rating applies to +25°C ambient. Observe dissipation limit and T_J.

CONNECTION DIAGRAMS

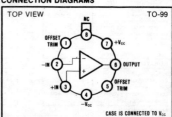

TOP VIEW TO-99

CASE IS CONNECTED TO V_{CC}

MECHANICAL

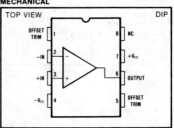

TOP VIEW DIP

3

TYPICAL PERFORMANCE CURVES

T_A = +25°C, V_{CC} = ±15VDC unless otherwise noted.

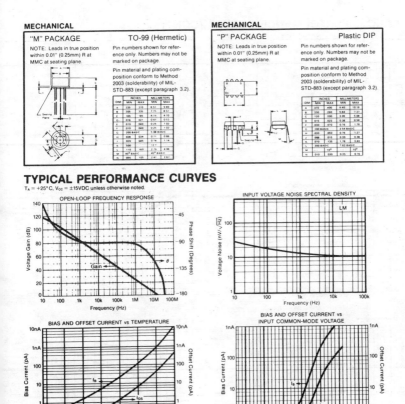

4

TYPICAL PERFORMANCE CURVES (CONT)

$T_A = +25°C$, $V_{CC} = \pm15VDC$ unless otherwise noted.

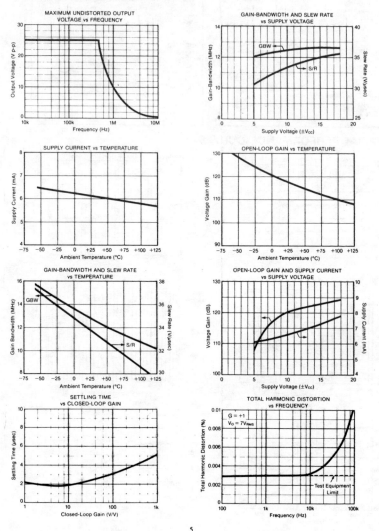

MAXIMUM UNDISTORTED OUTPUT
VOLTAGE vs FREQUENCY

GAIN-BANDWIDTH AND SLEW RATE
vs SUPPLY VOLTAGE

SUPPLY CURRENT vs TEMPERATURE

OPEN-LOOP GAIN vs TEMPERATURE

GAIN-BANDWIDTH AND SLEW RATE
vs TEMPERATURE

OPEN-LOOP GAIN AND SUPPLY CURRENT
vs SUPPLY VOLTAGE

SETTLING TIME
vs CLOSED-LOOP GAIN

TOTAL HARMONIC DISTORTION
vs FREQUENCY

5

TYPICAL PERFORMANCE CURVES (CONT)

$T_a = +25°C$, $V_{CC} = \pm15VDC$ unless otherwise noted.

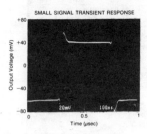

SMALL SIGNAL TRANSIENT RESPONSE

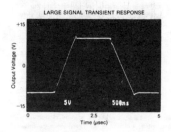

LARGE SIGNAL TRANSIENT RESPONSE

APPLICATIONS INFORMATION

OFFSET VOLTAGE ADJUSTMENT

The OPA606 offset voltage is laser-trimmed and will require no further trim for most applications. As with most amplifiers, externally trimming the remaining offset can change drift performance by about $0.5\mu V/°C$ for each millivolt of adjusted offset. Note that the trim (Figure I) is similar to operational amplifiers such as LF156 and OP-16. The OPA606 can replace most other amplifiers by leaving the external null circuit unconnected.

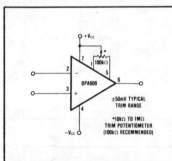

FIGURE I. Offset Voltage Trim.

INPUT PROTECTION

Static damage can cause subtle changes in amplifier input characteristics without necessarily destroying the device. In precision operational amplifiers (both bipolar and FET types), this may cause a noticeable degradation of offset voltage and drift. Static protection is recommended when handling any precision IC operational amplifier.

If the input voltage exceeds the amplifier's negative supply voltage, input current limiting must be used to prevent damage.

CIRCUIT LAYOUT

Wideband amplifiers require good circuit layout techniques and adequate power supply bypassing. Short, direct connections and good high frequency bypass capacitors (ceramic or tantalum) will help avoid noise pickup or oscillation.

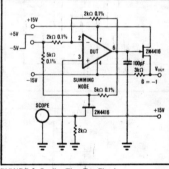

FIGURE 2. Settling Time Test Circuit.

6

GUARDING AND SHIELDING

As in any situation where high impedances are involved, careful shielding is required to reduce "hum" pickup in input leads. If large feedback resistors are used, they should also be shielded along with the external input circuitry.

Leakage currents across printed circuit boards can easily exceed the bias current of the OPA606. To avoid leakage problems, it is recommended that the signal input lead of the OPA606 be wired to a Teflon® standoff. If the OPA606 is to be soldered directly into a printed circuit board, utmost care must be used in planning the board layout.

A "guard" pattern should completely surround the high impedance input leads and should be connected to a low impedance point which is at the signal input potential (see Figure 3).

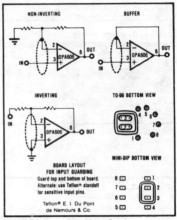

FIGURE 3. Connection of Input Guard.

APPLICATIONS CIRCUITS

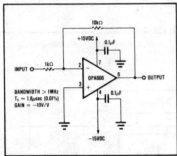

FIGURE 4. Inverting Amplifier.

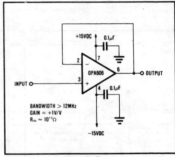

FIGURE 5. Noninverting Buffer.

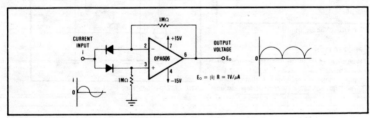

FIGURE 6. Absolute Value Current-to-Voltage Converter.

7

Appendix A

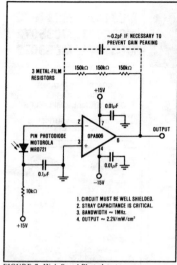

FIGURE 7. High-Speed Photodetector.

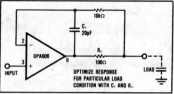

FIGURE 8. Isolating Load Capacitance from Buffer.

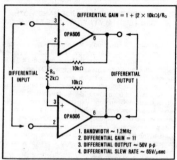

FIGURE 9. Differential Input/Differential Output Amplifier.

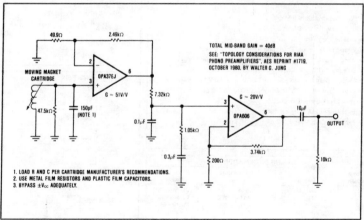

FIGURE 10. Low Noise/Low Distortion RIAA Preamplifier.

® 1985 Burr-Brown Corp. Reproduced with permission.

MOTOROLA

SEMICONDUCTORS

P.O. BOX 20912 • PHOENIX, ARIZONA 85036

MC34071, MC34072
MC35071, MC35072
MC33071, MC33072

Advance Information

HIGH PERFORMANCE
SINGLE SUPPLY
OPERATIONAL AMPLIFIERS

SILICON MONOLITHIC
INTEGRATED CIRCUIT

HIGH SLEW RATE, WIDE BANDWIDTH, SINGLE SUPPLY OPERATIONAL AMPLIFIERS

A standard low-cost Bipolar technology with innovative design concepts are employed for the MC34071/MC34072 series of monolithic operational amplifiers. These devices offer 4.5 MHz of gain bandwidth product, 13 V/μs slew rate, and fast settling time without the use of JFET device technology. In addition, low input offset voltage can economically be achieved. Although these devices can be operated from split supplies, they are particularly suited for single supply operation, since the common mode input voltage range includes ground potential (V_{EE}). The all NPN output stage, characterized by no deadband crossover distortion and large output voltage swing, also provides high capacitive drive capability, excellent phase and gain margins, low open-loop high frequency output impedance and symmetrical source/sink ac frequency response.

The MC34071/MC34072 series of devices are available in standard or prime performance (A Suffix) grades and specified over commercial, industrial/vehicular or military temperature ranges.

- Wide Bandwidth: 4.5 MHz
- High Slew Rate: 13 V/μs
- Fast Settling Time: 1.1 μs to 0.10%
- Wide Single Supply Operating Range: 3.0 to 44 Volts
- Wide Input Common Mode Range Including Ground (V_{EE})
- Low Input Offset Voltage: 1.5 mV Maximum (A Suffix)
- Large Output Voltage Swing: -14.7 V to $+14.0$ V for $V_S = \pm 15$ V
- Large Capacitance Drive Capability: 0 to 10,000 pF
- Low T.H.D. Distortion: 0.02%
- Excellent Phase Margins: 60°
- Excellent Gain Margin: 12 dB

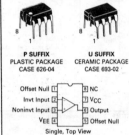

P SUFFIX
PLASTIC PACKAGE
CASE 626-04

U SUFFIX
CERAMIC PACKAGE
CASE 693-02

Offset Null ⬜1 8⬜ NC
Invt Input ⬜2 7⬜ V_{CC}
Noninvt Input ⬜3 6⬜ Output
V_{EE} ⬜4 5⬜ Offset Null

Single, Top View

Output A ⬜1 8⬜ V_{CC}
Inputs A ⬜2 7⬜ Output B
  ⬜3 6⬜ Inputs B
V_{EE} ⬜4 5⬜

Dual, Top View

SINGLE SUPPLY
3.0 V to 44 V

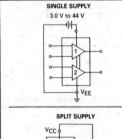

SPLIT SUPPLY

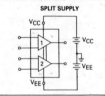

ORDERING INFORMATION

Op Amp Function	Device	Temperature Range	Package
Single	MC35071U,AU	-55 to $+125°$C	Ceramic DIP
	MC33071U,AU	-40 to $+85°$C	Ceramic DIP
	MC33071P,AP	-40 to $+85°$C	Plastic DIP
	MC34071U,AU	0 to $+70°$C	Ceramic DIP
	MC34071P,AP	0 to $+70°$C	Plastic DIP
Dual	MC35072U,AU	-55 to $+125°$C	Ceramic DIP
	MC33072U,AU	-40 to $+85°$C	Ceramic DIP
	MC33072P,AP	-40 to $+85°$C	Plastic DIP
	MC34072U,AU	0 to $+70°$C	Ceramic DIP
	MC34072P,AP	0 to $+70°$C	Plastic DIP
Quad	MC34074 Series	Refer to MC34074 Data Sheet	

This document contains information on a new product. Specifications and information herein are subject to change without notice.

© MOTOROLA INC., 1984

ADI1091

Courtesy Motorola Semiconductor Products Inc.

260   *Appendix A*

DC ELECTRICAL CHARACTERISTICS (V_{CC} = +15 V, V_{EE} = −15 V, R_L connected to ground, T_A = T_{low} to T_{high} [Note 3] unless otherwise noted)

Characteristic	Symbol	MC3507 A/MC3407 A/ MC3307 A			MC3507 /MC3407 / MC3307			Unit
		Min	Typ	Max	Min	Typ	Max	
Input Offset Voltage (V_{CM} = 0)	V_{IO}							mV
$\quad V_{CC}$ = +15 V, V_{EE} = −15 V, T_A = +25°C		—	0.5	1.5	—	1.0	3.5	
$\quad V_{CC}$ = +5.0 V, V_{EE} = 0 V, T_A = +25°C		—	0.5	2.0	—	1.5	4.0	
$\quad V_{CC}$ = +15 V, V_{EE} = −15 V, T_A = T_{low} to T_{high}		—	—	3.5	—	—	5.5	
Average Temperature Coefficient of Offset Voltage	$\Delta V_{IO}/\Delta T$	—	10	—	—	10	—	$\mu V/°C$
Input Bias Current (V_{CM} = 0)	I_{IB}							nA
$\quad T_A$ = +25°C		—	100	500	—	100	500	
$\quad T_A$ = T_{low} to T_{high}		—	—	700	—	—	700	
Input Offset Current (V_{CM} = 0)	I_{IO}							nA
$\quad T_A$ = +25°C		—	6.0	50	—	6.0	75	
$\quad T_A$ = T_{low} to T_{high}		—	—	300	—	—	300	
Large Signal Voltage Gain V_O = ±10 V, R_L = 2.0 k	A_{VOL}	50	100	—	25	100	—	V/mV
Output Voltage Swing	V_{OH}							V
$\quad V_{CC}$ = +5.0 V, V_{EE} = 0 V, R_L = 2.0 k, T_A = +25°C		3.7	4.0	—	3.7	4.0	—	
$\quad V_{CC}$ = +15 V, V_{EE} = −15 V, R_L = 10 k, T_A = +25°C		13.7	14	—	13.7	14	—	
$\quad V_{CC}$ = +15 V, V_{EE} −15 V, R_L = 2.0 k, T_A = T_{low} to T_{high}		13.5	—	—	13.5	—	—	
	V_{OL}							
$\quad V_{CC}$ = +5.0 V, V_{EE} = 0 V, R_L = 2.0 k, T_A = +25°C		—	0.1	0.2	—	0.1	0.2	
$\quad V_{CC}$ = +15 V, V_{EE} + −15 V, R_L = 10 k, T_A = +25°C		—	−14.7	−14.4	—	−14.7	−14.4	
$\quad V_{CC}$ = +15 V, V_{EE} = −15 V, R_L = 2.0 k, T_A = T_{low} to T_{high}		—	—	−13.8	—	—	−13.8	
Output Short-Circuit Current (T_A = +25°C) Input Overdrive = 1.0 V, Output to Ground	I_{SC}							mA
$\quad$ Source		10	30	—	10	30	—	
$\quad$ Sink		20	47	—	20	47	—	
Input Common Mode Voltage Range T_A = +25°C	V_{ICR}	V_{EE} to (V_{CC} − 1.8)			V_{EE} to (V_{CC} − 1.8)			V
$\quad T_A$ = T_{low} to T_{high}		V_{EE} to (V_{CC} − 2.2)			V_{EE} to (V_{CC} − 2.2)			
Common Mode Rejection Ratio (R_S ≤ 10 k)	CMRR	80	97	—	70	97	—	dB
Power Supply Rejection Ratio (R_S = 100 Ω)	PSRR	80	97	—	70	97	—	dB
Power Supply Current (Per Amplifier)	I_D							mA
$\quad V_{CC}$ = +5.0 V, V_{EE} = 0 V, T_A = +25°C		—	1.6	2.0	—	1.6	2.0	
$\quad V_{CC}$ = +15 V, V_{EE} = −15 V, T_A = +25°C		—	1.9	2.5	—	1.9	2.5	
$\quad V_{CC}$ = +15 V, V_{EE} = −15 V, T_A = T_{low} to T_{high}		—	—	2.8	—	—	2.8	

NOTES: (continued)
3. T_{low} = −55°C for MC35071,A/MC35072,A $\qquad T_{high}$ = + 125°C for MC35071,A/35072,A
$\quad$ = −40°C for MC33071,A/MC33072,A $\qquad$ = +85°C for MC33071,A/33072,A
$\quad$ = 0°C for MC34071,A/MC34072,A $\qquad$ = +70°C for MC34071,A/34072,A

 MOTOROLA Semiconductor Products Inc.

Courtesy Motorola Semiconductor Products Inc.

MAXIMUM RATINGS

Rating	Symbol	Value	Unit
Supply Voltage (from V_{CC} to V_{EE})	V_S	+44	Volts
Input Differential Voltage Range	V_{IDR}	Note 1	Volts
Input Voltage Range	V_{IR}	Note 1	Volts
Output Short-Circuit Duration (Note 2)	t_S	Indefinite	Seconds
Operating Ambient Temperature Range MC35071,A/MC35072,A MC33071,A/MC33072,A MC34071,A/MC34072,A	T_A	−55 to +125 −40 to +85 0 to +70	°C
Operating Junction Temperature	T_J	+150	°C
Storage Temperature Range Ceramic Package Plastic Package	T_{stg}	−65 to +150 −55 to +125	°C

NOTES:
1. Either or both input voltages must not exceed the magnitude of V_{CC} or V_{EE}.
2. Power dissipation must be considered to ensure maximum junction temperature (T_J) is not exceeded.

EQUIVALENT CIRCUIT SCHEMATIC (EACH AMPLIFIER)

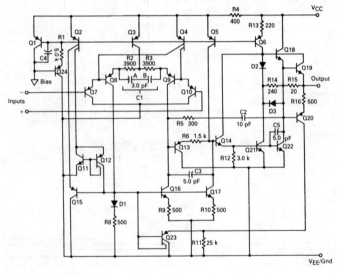

MOTOROLA Semiconductor Products Inc.

Courtesy Motorola Semiconductor Products Inc.

Appendix A

AC ELECTRICAL CHARACTERISTICS (V_{CC} = +15 V, V_{EE} = −15 V, R_L connected to ground, T_A = +25°C unless otherwise noted)

Characteristic	Symbol	MC3507_A/MC3407_A/ MC3307_A			MC3507_/MC3407_/ MC3307			Unit
		Min	Typ	Max	Min	Typ	Max	
Slew Rate (V_{in} = −10 V to +10 V, R_L = 2.0 k, C_L = 500 pF) A_V + 1.0 A_V − 1.0	SR	8.0 —	10 13	— —	— —	10 13	— —	V/µs
Settling Time (10 V Step, A_V = −1.0) To 0.10% (± 1/2 LSB of 9-Bits) To 0.01% (± 1/2 LSB of 12-Bits)	t_S	— —	1.1 2.2	— —	— —	1.1 2.2	— —	µs
Gain Bandwidth Product (f = 100 kHz)	GBW	3.5	4.5	—	—	4.5	—	MHz
Power Bandwidth A_V = +1.0, R_L = 2.0 k, V_O = 20 V_{p-p}, THD = 5.0%	BWp	—	200	—	—	200	—	kHz
Phase Margin R_L = 2.0 k R_L = 2.0 k, C_L = 300 pF	ϕm	— —	60 40	— —	— —	60 40	— —	Degrees
Gain Margin R_L = 2.0 k R_L = 2.0 k, C_L = 300 pF	A_m	— —	12 4.0	— —	— —	12 4.0	— —	dB
Equivalent Input Noise Voltage R_S = 100 Ω, f = 1.0 kHz	e_n	—	32	—	—	32	—	nV/√Hz
Equivalent Input Noise Current (f = 1.0 kHz)	I_n	—	0.22	—	—	0.22	—	pA/√Hz
Input Capacitance	C_i	—	0.8	—	—	0.8	—	pF
Total Harmonic Distortion A_V = +10, R_L = 2.0 k, 2.0 ≤ V_O ≤ 20 V_{p-p}, f = 10 kHz	THD	—	0.02	—	—	0.02	—	%
Channel Separation (f = 10 kHz, MC34072,A Only)	—	—	120	—	—	120	—	dB
Open-Loop Output Impedance (f = 1.0 MHz)	z_O	—	30	—	—	30	—	Ω

For typical performance curves and applications information refer to MC34074 series data sheet.

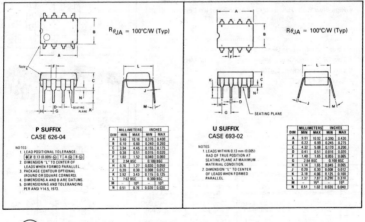

P SUFFIX
CASE 626-04

$R\theta_{JA}$ = 100°C/W (Typ)

U SUFFIX
CASE 693-02

$R\theta_{JA}$ = 100°C/W (Typ)

Courtesy Motorola Semiconductor Products Inc.

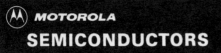

MOTOROLA

SEMICONDUCTORS

P.O. BOX 20912 • PHOENIX, ARIZONA 85036

MC34080/MC35080
thru
MC34085/MC35085

Advance Information

HIGH SLEW RATE, WIDE BANDWIDTH, JFET INPUT OPERATIONAL AMPLIFIERS

These devices are a new generation of high-speed JFET input monolithic operational amplifiers. Innovative design concepts along with JFET technology provide wide gain bandwidth product and high slew rate. Well matched JFET input devices and advanced trim techniques ensure low input offset errors and bias currents. The all NPN output stage features large output voltage swing, no deadband crossover distortion, high capacitive drive capability, excellent phase and gain margins, low open-loop output impedance, and symmetrical source/sink ac frequency response.

This series of devices are available in standard or prime performance (A suffix) grades, fully compensated or decompensated ($A_{VCL} \geq 2$) and are specified over commercial or Military temperature ranges. They are pin compatible with existing Industry standard operational amplifiers, and allow the designer to easily upgrade the performance of existing designs.

- Wide Gain Bandwidth: 8.0 MHz for Fully Compensated Devices
  16 MHz for Decompensated Devices
- High Slew Rate: 25 V/μs for Fully Compensated Devices
  50 V/μs for Decompensated Devices
- High Input Impedance: 10^{12} Ω
- Input Offset Voltage: 0.5 mV Maximum (Single Amplifier)
- Large Output Voltage Swing: -14.7 V to $+14$ V for $V_S = \pm 15$ V
- Low Open-Loop Output Impedance: 30 Ω @ 1.0 MHz
- Low THD Distortion: 0.01%
- Excellent Phase/Gain Margins: 55°/7.6 dB for Fully Compensated Devices

HIGH PERFORMANCE
JFET-INPUT
OPERATIONAL AMPLIFIERS

SILICON MONOLITHIC
INTEGRATED CIRCUITS

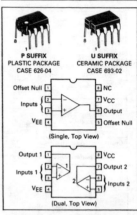

P SUFFIX
PLASTIC PACKAGE
CASE 626-04

U SUFFIX
CERAMIC PACKAGE
CASE 693-02

Offset Null [1   8] NC
Inputs { [2   7] V_{CC}
[3   6] Output
V_{EE} [4   5] Offset Null

(Single, Top View)

Output 1 [1   8] V_{CC}
Inputs 1 { [2   7] Output 2
[3   6] } Inputs 2
V_{EE} [4   5]

(Dual, Top View)

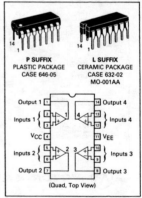

P SUFFIX
PLASTIC PACKAGE
CASE 646-05

L SUFFIX
CERAMIC PACKAGE
CASE 632-02
MO-001AA

Output 1 [1   14] Output 4
Inputs 1 { [2   13] } Inputs 4
[3   12]
V_{CC} [4   11] V_{EE}
Inputs 2 { [5   10] } Inputs 3
[6   9]
Output 2 [7   8] Output 3

(Quad, Top View)

ORDERING INFORMATION

Op Amp Function	Fully Compensated	$A_{VCL} \geq 2$ Decompensated	Temperature Range	Package
Single	MC35081U,AU	MC35080U,AU	-55 to $+125°C$	Ceramic DIP
	MC34081P,AP	MC34080P,AP	0 to 70°C	Plastic DIP
Dual	MC35082U,AU	MC35083U,AU	-55 to $+125°C$	Ceramic DIP
	MC34082P,AP	MC34083P,AP	0 to 70°C	Plastic DIP
Quad	MC35084L,AL	MC35085L,AL	-55 to $+125°C$	Ceramic DIP
	MC34084P,AP	MC34085P,AP	0 to 70°C	Plastic DIP

This document contains information on a new product. Specifications and information herein are subject to change without notice.

© MOTOROLA INC., 1985   ADI1150

Courtesy Motorola Semiconductor Products Inc.

MAXIMUM RATINGS

Rating	Symbol	Value	Unit
Supply Voltage (from V_{CC} to V_{EE})	V_S	+44	Volts
Input Differential Voltage Range	V_{IDR}	Note 1	Volts
Input Voltage Range	V_{IR}	Note 1	Volts
Output Short-Circuit Duration (Note 2)	t_S	Indefinite	Seconds
Operating Ambient Temperature Range MC35XXX MC34XXX	T_A	-55 to $+125$ 0 to $+70$	°C
Operating Junction Temperature Ceramic Package Plastic Package	T_J	$+165$ $+125$	°C
Storage Temperature Range Ceramic Package Plastic Package	T_{stg}	-65 to $+165$ -55 to $+125$	°C

NOTES:
1. Either or both input voltages must not exceed the magnitude of V_{CC} or V_{EE}.
2. Power dissipation must be considered to ensure maximum junction temperature (T_J) is not exceeded.

EQUIVALENT CIRCUIT SCHEMATIC (EACH AMPLIFIER)

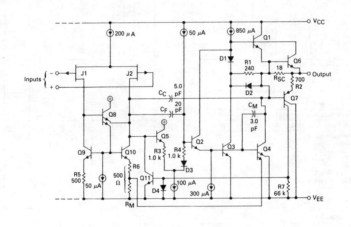

(M) **MOTOROLA** Semiconductor Products Inc.

2

Courtesy Motorola Semiconductor Products Inc.

DC ELECTRICAL CHARACTERISTICS ($V_S = \pm 15$ V, $T_A = T_{low}$ to T_{high} [Note 3], unless otherwise noted)

Characteristic	Symbol	A Suffix Min	A Suffix Typ	A Suffix Max	Non-Suffix Min	Non-Suffix Typ	Non-Suffix Max	Unit
Input Offset Voltage	V_{IO}							mV
Single								
$T_A = +25°C$		—	0.3	0.5	—	0.5	1.0	
$T_A = 0°C$ to $+70°C$ (MC34080, MC34081)		—	—	2.5	—	—	3.0	
$T_A = -55°C$ to $+125°C$ (MC35080, MC35081)		—	—	3.5	—	—	4.0	
Dual								
$T_A = +25°C$		—	0.6	1.0	—	1.0	3.0	
$T_A = 0°C$ to $+70°C$ (MC34082, MC34083)		—	—	3.0	—	—	5.0	
$T_A = -55°C$ to $+125°C$ (MC35082, MC35083)		—	—	4.0	—	—	6.0	
Quad								
$T_A = +25°C$		—	3.0	6.0	—	6.0	12	
$T_A = 0°C$ to $+70°C$ (MC34084, MC34085)		—	—	8.0	—	—	14	
$T_A = -55°C$ to $+125°C$ (MC35084, MC35085)		—	—	9.0	—	—	15	
Average Temperature Coefficient of Offset Voltage	$\Delta V_{IO}/\Delta T$	—	10	—	—	10	—	$\mu V/°C$
Input Bias Current ($V_{CM} = 0$ Note 4)	I_{IB}							nA
$T_A = +25°C$		—	0.06	0.2	—	0.06	0.2	
$T_A = 0°C$ to $+70°C$		—	—	4.0	—	—	4.0	
$T_A = -55°C$ to $+125°C$		—	—	50	—	—	50	
Input Offset Current ($V_{CM} = 0$ Note 4)	I_{IO}							nA
$T_A = +25°C$		—	0.02	0.1	—	0.02	0.1	
$T_A = 0°C$ to $+70°C$		—	—	2.0	—	—	20	
$T_A = -55°C$ to $+125°C$		—	—	25	—	—	25	
Large Signal Voltage Gain ($V_O = \pm 10$ V, $R_L = 2.0$ k)	A_{VOL}							V/mV
$T_A = +25°C$		50	80	—	25	80	—	
$T_A = T_{low}$ to T_{high}		25	—	—	15	—	—	
Output Voltage Swing	V_{OH}							V
$R_L = 2.0$ k, $T_A = +25°C$		13.2	13.7	—	13.2	13.7	—	
$R_L = 10$ k, $T_A = +25°C$		13.4	13.9	—	13.4	13.9	—	
$R_L = 10$ k, $T_A = T_{low}$ to T_{high}		13.4	—	—	13.4	—	—	
$R_L = 2.0$ k, $T_A = +25°C$	V_{OL}	—	−14.1	−13.5	—	−14.1	−13.5	
$R_L = 10$ k, $T_A = +25°C$		—	−14.7	−14.1	—	−14.7	−14.1	
$R_L = 10$ k, $T_A = T_{low}$ to T_{high}		—	—	−14.0	—	—	−14.0	
Output Short-Circuit Current ($T_A = +25°C$)	I_{SC}							mA
Input Overdrive = 1.0 V, Output to Ground								
Source		20	31	—	20	31	—	
Sink		20	28	—	20	28	—	
Input Common Mode Voltage Range	V_{ICR}	(V_{EE} + 4.0) to			(V_{EE} + 4.0) to			V
$T_A = +25°C$		(V_{CC} − 2.0)			(V_{CC} − 2.0)			
Common Mode Rejection Ratio ($R_S \le 10$ k, $T_A = +25°C$)	CMRR	75	90	—	70	90	—	dB
Power Supply Rejection Ratio ($R_S = 100 \ \Omega$, $T_A = 25°C$)	PSRR	75	86	—	70	86	—	dB
Power Supply Current	I_D							mA
Single								
$T_A = +25°C$		—	2.5	3.4	—	2.5	3.4	
$T_A = T_{low}$ to T_{high}		—	—	4.2	—	—	4.2	
Dual								
$T_A = +25°C$		—	4.9	6.0	—	4.9	6.0	
$T_A = T_{low}$ to T_{high}		—	—	7.5	—	—	7.5	
Quad								
$T_A = +25°C$		—	9.7	11	—	9.7	11	
$T_A = T_{low}$ to T_{high}		—	—	13	—	—	13	

NOTES: (CONTINUED)

3. $T_{low} = -55°C$ for MC35080,A $T_{low} = 0°C$ for MC34080,A $T_{high} = +125°C$ for MC35080,A $T_{high} = +70°C$ for MC34080,A

     MC35081,A   MC34081,A   MC35081,A   MC34081,A
     MC35082,A   MC34082,A   MC35082,A   MC34082,A
     MC35083,A   MC34083,A   MC35083,A   MC34083,A
     MC35084,A   MC34084,A   MC35084,A   MC34084,A
     MC35085,A   MC34085,A   MC35085,A   MC34085,A

4. Limits at $T_A = +25°$ are guaranteed by high temperature (T_{high}) testing.

 MOTOROLA Semiconductor Products Inc.

3

Courtesy Motorola Semiconductor Products Inc.

AC ELECTRICAL CHARACTERISTICS (V$_S$ = ± 15 V, T$_A$ = + 25°C unless otherwise noted)

Characteristic	Symbol	A Suffix			Non-Suffix			Unit
		Min	Typ	Max	Min	Typ	Max	
Slew Rate (V$_{in}$ = − 10 V to + 10 V, R$_L$ = 2.0 k, C$_L$ = 100 pF) Compensated A$_V$ = + 1.0	SR	20	25	—	20	25	—	V/μs
A$_V$ = − 1.0		—	30	—	—	30	—	
Decompensated A$_V$ = + 2.0		40	50	—	40	50	—	
A$_V$ = − 1.0		—	50	—	—	50	—	
Settling Time (10 V Step, A$_V$ = − 1.0) To 0.10% (± ½ LSB of 9-Bits)	t$_s$	—	0.72	—	—	0.72	—	μs
To 0.01% (± ½ LSB of 12-Bits)		—	1.6	—	—	1.6	—	
Gain Bandwidth Product (f = 200 kHz) Compensated	GBW	6.0	8.0	—	6.0	8.0	—	MHz
Decompensated		12	16	—	12	16	—	
Power Bandwidth (R$_L$ = 2.0 k, V$_O$ = 20 V$_{p-p}$, THD = 5.0%) Compensated A$_V$ = + 1.0	BWp	—	400	—	—	400	—	kHz
Decompensated A$_V$ = − 1.0		—	800	—	—	800	—	
Phase Margin (Compensated) R$_L$ = 2.0 k	φm	—	55	—	—	55	—	Degrees
R$_L$ = 2.0 k, C$_L$ = 100 pF		—	39	—	—	39	—	
Gain Margin (Compensated) R$_L$ = 2.0 k	A$_m$	—	7.6	—	—	7.6	—	dB
R$_L$ = 2.0 k, C$_L$ = 100 pF		—	4.5	—	—	4.5	—	
Equivalent Input Noise Voltage R$_S$ = 100 Ω, f = 1.0 kHz	e$_n$	—	30	—	—	30	—	nV/√Hz
Equivalent Input Noise Current (f = 1.0 kHz)	I$_n$	—	0.01	—	—	0.01	—	pA/√Hz
Input Capacitance	C$_i$	—	5.0	—	—	5.0	—	pF
Input Resistance	r$_i$	—	10^{12}	—	—	10^{12}	—	Ω
Total Harmonic Distortion A$_V$ = + 10, R$_L$ = 2.0 k, 2.0 ≤ V$_O$ ≤ 20 V$_{p-p}$, f = 10 kHz	THD	—	0.05	—	—	0.05	—	%
Channel Separation (f = 10 kHz)	—	—	120	—	—	120	—	dB
Open-Loop Output Impedance (f = 1.0 MHz)	z$_O$	—	35	—	—	35	—	Ω

TYPICAL PERFORMANCE CURVES

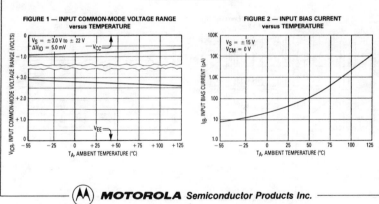

FIGURE 1 — INPUT COMMON-MODE VOLTAGE RANGE
versus TEMPERATURE

FIGURE 2 — INPUT BIAS CURRENT
versus TEMPERATURE

Ⓜ MOTOROLA *Semiconductor Products Inc.*

4

Courtesy Motorola Semiconductor Products Inc.

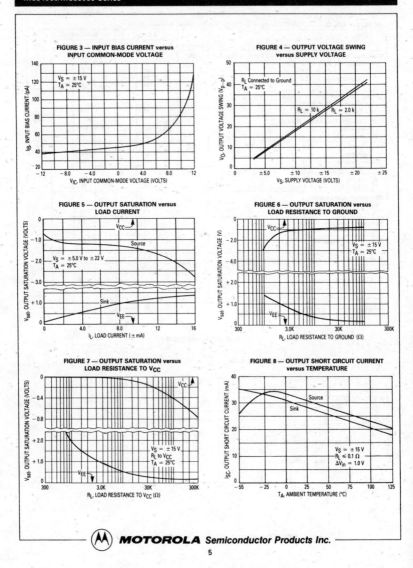

FIGURE 3 — INPUT BIAS CURRENT versus INPUT COMMON-MODE VOLTAGE

FIGURE 4 — OUTPUT VOLTAGE SWING versus SUPPLY VOLTAGE

FIGURE 5 — OUTPUT SATURATION versus LOAD CURRENT

FIGURE 6 — OUTPUT SATURATION versus LOAD RESISTANCE TO GROUND

FIGURE 7 — OUTPUT SATURATION versus LOAD RESISTANCE TO V_{CC}

FIGURE 8 — OUTPUT SHORT CIRCUIT CURRENT versus TEMPERATURE

MOTOROLA Semiconductor Products Inc.

5

Courtesy Motorola Semiconductor Products Inc.

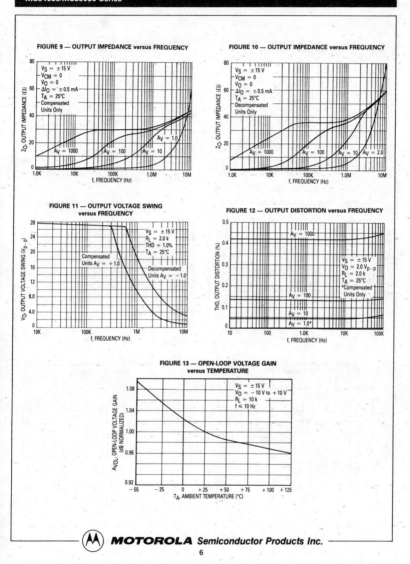

FIGURE 9 — OUTPUT IMPEDANCE versus FREQUENCY

FIGURE 10 — OUTPUT IMPEDANCE versus FREQUENCY

FIGURE 11 — OUTPUT VOLTAGE SWING versus FREQUENCY

FIGURE 12 — OUTPUT DISTORTION versus FREQUENCY

FIGURE 13 — OPEN-LOOP VOLTAGE GAIN versus TEMPERATURE

MOTOROLA Semiconductor Products Inc.

6

Courtesy Motorola Semiconductor Products Inc.

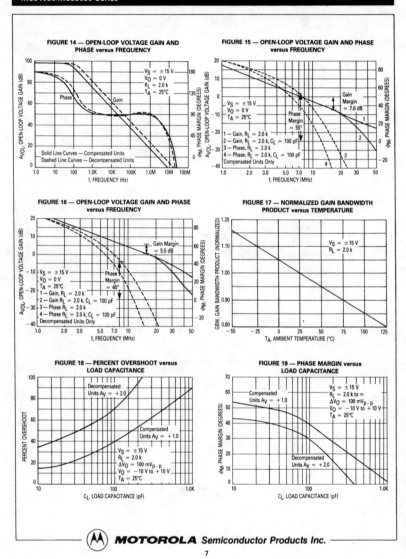

FIGURE 14 — OPEN-LOOP VOLTAGE GAIN AND PHASE versus FREQUENCY

FIGURE 15 — OPEN-LOOP VOLTAGE GAIN AND PHASE versus FREQUENCY

FIGURE 16 — OPEN-LOOP VOLTAGE GAIN AND PHASE versus FREQUENCY

FIGURE 17 — NORMALIZED GAIN BANDWIDTH PRODUCT versus TEMPERATURE

FIGURE 18 — PERCENT OVERSHOOT versus LOAD CAPACITANCE

FIGURE 19 — PHASE MARGIN versus LOAD CAPACITANCE

MOTOROLA Semiconductor Products Inc.

7

Courtesy Motorola Semiconductor Products Inc.

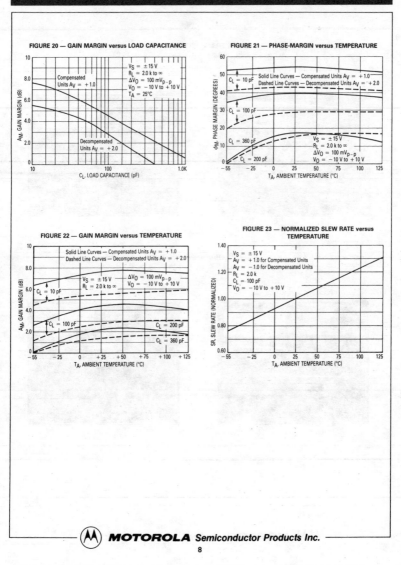

FIGURE 20 — GAIN MARGIN versus LOAD CAPACITANCE

FIGURE 21 — PHASE-MARGIN versus TEMPERATURE

FIGURE 22 — GAIN MARGIN versus TEMPERATURE

FIGURE 23 — NORMALIZED SLEW RATE versus TEMPERATURE

MOTOROLA Semiconductor Products Inc.

8

Courtesy Motorola Semiconductor Products Inc.

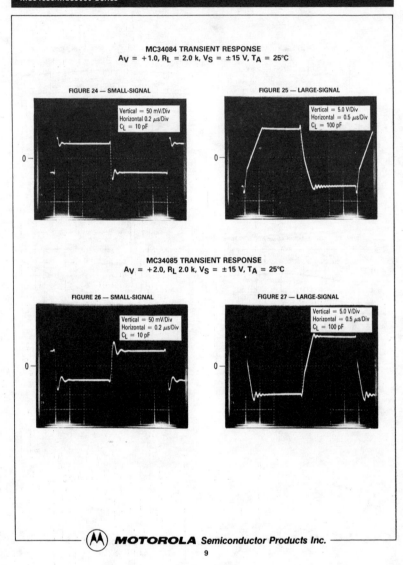

MC34084 TRANSIENT RESPONSE
$A_V = +1.0$, $R_L = 2.0$ k, $V_S = \pm15$ V, $T_A = 25°C$

FIGURE 24 — SMALL-SIGNAL

Vertical = 50 mV/Div
Horizontal 0.2 μs/Div
$C_L = 10$ pF

FIGURE 25 — LARGE-SIGNAL

Vertical = 5.0 V/Div
Horizontal = 0.5 μs/Div
$C_L = 100$ pF

MC34085 TRANSIENT RESPONSE
$A_V = +2.0$, R_L 2.0 k, $V_S = \pm15$ V, $T_A = 25°C$

FIGURE 26 — SMALL-SIGNAL

Vertical = 50 mV/Div
Horizontal = 0.2 μs/Div
$C_L = 10$ pF

FIGURE 27 — LARGE-SIGNAL

Vertical = 5.0 V/Div
Horizontal = 0.5 μs/Div
$C_L = 100$ pF

MOTOROLA Semiconductor Products Inc.

9

Courtesy Motorola Semiconductor Products Inc.

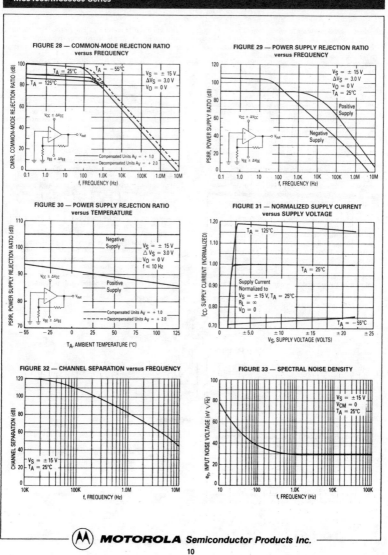

FIGURE 28 — COMMON-MODE REJECTION RATIO versus FREQUENCY

FIGURE 29 — POWER SUPPLY REJECTION RATIO versus FREQUENCY

FIGURE 30 — POWER SUPPLY REJECTION RATIO versus TEMPERATURE

FIGURE 31 — NORMALIZED SUPPLY CURRENT versus SUPPLY VOLTAGE

FIGURE 32 — CHANNEL SEPARATION versus FREQUENCY

FIGURE 33 — SPECTRAL NOISE DENSITY

MOTOROLA Semiconductor Products Inc.

10

Courtesy Motorola Semiconductor Products Inc.

APPLICATIONS INFORMATION

The bandwidth and slew rate of the MC34080 series is nearly double that of currently available general purpose JFET op-amps. This improvement in ac performance is due to the P-channel JFET differential input stage driving a compensated miller integration amplifier in conjunction with an all NPN output stage.

The all NPN output stage offers unique advantages over the more conventional NPN/PNP transistor Class AB output stage. With a 10 k load resistance, the op-amp can typically swing within I.0 V of the positive rail (V_{CC}), and within 0.3 volts of the negative rail (V_{EE}), providing a 28.7 Vp−p swing from ±15 volt supplies. This large output swing becomes most noticeable at lower supply voltages. If the load resistance is referenced to V_{CC} instead of ground, the maximum possible output swing can be achieved for a given supply voltage. For light load currents, the load resistance offers will pull the output to V_{CC} during the positive swing and the NPN output transistor will pull the output very near V_{EE} during the negative swing. The load resistance value should be much less than that of the feedback resistance to maximize pull-up capability.

The all NPN transistor output stage is also inherently fast, contributing to the operational amplifier's high gain-bandwidth product and fast settling time. The associated high frequency output impedance is 50 ohms (typical) at 8.0 MHz. This allows driving capacitive loads from 0 to 300 pF without oscillations over the military temperature range, and over the full range of output swing. The 55° phase margin and 7.6 dB gain margin as well as the general gain and phase characteristics are virtually independent of the sink/source output swing conditions. The high frequency characteristics of the MC34080 series is especially useful for active filter applications.

The common mode input range is from 2.0 volts below the positive rail (V_{CC}) to 4.0 volts above the negative rail (V_{EE}). The amplifier remains active if the inputs are biased at the positive rail. This may be useful for some applications in that single supply operation is possible with a single negative supply. However, a degradation of offset voltage and voltage gain may result.

Phase reversal does not occur if either the inverting or noninverting input exceeds the positive common mode limit. If either input (or both) exceeds the negative common mode limit, the output will be in the high state. The input stage also allows a differential up to ±44 volts, provided the maximum input voltage range is not exceeded. The supply voltage operating range is from ±5.0 V to ±22 V.

For optimum frequency performance and stability careful component placement and printed circuit board layout should be exercised. For example, long unshielded input or output leads may result in unwanted input-output coupling. In order to reduce the input capacitance, resistors connected to the input pins should be physically close to these pins. This not only minimizes the input pole for optimum frequency response, but also minimizes extraneous "pickup" at this node.

Supply decoupling with adequate capacitance close to the supply pin is also important, particularly over temperature, since many types of decoupling capacitors exhibit large impedance changes over temperature.

FIGURE 34 — OFFSET NULLING CIRCUIT

THERMAL INFORMATION

The maximum power consumption an integrated circuit can tolerate at a given operating ambient temperature, can be found from the equation:

$$P_{D(T_A)} = \frac{T_{J(max)} - T_A}{R_{\theta JA}(Typ)}$$

Where: $P_{D(T_A)}$ = Power Dissipation allowable at a given operating ambient temperature. This must be greater than the sum of the products of the supply voltages and supply currents at the worst case operating condition.

$T_{J(max)}$ = Maximum Operating Junction Temperature as listed in the Maximum Ratings Section

T_A = Maximum Desired Operating Ambient Temperature

$R_{\theta JA}(Typ)$ = Typical Thermal Resistance Junction to Ambient

Ⓜ MOTOROLA Semiconductor Products Inc.

11

Courtesy Motorola Semiconductor Products Inc.

Appendix A

FEATURES

- **Low Noise** .... { ... 80nV$_{p-p}$ (0.1Hz to 10Hz)
  .... 3nV/$\sqrt{Hz}$
- **Low Drift** .... 0.2μV/°C
- **High Speed** .... { ...... 2.8V/μs Slew Rate
  .... 8MHz Gain Bandwidth
- **Low V$_{OS}$** 10μV
- **Excellent CMRR** .... 126dB at V$_{CM}$ of ±11V
- **High Open-Loop Gain** .... 1.8 Million
- Fits 725, OP-07, OP-05, AD510, AD517, 5534A sockets

ORDERING INFORMATION†

	PACKAGE			
T$_A$ = 25°C V$_{OS}$ MAX (μV)	HERMETIC TO-99 8-PIN	HERMETIC DIP 8-PIN	PLASTIC DIP 8-PIN	OPERATING TEMPERATURE RANGE
25	OP27AJ*	OP27AZ*		MIL
25	OP27EJ	OP27EZ	OP27EP	IND/COM
60	OP27BJ*	OP27BZ*		MIL
60	OP27FJ	OP27FZ	OP27FP	IND/COM
100	OP27CJ*	OP27CZ*		MIL
100	OP27GJ	OP27GZ	OP27GP	IND/COM

*Also available with MIL-STD-883B processing. To order add /883 as a suffix to the part number. Screening Procedure: 1984 Data Book, Section 3.
†All commercial and industrial temperature range parts are available with burn-in per MIL-STD-883. Ordering Information: 1984 Data Book, Section 2.

GENERAL DESCRIPTION

The OP-27 precision operational amplifier combines the low offset and drift of the OP-07 with both high-speed and low-noise. Offsets down to 25μV and drift of 0.6μV/°C maximum make the OP-27 ideal for precision instrumentation applications. Exceptionally low noise, e$_n$ = 3.5nV/$\sqrt{Hz}$, at 10Hz, a low 1/f noise corner frequency of 2.7Hz, and high gain (1.8 million), allow accurate high-gain amplification of low-level signals. A gain-bandwidth product of 8MHz and a 2.8V/μsec slew rate provides excellent dynamic accuracy in high-speed data-acquisition systems.

A low input bias current of ±10nA is achieved by use of a bias-current-cancellation circuit. Over the military temperature range, this circuit typically holds I$_B$ and I$_{OS}$ to ±20nA and 15nA respectively.

The output stage has good load driving capability. A guaranteed swing of ±10V into 600Ω and low output distortion make the OP-27 an excellent choice for professional audio applications.

PSRR and CMRR exceed 120dB. These characteristics, coupled with long-term drift of 0.2μV/month, allow the circuit designer to achieve performance levels previously attained only by discrete designs.

Low cost, high-volume production of OP-27 is achieved by using an on-chip zener-zap trimming network. This reliable and stable offset trimming scheme has proved its effectiveness over many years of production history.

The OP-27 provides excellent performance in low-noise high-accuracy amplification of low-level signals. Applications include stable integrators, precision summing amplifiers, precision voltage-threshold detectors, comparators, and professional audio circuits such as tape-head and microphone preamplifiers.

The OP-27 is a direct replacement for 725, OP-06, OP-07 and OP-05 amplifiers; 741 types may be directly replaced by removing the 741's nulling potentiometer.

PIN CONNECTIONS

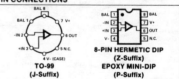

8-PIN HERMETIC DIP (Z-Suffix)
EPOXY MINI-DIP (P-Suffix)

TO-99 (J-Suffix)

SIMPLIFIED SCHEMATIC

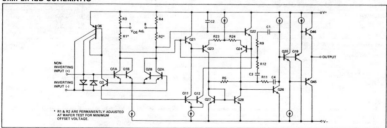

* R1 & R2 ARE PERMANENTLY ADJUSTED AT WAFER TEST FOR MINIMUM OFFSET VOLTAGE.

— Precision Monolithics Incorporated —

Printed with permission from Precision Monolithics Incorporated.

ABSOLUTE MAXIMUM RATINGS (Note 4)

Supply Voltage .... ±22V
Internal Power Dissipation (Note 1) 500mW
Input Voltage (Note 3) .... ±22V
Output Short-Circuit Duration .... Indefinite
Differential Input Voltage (Note 2) .... ±0.7V
Differential Input Current (Note 2) .... ±25mA
Storage Temperature Range .... −65°C to +150°C
Operating Temperature Range
  OP-27A, OP-27B, OP-27C (J, Z) ..... −55°C to +125°C
  OP-27E, OP-27F, OP-27G (J, Z) ..... −25°C to +85°C
  OP-27E, OP-27F, OP-27G (P) .... 0°C to +70°C
Lead Temperature Range (Soldering, 60 sec) ...... 300°C
DICE Junction Temperature .... −65°C to +150°C

NOTES:
1. See table for maximum ambient temperature rating and derating factor.

PACKAGE TYPE	MAXIMUM AMBIENT TEMPERATURE FOR RATING	DERATE ABOVE MAXIMUM AMBIENT TEMPERATURE
TO-99 (J)	80°C	7.1mW/°C
8-Pin Hermetic DIP (Z)	75°C	6.7mW/°C
8-Pin Plastic DIP (P)	62°C	5.6mW/°C

2. The OP-27's inputs are protected by back-to-back diodes. Current limiting resistors are not used in order to achieve low noise. If differential input voltage exceeds ±0.7V, the input current should be limited to 25mA.
3. For supply voltages less than ±22V, the absolute maximum input voltage is equal to the supply voltage.
4. Absolute maximum ratings apply to both DICE and packaged parts, unless otherwise noted.

ELECTRICAL CHARACTERISTICS at $V_S = \pm15V$, $T_A = 25°C$, unless otherwise noted.

PARAMETER	SYMBOL	CONDITIONS	OP-27A/E MIN	TYP	MAX	OP-27B/F MIN	TYP	MAX	OP-27C/G MIN	TYP	MAX	UNITS
Input Offset Voltage	V_{OS}	(Note 1)	—	10	25	—	20	60	—	30	100	μV
Long-Term V_{OS} Stability	V_{OS}/Time	(Note 2)	—	0.2	1.0	—	0.3	1.5	—	0.4	2.0	$\mu V/Mo$
Input Offset Current	I_{OS}		—	7	35	—	9	50	—	12	75	nA
Input Bias Current	I_B		—	±10	±40	—	±12	±55	—	±15	±80	nA
Input Noise Voltage	e_{np-p}	0.1Hz to 10Hz (Notes 3, 5)	—	0.08	0.18	—	0.08	0.18	—	0.09	0.25	$\mu Vp-p$
Input Noise Voltage Density	e_n	$f_O = 10Hz$ (Note 3)	—	3.5	5.5	—	3.5	5.5	—	3.8	8.0	$nV/\sqrt{Hz}$
		$f_O = 30Hz$ (Note 3)	—	3.1	4.5	—	3.1	4.5	—	3.3	5.6	
		$f_O = 1000Hz$ (Note 3)	—	3.0	3.8	—	3.0	3.8	—	3.2	4.5	
Input Noise Current Density	i_n	$f_O = 10Hz$ (Notes 3,6)	—	1.7	4.0	—	1.7	4.0	—	1.7	—	$pA/\sqrt{Hz}$
		$f_O = 30Hz$ (Notes 3,6)	—	1.0	2.3	—	1.0	2.3	—	1.0	—	
		$f_O = 1000Hz$ (Notes 3, 6)	—	0.4	0.6	—	0.4	0.6	—	0.4	0.6	
Input Resistance — Differential-Mode	R_{IN}	(Note 4)	1.5	6	—	1.2	5	—	0.8	4	—	$M\Omega$
Input Resistance — Common-Mode	R_{INCM}		—	3	—	—	2.5	—	—	2	—	$G\Omega$
Input Voltage Range	IVR		±11.0	±12.3	—	±11.0	±12.3	—	±11.0	±12.3	—	V
Common-Mode Rejection Ratio	CMRR	$V_{CM} = \pm11V$	114	126	—	106	123	—	100	120	—	dB
Power Supply Rejection Ratio	PSRR	$V_S = \pm4V$ to ±18V	—	1	10	—	1	10	—	2	20	$\mu V/V$
Large-Signal Voltage Gain	A_{VO}	$R_L \geq 2k\Omega$, $V_O = \pm10V$	1000	1800	—	1000	1800	—	700	1500	—	V/mV
		$R_L \geq 600\Omega$, $V_O = \pm10V$	800	1500	—	800	1500	—	600	1500	—	
Output Voltage Swing	V_O	$R_L \geq 2k\Omega$	±12.0	±13.8	—	±12.0	±13.8	—	±11.5	±13.5	—	V
		$R_L \geq 600\Omega$	±10.0	±11.5	—	±10.0	±11.5	—	±10.0	±11.5	—	
Slew Rate	SR	$R_L \geq 2k\Omega$ (Note 4)	1.7	2.8	—	1.7	2.8	—	1.7	2.8	—	V/μs
Gain Bandwidth Prod.	GBW	(Note 4)	5.0	8.0	—	5.0	8.0	—	5.0	8.0	—	MHz
Open-Loop Output Resistance	R_O	$V_O = 0$, $I_O = 0$	—	70	—	—	70	—	—	70	—	Ω
Power Consumption	P_d	V_O	—	90	140	—	90	140	—	100	170	mW
Offset Adjustment Range		$R_P = 10k\Omega$	—	±4.0	—	—	±4.0	—	—	±4.0	—	mV

NOTES:
1. Input offset voltage measurements are performed ~ 0.5 seconds after application of power. A/E grades guaranteed fully warmed-up.
2. Long-term input offset voltage stability refers to the average trend line of V_{OS} vs. Time over extended periods after the first 30 days of operation. Excluding the initial hour of operation, changes in V_{OS} during the first 30 days are typically 2.5μV — refer to typical performance curve.
3. Sample tested.
4. Guaranteed by design.
5. See test circuit and frequency response curve for 0.1Hz to 10Hz tester.
6. See test circuit for current noise measurement.

Printed with permission from Precision Monolithics Incorporated.

ELECTRICAL CHARACTERISTICS for $V_S = \pm 15V$, $-55°C \leq T_A \leq +125°C$, unless otherwise noted.

PARAMETER	SYMBOL	CONDITIONS	OP-27A			OP-27B			OP-27C			UNITS
			MIN	TYP	MAX	MIN	TYP	MAX	MIN	TYP	MAX	
Input Offset Voltage	V_{OS}	(Note 1)	—	30	60	—	50	200	—	70	300	μV
Average Input Offset Drift	TCV_{OS} TCV_{OSn}	(Note 2)	—	0.2	0.6	—	0.3	1.3	—	0.4	1.8	$\mu V/°C$
Input Offset Current	I_{OS}		—	15	50	—	22	85	—	30	135	nA
Input Bias Current	I_B		—	± 20	± 60	—	± 28	± 95	—	± 35	± 150	nA
Input Voltage Range	IVR		± 10.3	± 11.5	—	± 10.3	± 11.5	—	± 10.2	± 11.5	—	V
Common-Mode Rejection Ratio	CMRR	$V_{CM} = \pm 10V$	108	122	—	100	119	—	94	116	—	dB
Power Supply Rejection Ratio	PSRR	$V_S = \pm 4.5V$ to $\pm 18V$	—	2	16	—	2	20	—	4	51	$\mu V/V$
Large-Signal Voltage Gain	A_{VO}	$R_L \geq 2k\Omega$, $V_O = \pm 10V$	600	1200	—	500	1000	—	300	800	—	V/mV
Output Voltage Swing	V_O	$R_L \geq 2k\Omega$	± 11.5	± 13.5	—	± 11.0	± 13.2	—	± 10.5	± 13.0	—	V

ELECTRICAL CHARACTERISTICS for $V_S = \pm 15V$, $-25°C \leq T_A \leq +85°C$ for OP-27J and OP-27Z, $0°C \leq T_A \leq +70°C$ for OP-27P, unless otherwise noted.

PARAMETER	SYMBOL	CONDITIONS	OP-27E			OP-27F			OP-27G			UNITS
			MIN	TYP	MAX	MIN	TYP	MAX	MIN	TYP	MAX	
Input Offset Voltage	V_{OS}		—	20	50	—	40	140	—	55	220	μV
Average Input Offset Drift	TCV_{OS} TCV_{OSn}	(Note 2)	—	0.2	0.6	—	0.3	1.3	—	0.4	1.8	$\mu V/°C$
Input Offset Current	I_{OS}		—	10	50	—	14	85	—	20	135	nA
Input Bias Current	I_B		—	± 14	± 60	—	± 18	± 95	—	± 25	± 150	nA
Input Voltage Range	IVR		± 10.5	± 11.8	—	± 10.5	± 11.8	—	± 10.5	± 11.8	—	V
Common-Mode Rejection Ratio	CMRR	$V_{CM} = \pm 10V$	110	124	—	102	121	—	96	118	—	dB
Power Supply Rejection Ratio	PSRR	$V_S = \pm 4.5V$ to $\pm 18V$	—	2	15	—	2	16	—	2	32	$\mu V/V$
Large-Signal Voltage Gain	A_{VO}	$R_L \geq 2k\Omega$, $V_O = \pm 10V$	750	1500	—	700	1300	—	450	1000	—	V/mV
Output Voltage Swing	V_O	$R_L \geq 2k\Omega$	± 11.7	± 13.6	—	± 11.4	± 13.5	—	± 11.0	± 13.3	—	V

NOTES:

1. Input offset voltage measurements are performed by automated test equipment approximately 0.5 seconds after application of power. A/E grades guaranteed fully warmed-up.
2. The TCV_{OS} performance is within the specifications unnulled or when nulled with $R_P = 8k\Omega$ to $20k\Omega$.

Printed with permission from Precision Monolithics Incorporated.

DICE CHARACTERISTICS

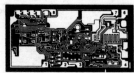

DIE SIZE 0.054 × 0.108 inch, 5832 sq. mils
(1.37 × 2.74mm, 3.76 sq. mm)

1. NULL
2. (–) INPUT
3. (+) INPUT
4. V–
6. OUTPUT
7. V+
8. NULL

For additional DICE information refer to
1984 Data Book, Section 2.

WAFER TEST LIMITS at $V_S = \pm 15V$, $T_A = 25°C$ for OP-27N, OP-27G, and OP-27GR devices; $T_A = 125°C$ for OP-27NT and OP-27GT devices, unless otherwise noted.

PARAMETER	SYMBOL	CONDITIONS	OP-27NT LIMIT	OP-27N LIMIT	OP-27GT LIMIT	OP-27G LIMIT	OP-27GR LIMIT	UNITS
Input Offset Voltage	V_{OS}	(Note 1)	60	35	200	60	100	µV MAX
Input Offset Current	I_{OS}		50	35	85	50	75	nA MAX
Input Bias Current	I_B		±60	±40	±95	±55	±80	nA MAX
Input Voltage Range	IVR		±10.3	±11	±10.3	±11	±11	V MIN
Common-Mode Rejection Ratio	CMRR	$V_{CM} = IVR$	108	114	100	106	100	dB MIN
Power Supply Rejection Ratio	PSRR	$V_S = \pm 4V$ to ±18V	—	10	—	10	20	µV/V MAX
Large-Signal Voltage Gain	A_{VO}	$R_L \geq 2k\Omega$, $V_O = \pm 10V$ $R_L \geq 600\Omega$, $V_O = \pm 10V$	600 —	1000 800	500 —	1000 800	700 600	V/mV MIN
Output Voltage Swing	V_O	$R_L \geq 2k\Omega$ $R_L \geq 600\Omega$	±11.5 —	±12.0 ±10.0	±11.0 —	±12.0 ±10.0	±11.5 ±10.0	V MIN
Power Consumption	P_d	$V_O = 0$	—	140	—	140	170	mW MAX

NOTE:
Electrical tests are performed at wafer probe to the limits shown. Due to variations in assembly methods and normal yield loss, yield after packaging is not guaranteed for standard product dice. Consult factory to negotiate specifications based on dice lot qualification through sample lot assembly and testing.

TYPICAL ELECTRICAL CHARACTERISTICS at $V_S = \pm 15V$, $T_A = +25°C$, unless otherwise noted.

PARAMETER	SYMBOL	CONDITIONS	OP-27N TYPICAL	OP-27G TYPICAL	OP-27GR TYPICAL	UNITS
Average Input Offset Voltage Drift	TCV_{OS} or TCV_{OSn}	Nulled or Unnulled $R_P = 8k\Omega$ to 20kΩ	0.2	0.3	0.4	µV/°C
Average Input Offset Current Drift	TCI_{OS}		80	130	180	pA/°C
Average Input Bias Current Drift	TCI_B		100	160	200	pA/°C
Input Noise Voltage Density	e_n	$f_O = 10Hz$ $f_O = 30Hz$ $f_O = 1000Hz$	3.5 3.1 3.0	3.5 3.1 3.0	3.8 3.3 3.2	nV/$\sqrt{Hz}$
Input Noise Current Density	i_n	$f_O = 10Hz$ $f_O = 30Hz$ $f_O = 1000Hz$	1.7 1.0 0.4	1.7 1.0 0.4	1.7 1.0 0.4	pA/$\sqrt{Hz}$
Input Noise Voltage	e_{np-p}	0.1Hz to 10Hz	0.08	0.08	0.09	µVp-p
Slew Rate	SR	$R_L \geq 2k\Omega$	2.8	2.8	2.8	V/µs
Gain Bandwidth Product	GBW		8	8	8	MHz

NOTE:
1. Input offset voltage measurements are performed by automated test equipment approximately 0.5 seconds after application of power.

Printed with permission from Precision Monolithics Incorporated.

TYPICAL PERFORMANCE CHARACTERISTICS

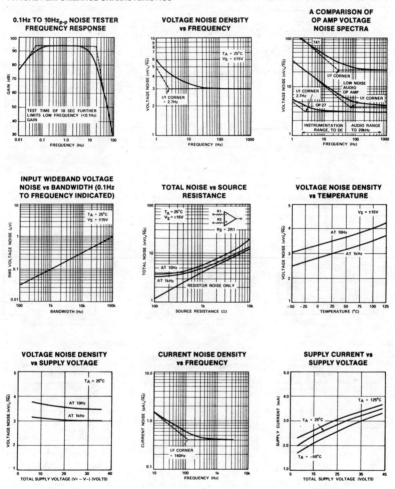

0.1Hz TO 10Hz_p-p NOISE TESTER FREQUENCY RESPONSE

VOLTAGE NOISE DENSITY vs FREQUENCY

A COMPARISON OF OP AMP VOLTAGE NOISE SPECTRA

INPUT WIDEBAND VOLTAGE NOISE vs BANDWIDTH (0.1Hz TO FREQUENCY INDICATED)

TOTAL NOISE vs SOURCE RESISTANCE

VOLTAGE NOISE DENSITY vs TEMPERATURE

VOLTAGE NOISE DENSITY vs SUPPLY VOLTAGE

CURRENT NOISE DENSITY vs FREQUENCY

SUPPLY CURRENT vs SUPPLY VOLTAGE

Printed with permission from Precision Monolithics Incorporated.

Appendix A

279

TYPICAL PERFORMANCE CHARACTERISTICS

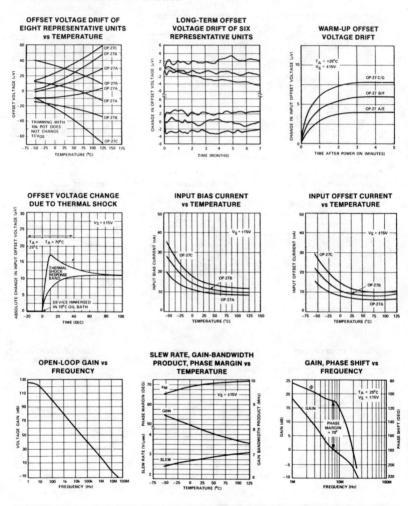

Printed with permission from Precision Monolithics Incorporated.

TYPICAL PERFORMANCE CHARACTERISTICS

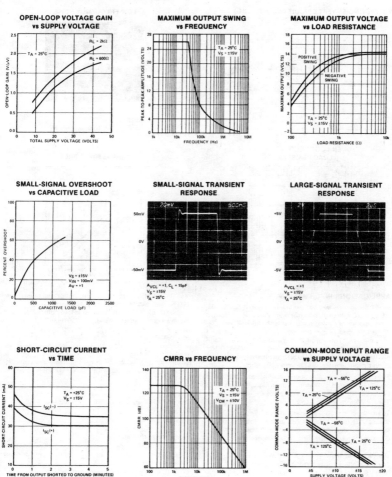

TYPICAL PERFORMANCE CHARACTERISTICS

VOLTAGE NOISE TEST CIRCUIT (0.1Hz-TO-10Hz)

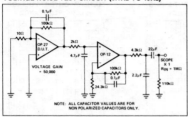

NOTE: ALL CAPACITOR VALUES ARE FOR NON POLARIZED CAPACITORS ONLY.

LOW-FREQUENCY NOISE

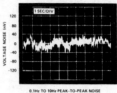

0.1Hz TO 10Hz PEAK-TO-PEAK NOISE

NOTE:
Observation time limited to 10 seconds.

OPEN-LOOP VOLTAGE GAIN vs LOAD RESISTANCE

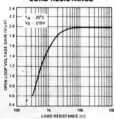

PSRR vs FREQUENCY

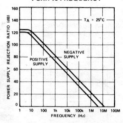

APPLICATIONS INFORMATION

OP-27 Series units may be inserted directly into 725, OP-06, OP-07 and OP-05 sockets with or without removal of external compensation or nulling components. Additionally, the OP-27 may be fitted to unnulled 741-type sockets; however, if conventional 741 nulling circuitry is in use, it should be modified or removed to ensure correct OP-27 operation. OP-27 offset voltage may be nulled to zero (or other desired setting) using a potentiometer (see Offset Nulling Circuit).

The OP-27 provides stable operation with load capacitances of up to 2000pF and ± 10V swings; larger capacitances should be decoupled with a 50Ω resistor inside the feedback loop. The OP-27 is unity-gain stable.

Thermoelectric voltages generated by dissimilar metals at the input terminal contacts can degrade the drift performance. Best operation will be obtained when both input contacts are maintained at the same temperature.

OFFSET VOLTAGE ADJUSTMENT

The input offset voltage of the OP-27 is trimmed at wafer level. However, if further adjustment of V_{OS} is necessary, a 10kΩ trim potentiometer may be used. TCV_{OS} is not degraded

(see Offset Nulling Circuit). Other potentiometer values from 1kΩ to 1MΩ can be used with a slight degradation (0.1 to 0.2μV/°C) of TCV_{OS}. Trimming to a value other than zero creates a drift of approximately $(V_{OS}/300)$ μV/°C. For example, the change in TCV_{OS} will be 0.33μV/°C if V_{OS} is adjusted to 100μV. The offset-voltage adjustment range with a 10kΩ potentiometer is ±4mV. If smaller adjustment range is required, the nulling sensitivity can be reduced by using a smaller pot in conjuction with fixed resistors. For example, the network below will have a ±280μV adjustment range.

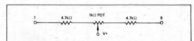

NOISE MEASUREMENTS

To measure the 80nV peak-to-peak noise specification of the OP-27 in the 0.1Hz to 10Hz range, the following precautions must be observed:

(1) The device has to be warmed-up for at least five minutes. As shown in the warm-up drift curve, the offset voltage

Printed with permission from Precision Monolithics Incorporated.

Appendix A

typically changes 4µV due to increasing chip temperature after power-up. In the 10-second measurement interval, these temperature-induced effects can exceed tens-of-nanovolts.

(2) For similar reasons, the device has to be well-shielded from air currents. Shielding minimizes thermocouple effects.

(3) Sudden motion in the vicinity of the device can also "feed-through" to increase the observed noise.

(4) The test time to measure 0.1Hz-to-10Hz noise should not exceed 10 seconds. As shown in the noise-tester frequency-response curve, the 0.1Hz corner is defined by only one zero. The test time of 10 seconds acts as an additional zero to eliminate noise contributions from the frequency band below 0.1Hz.

(5) A noise-voltage-density test is recommended when measuring noise on a large number of units. A 10Hz noise-voltage-density measurement will correlate well with a 0.1Hz-to-10Hz peak-to-peak noise reading, since both results are determined by the white noise and the location of the 1/f corner frequency.

UNITY-GAIN BUFFER APPLICATIONS

When $R_f \le 100\Omega$ and the input is driven with a fast, large signal pulse (>1V), the output waveform will look as shown in the pulsed operation diagram below.

During the fast feedthrough-like portion of the output, the input protection diodes effectively short the output to the input and a current, limited only by the output short-circuit protection, will be drawn by the signal generator. With $R_f \ge 500\Omega$, the output is capable of handling the current requirements ($I_L \le 20mA$ at 10V); the amplifier will stay in its active mode and a smooth transition will occur.

When $R_f > 2k\Omega$, a pole will be created with R_f and the amplifier's input capacitance (8pF) that creates additional phase shift and reduces phase margin. A small capacitor (20 to 50pF) in parallel with R_f will eliminate this problem.

PULSED OPERATION

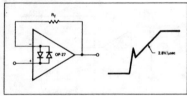

COMMENTS ON NOISE

The OP-27 is a very low-noise monolithic op amp. The outstanding input voltage noise characteristics of the OP-27 are achieved mainly by operating the input stage at a high quiescent current. The input bias and offset currents, which would normally increase, are held to reasonable values by the input-

bias-current cancellation circuit. The OP-27A/E has I_B and I_{OS} of only ±40nA and 35nA respectively at 25°C. This is particularly important when the input has a high source-resistance. In addition, many audio amplifier designers prefer to use direct coupling. The high I_B, V_{OS}, TCV_{OS} of previous designs have made direct coupling difficult, if not impossible, to use.

Voltage noise is inversely proportional to the square-root of bias current, but current noise is proportional to the square-root of bias current. The OP-27's noise advantage disappears when high source-resistors are used. Figures 1, 2, and 3 compare OP-27 observed total noise with the noise performance of other devices in different circuit applications.

Total noise = $[(\text{Voltage noise})^2 + (\text{current noise} \times R_S)^2 + (\text{resistor noise})^2]^{1/2}$

Figure 1 shows noise-versus-source-resistance at 1000Hz. The same plot applies to wideband noise. To use this plot, just multiply the vertical scale by the square-root of the bandwidth.

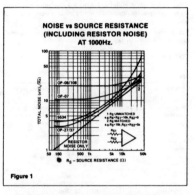

NOISE vs SOURCE RESISTANCE (INCLUDING RESISTOR NOISE) AT 1000Hz.

Figure 1

At $R_S < 1k\Omega$, the OP-27's low voltage noise is maintained. With $R_S > 1k\Omega$, total noise increases, but is dominated by the resistor noise rather than current or voltage noise. It is only beyond R_S of 20kΩ that current noise starts to dominate. The argument can be made that current noise is not important for applications with low-to-moderate source resistances. The crossover between the OP-27 and OP-07 and OP-08 noise occurs in the 15-to-40kΩ region.

Figure 2 shows the 0.1Hz-to-10Hz peak-to-peak noise. Here the picture is less favorable; resistor noise is negligible, current noise becomes important because it is inversely proportional to the square-root of frequency. The crossover with the OP-07 occurs in the 3-to-5kΩ range depending on whether balanced or unbalanced source resistors are used (at 3kΩ the I_B, I_{OS} error also can be three times the V_{OS} spec.).

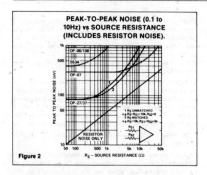

Figure 2

PEAK-TO-PEAK NOISE (0.1 to 10Hz) vs SOURCE RESISTANCE (INCLUDES RESISTOR NOISE).

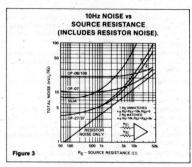

Figure 3

10Hz NOISE vs SOURCE RESISTANCE (INCLUDES RESISTOR NOISE).

Therefore, for low-frequency applications, the OP-07 is better than the OP-27/37 when $R_S > 3k\Omega$. The only exception is when gain error is important. Figure 3 illustrates the 10Hz noise. As expected, the results are between the previous two figures.

For reference, typical source resistances of some signal sources are listed in Table 1.

Table 1

DEVICE	SOURCE IMPEDANCE	COMMENTS
Strain gauge	<500Ω	Typically used in low-frequency applications.
Magnetic tapehead	<1500Ω	Low I_B very important to reduce self-magnetization problems when direct coupling is used. OP-27 I_B can be neglected.
Magnetic phonograph cartridges	<1500Ω	Similar need for low I_B in direct coupled applications. OP-27 will not introduce any self-magnetization problem.
Linear variable differential transformer	<1500Ω	Used in rugged servo-feedback applications. Bandwidth of interest is 400Hz to 5kHz.

OPEN-LOOP GAIN			
FREQUENCY AT:	OP-07	OP-27	OP-37
3Hz	100dB	124dB	125dB
10Hz	100dB	120dB	125dB
30Hz	90dB	110dB	124dB

For further information regarding noise calculations, see "Minimization of Noise in Op-Amp Applications", Application Note AN-15.

AUDIO APPLICATIONS

The following applications information has been abstracted from a PMI article in the 12/20/80 issue of Electronic Design magazine and updated.

Figure 4 is an example of a phono pre-amplifier circuit using the OP-27 for A1; R1-R2-C1-C2 form a very accurate RIAA network with standard component values. The popular method to accomplish RIAA phono equalization is to employ frequency-dependent feedback around a high-quality gain block. Properly chosen, an RC network can provide the three necessary time constants of 3180, 318, and 75µs.[1]

For initial equalization accuracy and stability, precision metal-film resistors and film capacitors of polystyrene or polypropylene are recommended since they have low voltage coefficients, dissipation factors, and dielectric absorption.[4] (High-K ceramic capacitors should be avoided here, though low-K ceramics — such as NPO types, which have excellent dissipation factors, and somewhat lower dielectric absorption — can be considered for small values.)

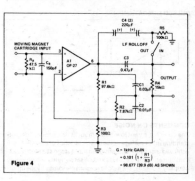

Figure 4

Printed with permission from Precision Monolithics Incorporated.

The OP-27 brings a $3.2nV/\sqrt{Hz}$ voltage noise and 0.45 $pA/\sqrt{Hz}$ current noise to this circuit. To minimize noise from other sources, R_3 is set to a value of 100Ω, which generates a voltage noise of $1.3nV/\sqrt{Hz}$. The noise increases the $3.2nV/\sqrt{Hz}$ of the amplifier by only 0.7dB. With a $1k\Omega$ source, the circuit noise measures 63dB below a 1mV reference level, unweighted, in a 20kHz noise bandwidth.

Gain (G) of the circuit at 1kHz can be calculated by the expression:

$$G = 0.101 \left(1 + \frac{R_1}{R_3}\right)$$

For the values shown, the gain is just under 100 (or 40dB). Lower gains can be accommodated by increasing R_3, but gains higher than 40dB will show more equalization errors because of the 8MHz gain-bandwidth of the OP-27.

This circuit is capable of very low distortion over its entire range, generally below 0.01% at levels up to 7V rms. At 3V output levels, it will produce less than 0.03% total harmonic distortion at frequencies up to 20kHz.

Capacitor C_3 and resistor R_4 form a simple $-6dB$-per-octave rumble filter, with a corner at 22Hz. As an option, the switch-selected shunt capacitor C_4, a nonpolarized electrolytic, bypasses the low-frequency rolloff. Placing the rumble filter's high-pass action after the preamp has the desirable result of discriminating against the RIAA-amplified low-frequency noise components and pickup-produced low-frequency disturbances.

A preamplifier for NAB tape playback is similar to an RIAA phono preamp, though more gain is typically demanded, along with equalization requiring a heavy low-frequency boost. The circuit in Fig. 4 can be readily modified for tape use, as shown by Fig. 5.

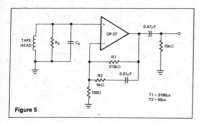

Figure 5

While the tape-equalization requirement has a flat high-frequency gain above 3kHz ($T_2 = 50\mu s$), the amplifier need not be stabilized for unity gain. The decompensated OP-37 provides a greater bandwidth and slew rate. For many applications, the idealized time constants shown may require trimming of R_1 and R_2 to optimize frequency response for nonideal tape-head performance and other factors.[5]

The network values of the configuration yield a 50dB gain at 1kHz, and the dc gain is greater than 70dB. Thus, the worst-case output offset is just over 500mV. A single $0.47\mu F$ output capacitor can block this level without affecting the dynamic range.

The tape head can be coupled directly to the amplifier input, since the worst-case bias current of 80nA with a 400mH, 100 μin. head (such as the PRB2H7K) will not be troublesome.

One potential tape-head problem is presented by amplifier bias-current transients which can magnetize a head. The OP-27 and OP-37 are free of bias-current transients upon power up or power down. However, it is always advantageous to control the speed of power supply rise and fall, to eliminate transients.

In addition, the dc resistance of the head should be carefully controlled, and preferably below $1k\Omega$. For this configuration, the bias-current-induced offset voltage can be greater than the $100\mu V$ maximum offset if the head resistance is not sufficiently controlled.

A simple, but effective, fixed-gain transformerless microphone preamp (Fig. 6) amplifies differential signals from low-impedance microphones by 50dB, and has an input impedance of $2k\Omega$. Because of the high working gain of the circuit, an OP-37 helps to preserve bandwidth, which will be 110kHz. As the OP-37 is a decompensated device (minimum stable gain of 5), a dummy resistor, R_p, may be necessary, if the microphone is to be unplugged. Otherwise the 100% feedback from the open input may cause the amplifier to oscillate.

Common-mode input-noise rejection will depend upon the match of the bridge-resistor ratios. Either close-tolerance (0.1%) types should be used, or R_4 should be trimmed for best CMRR. All resistors should be metal-film types for best stability and low noise.

Noise performance of this circuit is limited more by the input resistors R_1 and R_2 than by the op amp, as R_1 and R_2 each generate a $4nV/\sqrt{Hz}$ noise, while the op amp generates a $3.2nV/\sqrt{Hz}$ noise. The rms sum of these predominant noise sources will be about $6nV/\sqrt{Hz}$, equivalent to $0.9\mu V$ in a 20kHz noise bandwidth, or nearly 61dB below a 1mV input signal. Measurements confirm this predicted performance.

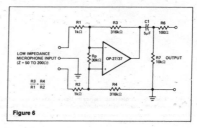

Figure 6

For applications demanding appreciably lower noise, a high-quality microphone-transformer-coupled preamp (Fig. 7) incorporates the internally-compensated OP-27. T_1 is a JE-115K-E $150\Omega/15k\Omega$ transformer which provides an optimum source resistance for the OP-27 device. The circuit has an overall gain of 40dB, the product of the transformer's voltage setup and the op amp's voltage gain.

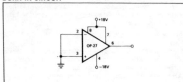

Figure 7

Gain may be trimmed to other levels, if desired, by adjusting R_2 or R_1. Because of the low offset voltage of the OP-27, the output offset of this circuit will be very low, 1.7mV or less, for a 40dB gain. The typical output blocking capacitor can be

eliminated in such cases, but is desirable for higher gains to eliminate switching transients.

Capacitor C_2 and resistor R_2 form a $2\mu s$ time constant in this circuit, as recommended for optimum transient response by the transformer manufacturer. With C_2 in use, A_1 must have unity-gain stability. For situations where the $2\mu s$ time constant is not necessary, C_2 can be deleted, allowing the faster OP-37 to be employed.

Some comment on noise is appropriate to understand the capability of this circuit. A 150Ω resistor and R_1 and R_2 gain resistors connected to a noiseless amplifier will generate 220 nV of noise in a 20kHz bandwidth, or 73dB below a 1mV reference level. Any practical amplifier can only approach this noise level; it can never exceed it. With the OP-27 and T_1 specified, the additional noise degradation will be close to 3.6dB (or −69.5 referenced to 1mV).

References

1. Lipshitz, S.P., "On RIAA Equalization Networks," *JAES*, Vol. 27, June 1979, p. 458-481.

2. Jung, W.G., *IC Op Amp Cookbook*, 2nd Ed., H.W. Sams and Company, 1980.

3. Jung, W.G., *Audio IC Op Amp Applications*, 2nd Ed., H.W. Sams and Company, 1978.

4. Jung, W.G., and Marsh, R.M., "Picking Capacitors," *Audio*, February & March, 1980.

5. Otala, M., "Feedback-Generated Phase Nonlinearity in Audio Amplifiers," London AES Convention, March 1980, preprint 1976.

6. Stout, D.F., and Kaufman, M., *Handbook of Operational Amplifier Circuit Design*, New York, McGraw Hill, 1976.

BURN-IN CIRCUIT

OFFSET NULLING CIRCUIT

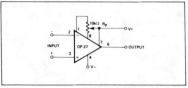

PMI **Precision Monolithics Incorporated** A Bourns Subsidiary
® 1500 SPACE PARK DR., SANTA CLARA, CA 95050 • TEL (408) 727-9222 • TWX 910-338-0218 • TLX 172 070
06840137G5M PRINTED IN USA

Printed with permission from Precision Monolithics Incorporated.

Appendix A

HIGH SLEW RATE OPERATIONAL AMPLIFIER

SE/NE530

DESCRIPTION
The 530 is a new generation operational amplifier featuring a high slew rate combined with improved input characteristics. Internally compensated, the SE530 guarantees slew rates of 25V/μs with 2mV maximum offset voltage. Industry standard pinout and internal compensation allow the user to upgrade system performance by directly replacing general purpose amplifiers such as the 741 and LF356 types.

FEATURES
- Gain bandwidth product—3MHz
- 35V/μs slew rate (Gain = -1)
- Internal frequency compensation
- Low input offset voltage 2mV max
- Low input bias current-60nA max
- Short circuit protection
- Offset null capability
- Large common mode and differential voltage ranges

PIN CONFIGURATIONS

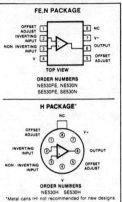

FE,N PACKAGE

OFFSET ADJUST 1
INVERTING INPUT 2
NON INVERTING INPUT 3
V 4

8 NC
7 V+
6 OUTPUT
5 OFFSET ADJUST

TOP VIEW

ORDER NUMBERS
NE530FE, NE530N
SE530FE, SE530N

H PACKAGE*
NC

OFFSET ADJUST
INVERTING INPUT
NON-INVERTING INPUT
V+
OUTPUT
OFFSET ADJUST
V

ORDER NUMBERS
NE530H   SE530H
*Metal cans (H) not recommended for new designs.

ABSOLUTE MAXIMUM RATINGS

PARAMETER	RATING	UNIT
Supply voltage		
SE530	±22	V
NE530	±18	V
Internal power dissipation		
N Package	500	mW
H Package	800	mW
FE Package	1000	mW
Differential input voltage	±30	V
Input voltage	±15	V
Operating temperature range		
SE530	-55 to +125	°C
NE530	0 to +70	°C
Storage temperature range	-65 to +150	°C
Lead temperature range (Solder, 60sec)	300	°C
Output short circuit	Indefinite	

EQUIVALENT SCHEMATIC EACH AMPLIFIER

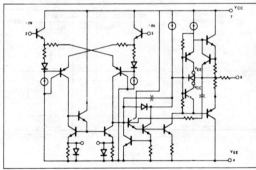

Signetics

Courtesy Signetics Corporation.

HIGH SLEW RATE OPERATIONAL AMPLIFIER

SE/NE530

DC ELECTRICAL CHARACTERISTICS $T_A = 25°C$, $V_{CC} = \pm 15V$ unless otherwise specified.[1]

PARAMETER		TEST CONDITIONS	SE530			NE530			UNIT
			Min	Typ	Max	Min	Typ	Max	
V_{OS}	Input offset voltage	$R_S \leq 10k\Omega$		0.7	4.0		2.0	6.0	mV
		Over temperature			5.0			7.0	mV
ΔV_{OS}	Temperature coefficient of input offset voltage	Over temperature		3	15		6		$\mu V/°C$
I_{OS}	Input offset current			5	20		15	40	nA
		Over temperature			40			80	nA
ΔI_{OS}	Input offset current	Over temperature		25			40		pA/°C
I_B	Input bias current			45	80		65	150	nA
		Over temperature			200			200	nA
ΔI_B	Input current	Over temperature		50			80		pA/°C
R_{IN}	Input resistance		3	10		1	6		$M\Omega$
V_{CM}	Input common mode voltage range		± 12	± 13		± 12	± 13		V
A_{VOL}	Large signal voltage gain	$R_L \geq 2k\Omega$, $V_O = \pm 10V$	50	200		50	200		V/mV
		Over temperature	25			25			V/mV
V_{OUT}	Output voltage swing	$R_L \geq 10k\Omega$	± 12	± 14		± 12	± 14		V
		$R_L \geq 2k\Omega$	± 10	± 13		± 10	± 13		V
I_{SC}	Output short circuit current		10	25	50	10	25	50	mA
R_{OUT}	Output resistance			100			100		Ω
I_{CC}	Supply current	Each amplifier		2.0	3.0		2.0	3.0	mA
		Over temperature		2.2	3.6		2.2		mA
CMRR	Common mode rejection ratio	$R_S \leq 10k\Omega$	70	90		70	90		dB
		Over temperature							
PSRR	Power supply rejection ratio	$R_S \leq 10k\Omega$		30	150		30	150	$\mu V/V$
		Over temperature							

AC ELECTRICAL CHARACTERISTICS $T_A = 25°C$, $V_{CC} = \pm 15V$ unless otherwise specified.

PARAMETER	TEST CONDITIONS	SE530/5530			NE530/5530			UNIT
		Min	Typ	Max	Min	Typ	Max	
Transient Response								
Small signal rise time			.06			.06		μs
Small signal overshoot			13			13		%
Settling time	TO 0.1% (10V step)		0.9			0.9		μs
Slew rate	$\pm 15V$ supply, $V_O = \pm 10V$, $R_L \geq 2k\Omega$							
Unity gain inverting		25	35		20	35		V/μs
Unity gain non-inverting		18	25		12	25		V/μs
Power bandwidth	5% THD, $V_O = \pm 10V$, $R_L \geq 2k\Omega$	360	500		280	500		kHz
Small signal bandwidth	Open loop		3			3		MHz
Input noise voltage	$f = 1kHz$		30			30		nV/$\sqrt{Hz}$

NOTE
1. Operating temperature range for the SE530 is −55°C to +125°C
   Operating temperature range for the NE530 is 0°C to +70°C

Signetics

6-27

Courtesy Signetics Corporation.

Appendix A

HIGH SLEW RATE OPERATIONAL AMPLIFIER

SE/NE530

TYPICAL PERFORMANCE CHARACTERISTICS

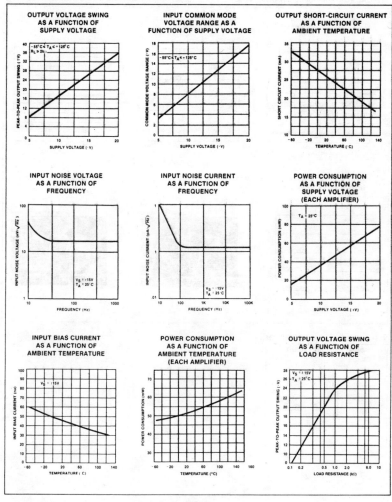

Signetics

Courtesy Signetics Corporation.

Appendix A

289

HIGH SLEW RATE OPERATIONAL AMPLIFIER

SE/NE530

TYPICAL PERFORMANCE CHARACTERISTICS (Cont'd)

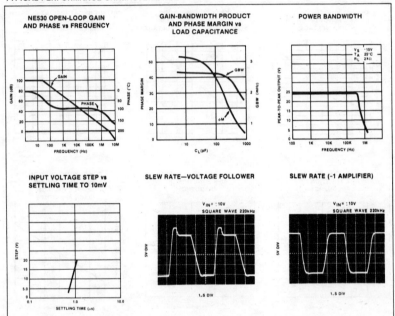

TYPICAL CIRCUIT CONNECTION

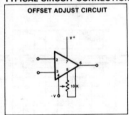

OFFSET ADJUST CIRCUIT

Courtesy Signetics Corporation.

HIGH SLEW RATE OPERATIONAL AMPLIFIER   SE/NE530

TEST LOAD CIRCUITS

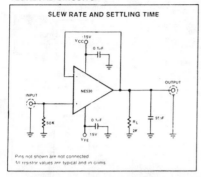

SLEW RATE AND SETTLING TIME

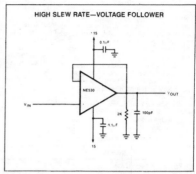

HIGH SLEW RATE—VOLTAGE FOLLOWER

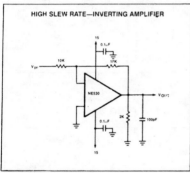

HIGH SLEW RATE—INVERTING AMPLIFIER

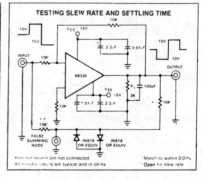

TESTING SLEW RATE AND SETTLING TIME

VOLTAGE WAVEFORMS

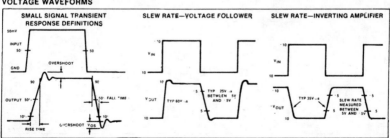

SMALL SIGNAL TRANSIENT RESPONSE DEFINITIONS

SLEW RATE—VOLTAGE FOLLOWER

SLEW RATE—INVERTING AMPLIFIER

6-30   **Signetics**

Courtesy Signetics Corporation.

INTERNALLY COMPENSATED DUAL LOW NOISE OP AMP　　SE/NE5532/5532A

DESCRIPTION
The 5532 is a dual high-performance low noise operational amplifier. Compared to most of the standard operational amplifiers, such as the 1458, it shows better noise performance, improved output drive capability and considerably higher small-signal and power bandwidths.

This makes the device especially suitable for application in high quality and professional audio equipment, instrumentation and control circuits, and telephone channel amplifiers. The op amp is internally compensated for gains equal to one. If very low noise is of prime importance, it is recommended that the 5532A version be used which has guaranteed noise voltage specifications.

FEATURES
- Small-signal bandwidth: 10MHz
- Output drive capability: 600Ω, 10V (rms)
- Input noise voltage: 5nV/$\sqrt{Hz}$ (typical)
- DC voltage gain: 50000
- AC voltage gain: 2200 at 10kHz
- Power bandwidth: 140kHz
- Slew-rate: 9V/μs
- Large supply voltage range: ±3 to ±20V
- Compensated for unity gain

PIN CONFIGURATION

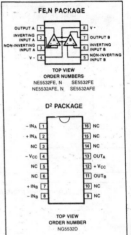

FE,N PACKAGE

TOP VIEW
ORDER NUMBERS
NE5532FE, N　　SE5532FE
NE5532AFE, N　SE5532AFE

D² PACKAGE

TOP VIEW
ORDER NUMBER
NG5532D

ABSOLUTE MAXIMUM RATINGS

	PARAMETER	RATING	UNIT
V_S	Supply voltage	± 22	V
V_{IN}	Input voltage	± V supply	V
V_{DIFF}	Differential input voltage[1]	±.5	V
T_A	Operating temperature range		
	NE5532/A	0 to 70	°C
	SE5532/A	− 55 to + 125	°C
T_{STG}	Storage temperature	− 65 to + 150	°C
T_J	Junction temperature	150	°C
P_D	Power dissipation		
	5532FE	1000	mW
	Lead temperature (soldering, 10 sec)	300	°C

NOTES:

1. Diodes protect the inputs against over-voltage. Therefore, unless current-limiting resistors are used, large currents will flow if the differential input voltage exceeds 0.6V. Maximum current should be limited to ± 10mA.
2. Thermal resistance of the FE package is 125°C/W.

EQUIVALENT SCHEMATIC (EACH AMPLIFIER)

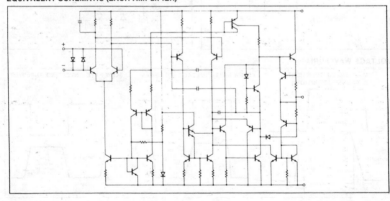

Signetics

Courtesy Signetics Corporation.

INTERNALLY COMPENSATED DUAL LOW NOISE OP AMP — SE/NE5532/5532A

DC ELECTRICAL CHARACTERISTICS $T_A = 25°C$, $V_S = \pm 15V$ unless otherwise specified.[1,2]

PARAMETER		TEST CONDITIONS	SE5532/55232A			NE5532/5532A			UNIT
			Min	Typ	Max	Min	Typ	Max	
V_{OS}	Offset voltage			0.5	2		0.5	4	mV
		Over temperature			3			5	mV
$\Delta V_{OS}/\Delta T$				5			5		$\mu V/°C$
I_{OS}	Offset current				100		10	150	nA
		Over temperature			200			200	nA
$\Delta I_{OS}/\Delta T$				200			200		pA/°C
I_B	Input current			200	400		200	800	nA
		Over temperature			700			1000	nA
$\Delta I_B/\Delta T$				5			5		mA/°C
I_{CC}	Supply current						8	16	mA
		Over temperature			13				mA
V_{CM}	Common mode input range		± 12	± 13		± 12	± 13		V
CMRR	Common mode rejection ratio		80	100		70	100		dB
PSRR	Power supply rejection ratio			10	50		10	100	$\mu V/V$
A_{VOL}	Large signal voltage gain	$R_L \geq 2k\Omega$, $V_0 = \pm 10V$	50			25	100		V/mV
		Over temperature	25			15			V/mV
		$R_L \geq 600\Omega$, $V_0 = \pm 10V$	40			15	50		V/mV
		Over temperature	20			10			V/mV
V_{OUT}	Output swing	$R_L \geq 600\Omega$				± 12	± 13		V
		Over temperature				± 10	± 12		V
		$R_L \geq 600\Omega$, $V_S = \pm 18V$	± 15	± 16					V
		Over temperature				± 12	± 14		V
		$R_L \geq 2k\Omega$ over temp.	± 12	± 13		± 10	± 13		V
R_{IN}	Input resistance		30	300		30	300		$k\Omega$
I_{SC}	Output short circuit current		10	38	60	10	38	60	mA

AC ELECTRICAL CHARACTERISTICS $T_A = 25°C$, $V_S = \pm 15V$ unless otherwise specified.

PARAMETER		TEST CONDITIONS	SE/NE5532/5532A			UNIT
			Min	Typ	Max	
R_{OUT}	Output resistance	$A_V = 30dB$ Closed loop $f = 10kHz$, $R_L = 600\Omega$		0.3		Ω
	Overshoot	Voltage follower $V_{IN} = 100mV$ p-p $C_L = 100pF$ $R_L = 600\Omega$		10		%
	Gain	$f = 10kHz$		2.2		V/mV
	Gain bandwidth product	$C_L = 100pF$ $R_L = 600\Omega$		10		MHz
	Slew rate			9		V/μs
	Power bandwidth	$V_{OUT} = \pm 10V$		140		kHz
		$V_{OUT} = \pm 14V$, $R_L = 600\Omega$, $V_{CC} = \pm 18V$		100		kHz

ELECTRICAL CHARACTERISTICS $T_A = 25°C$, $V_S = \pm 15V$ unless otherwise specified.

PARAMETER	TEST CONDITIONS	SE/NE5532			SE/NE5532A			UNIT
		Min	Typ	Max	Min	Typ	Max	
Input noise voltage	$f_0 = 30Hz$		8			8	12	nV/$\sqrt{Hz}$
	$f_0 = 1kHz$		5			5	6	nV/$\sqrt{Hz}$
Input noise current	$f_0 = 30Hz$		2.7			2.7		pA/$\sqrt{Hz}$
	$f_0 = 1kHz$		0.7			0.7		pA/$\sqrt{Hz}$
Channel separation	$f = 1kHz$, RS = 5kΩ		110			110		dB

Signetics

6-49

Courtesy Signetics Corporation.

INTERNALLY COMPENSATED DUAL LOW NOISE OP AMP   SE/NE5532/5532A

TYPICAL PERFORMANCE CHARACTERISTICS

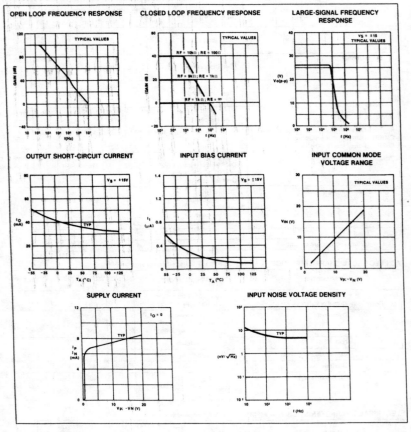

Signetics

Courtesy Signetics Corporation

Appendix A

INTERNALLY COMPENSATED DUAL LOW NOISE OP AMP   SE/NE5532/5532A

TEST CIRCUITS

CLOSED LOOP FREQUENCY RESPONSE

VOLTAGE FOLLOWER

AUDIO CIRCUITS USING THE NE5532/33/34

More detailed information is available in the communications section of this manual, regarding other audio circuits. The following will explain the Signetics line of low noise op amps and show their use in some audio applications.

DESCRIPTION

The 5532 is a dual high-performance low noise operational amplifier. Compared to most of the standard operational amplifiers, such as the 1458, it shows better noise performance, improved output drive capability and considerably higher small-signal and power bandwidths.

This makes the device especially suitable for application in high quality and professional audio equipment, instrumentation and control circuits, and telephone channel amplifiers. The op amp is internally compensated for gains equal to one. If very low noise is of prime importance, it is recommended that the 5532A version be used which has guaranteed noise voltage specifications.

APPLICATIONS

The Signetics 5532 High Performance Op Amp is an ideal amplifier for use in high quality and professional audio equipment which requires low noise and low distortion.

The circuit included in this application note has been assembled on a P.C. board, and tested with actual audio input devices (Tuner and Turntable). It consists of an RIAA pre-amp, input buffer, 5-band equalizer, and mixer. Although the circuit design is not new, its performance using the 5532 has been improved.

The RIAA pre-amp section is a standard compensation configuration with low frequency boost provided by the Magnetic cartridge and the RC network in the op amp feedback loop. Cartridge loading is accomplished via R1. 47k was chosen as a typical value, and may differ from cartridge to cartridge.

The Equalizer section consists of an input buffer, 5 active variable band pass/notch (depending on R9's setting) filters, and an output summing amplifier. The input buffer is a standard unity gain design providing impedance matching between the pre amplifiers and the equalizer section. Because the 5532 is internally compensated, no external compensation is required. The 5-band active filter section is actually 5 individual active filters with the same feedback design for all 5. The main difference in all five stages is the values of C5 and C6 which are responsible for setting the center frequency of each stage. Linear pots are recommended for R9. To simplify use of this circuit, a component value table is provided, which lists center frequencies and their associated capacitor values. Notice that C5 equals (10) C6, and that the value of R8 and R10 are related to R9 by a factor of 10 as well. The values listed in the table are common and easily found standard values.

RIAA EQUALIZATION AUDIO PREAMPLIFIER USING NE5532A

With the onset of new recording techniques along with sophisticated playback equipment, a new breed of low noise operational amplifiers was developed to complement the state-of-the-art in audio reproduction. The first ultra low noise op amp introduced by Signetics was called the NE5534A. This is a single operational amplifier with less

than 4nV/$\sqrt{Hz}$ input noise voltage. The NE5534A is internally compensated at a gain of three. This device has been used in many audio preamp and equalizer (active filter) applications since its introduction early last year.

Many of the amplifiers that are being designed today are dc coupled. This means that very low frequencies (2-15Hz) are being amplified. These low frequencies are common to turntables because of rumble and tone arm resonancys. Since the amplifiers can reproduce these sub-audible tones, they become quite objectionable because the speakers try to reproduce these tones. This causes non-linearities when the actual recorded material is amplified and converted to sound waves.

The RIAA has proposed a change in its standard playback response curve in order to alleviate some of the problems that were previously discussed. The changes occur primarily at the low frequency range with a slight modification to the high frequency range. (See Figure 2). Note that the response peak for the bass section of the playback curve now occurs at 31.5Hz and begins to roll off below that frequency. The rolloff occurs by introducing a fourth R/C network by introducing a fourth R/C network with a 7950μs time constant to the three existing networks that make up the equalization circuit. The high end of the equalization curve is extended to 20kHz, because recordings at these frequencies are achievable on many current discs.

NE5533/34 DESCRIPTION

The 5533/5534 are dual and single high-performance low noise operational amplifiers. Compared to other operational amplifiers

6

Signetics

6-51

Courtesy Signetics Corporation.

INTERNALLY COMPENSATED DUAL LOW NOISE OP AMP   SE/NE5532/5532A

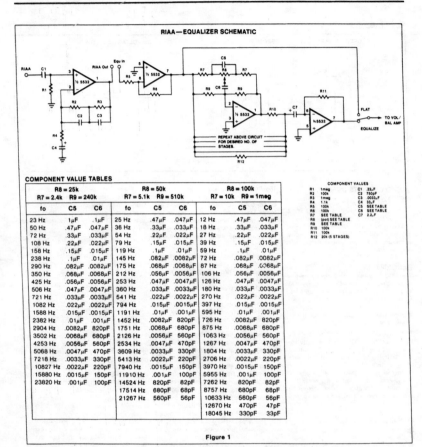

COMPONENT VALUE TABLES

R8 = 25k R7 = 2.4k R9 = 240k			R8 = 50k R7 = 5.1k R9 = 510k			R8 = 100k R7 = 10k R9 = 1meg		
fo	C5	C6	fo	C5	C6	fo	C5	C6
23 Hz	1µF	.1µF	25 Hz	.47µF	.047µF	12 Hz	.47µF	.047µF
50 Hz	.47µF	.047µF	36 Hz	.33µF	.033µF	18 Hz	.33µF	.033µF
72 Hz	.33µF	.033µF	54 Hz	.22µF	.022µF	27 Hz	.22µF	.022µF
108 Hz	.22µF	.022µF	79 Hz	.15µF	.015µF	39 Hz	.15µF	.015µF
158 Hz	.15µF	.015µF	119 Hz	.1µF	.01µF	59 Hz	.1µF	.01µF
238 Hz	.1µF	.01µF	145 Hz	.082µF	.0082µF	72 Hz	.082µF	.0082µF
290 Hz	.082µF	.0082µF	175 Hz	.068µF	.0068µF	87 Hz	.068µF	.0068µF
350 Hz	.068µF	.0068µF	212 Hz	.056µF	.0056µF	106 Hz	.056µF	.0056µF
425 Hz	.056µF	.0056µF	253 Hz	.047µF	.0047µF	126 Hz	.047µF	.0047µF
506 Hz	.047µF	.0047µF	360 Hz	.033µF	.0033µF	180 Hz	.033µF	.0033µF
721 Hz	.033µF	.0033µF	541 Hz	.022µF	.0022µF	270 Hz	.022µF	.0022µF
1082 Hz	.022µF	.0022µF	794 Hz	.015µF	.0015µF	397 Hz	.015µF	.0015µF
1588 Hz	.015µF	.0015µF	1191 Hz	.01µF	.001µF	595 Hz	.01µF	.001µF
2382 Hz	.01µF	.001µF	1452 Hz	.0082µF	820pF	726 Hz	.0082µF	820pF
2904 Hz	.0082µF	820pF	1751 Hz	.0068µF	680pF	875 Hz	.0068µF	680pF
3502 Hz	.0068µF	680pF	2126 Hz	.0056µF	560pF	1063 Hz	.0056µF	560pF
4253 Hz	.0056µF	560pF	2534 Hz	.0047µF	470pF	1267 Hz	.0047µF	470pF
5068 Hz	.0047µF	470pF	3609 Hz	.0033µF	330pF	1804 Hz	.0033µF	330pF
7218 Hz	.0033µF	330pF	5413 Hz	.0022µF	220pF	2706 Hz	.0022µF	220pF
10827 Hz	.0022µF	220pF	7940 Hz	.0015µF	150pF	3970 Hz	.0015µF	150pF
15880 Hz	.0015µF	150pF	11910 Hz	.001µF	100pF	5955 Hz	.001µF	100pF
23820 Hz	.001µF	100pF	14524 Hz	820pF	82pF	7262 Hz	820pF	82pF
			17514 Hz	680pF	68pF	8757 Hz	680pF	68pF
			21267 Hz	560pF	56pF	10633 Hz	560pF	56pF
						12670 Hz	470pF	47pF
						18045 Hz	330pF	33pF

COMPONENT VALUES			
R1	1meg	C1	.22µF
R2	100k	C2	750pF
R3	1meg	C3	.0033µF
R4	1.1k	C4	33µF
R5	100k	C5	SEE TABLE
R6	100k	C6	SEE TABLE
R7	SEE TABLE	C7	2.2µF
R8	(pot) SEE TABLE		
R9	SEE TABLE		
R10	100k		
R11	100k		
R12	20k (5 STAGES)		

Figure 1

such as TL083, they show better noise performance, improved output drive capability and considerably higher small-signal and power bandwidths.

This makes the devices especially suitable for application in high quality and professional audio equipment, in instrumentation and control circuits and telephone channel amplifiers. The op amps are internally compensated for

gain equal to, or higher than, three. The frequency response can be optimized with an external compensation capacitor for various applications (unity gain amplifier, capacitive load, slew-rate, low overshoot, etc.) If very low noise is of prime importance, it is recommended that the 5533A/5534A version be used which has guaranteed noise specifications.

APPLICATIONS

Diode Protection of Input

The input leads of the device are protected from differential transients above ±0.6V by internal back-to-back diodes. Their presence imposes certain limitations on the amplifier dynamic characteristics related to closed-loop gain and slew rate.

Signetics

Courtesy Signetics Corporation.

INTERNALLY COMPENSATED DUAL LOW NOISE OP AMP   SE/NE5532/5532A

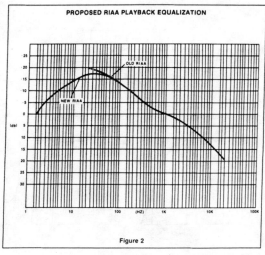

Figure 2

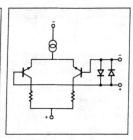

Consider the unity gain follower as an example:

Assume a signal input square wave with dV/dt of 250V per μs and 2V peak amplitude as shown. If a 22 pF compensation capacitor is inserted and the R_1 C_1 circuit deleted, the device slew rate falls to approximately 7V/μs. The input waveform will reach 2V/250V/μs or 8 ns, while the output will have changed (8×10^{-3}) (7) only 56 mV. The differential input signal is then $(V_{IN} - V_O) R_i/R_i + R_f$ or approximately 1V.

The diode limiter will definitely be active and output distortion will occur; therefore, $V_{in} < 1V$ as indicated.

Next, a sine wave input is used with a similar circuit.

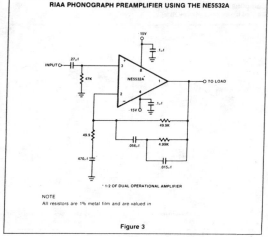

Figure 3

NOTE
All resistors are 1% metal film and are valued in

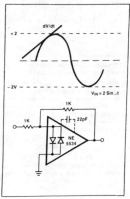

Signetics

6-53

Courtesy Signetics Corporation.

INTERNALLY COMPENSATED DUAL LOW NOISE OP AMP   SE/NE5532/5532A

The slew rate of the input waveform now depends on frequency and the exact expression is

$$\frac{dv}{dt} = 2\omega \cos \omega t$$

The upper limit before slew rate distortion occurs for *small signal* ($V_{IN} < 100$ mV) conditions is found by setting the slew rate to $7V/\mu s$. That is:

$$7 \times 10^6 \text{ V}/\mu s = 2\omega \cos \omega t$$

at $\quad \omega t = 0$

$$\omega_{LIMIT} = \frac{7 \times 10^6}{2} = 3.5 \times 10^6 \text{ rad/s}$$

$$f_{LIMIT} \frac{3.5 \times 10^6}{2\pi} \cong 560 \text{ kHz}$$

External Compensation Network Improves Bandwidth

By using an external lead-lag network, the follower circuit slew rate and small signal bandwidth can be increased. This may be useful in situations where a closed-loop gain less than 3 to 5 is indicated. A number of examples are shown in subsequent figures. The principle benefit of using the network approach is that the full slew rate and bandwidth of the device is retained, while impulse-related parameters such as damping and phase margin are controlled by choosing the appropriate circuit constants. For example, consider the following configuration:

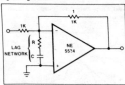

The major problem to be overcome is poor phase margin leading to instability.

By choosing the lag network break frequency one decade below the unity gain crossover frequency (30–50 MHz), the phase and gain margin are improved. An appropriate value for R is 270Ω. Setting the lag network break frequency at 5 MHz, C may be calculated

$$C = \frac{1}{2\pi \cdot 270 \cdot 5 \times 10^6}$$

$$118 = pF$$

A single pole and zero inserted in the transfer function will give an added 45° of phase margin depending on the network values.

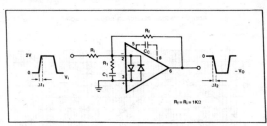

$R_f = R_i = 1K\Omega$

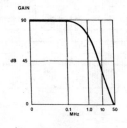

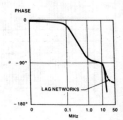

RULES AND EXAMPLES

Compensation Using Pins 5 and 8
(Limited Bandwidth and Slew Rate)

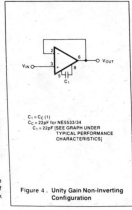

$C_1 = C_C$ (1)
$C_C = 22pF$ for NE5533/34
$C_1 = 22pF$ [SEE GRAPH UNDER TYPICAL PERFORMANCE CHARACTERISTICS]

Figure 4 . Unity Gain Non-Inverting Configuration

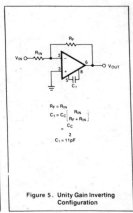

$R_F = R_{IN}$
$C_1 = C_C \left[\dfrac{R_{IN}}{R_F + R_{IN}} \right]$
$\qquad = \dfrac{C_C}{2}$
$C_1 = 11pF$

Figure 5 . Unity Gain Inverting Configuration

Signetics

INTERNALLY COMPENSATED DUAL LOW NOISE OP AMP   SE/NE5532/5532A

External Compensation for Wideband Voltage Follower

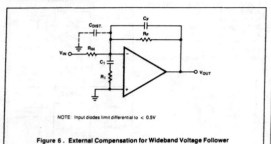

NOTE: Input diodes limit differential to < 0.5V

Figure 6 . External Compensation for Wideband Voltage Follower

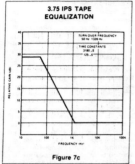

Figure 7c

Calculating the Lead-Lag Network

$$C_1 = \frac{1}{2\pi F_1 R_1}$$ Let $R_1 = \frac{R_{IN}}{10}$

where $F_1 = \frac{1}{10}$ (UGBW)

   UGBW = 30 MHz

Shunt Capacitance Compensation

$$C_F = \frac{1}{2\pi F_F R_F}, F_F \cong 30 \text{ MHz}$$

or $$C_F \cong \frac{C_{DIST}}{A_{CL}}$$

$C_{DIST} \cong$ Distributed Capacitance $\cong$ 2-3pF

Many audio circuits involve carefully tailored frequency responses. Pre-emphasis is used in all recording mediums to reduce noise and produce flat frequency response. The most often used de-emphasis curves for broadcast and home entertainment systems are shown in Figure 7. Operational amplifiers are well suited to these applications because of their high gain and easily tailored frequency response.

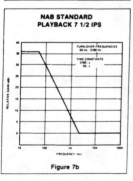

Figure 7b

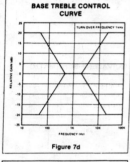

Figure 7d

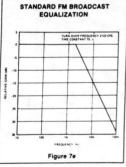

Figure 7e

Signetics

SINGLE AND DUAL LOW NOISE OP AMP   NE5533/5533A/SA/SE/NE5534/5534A

DESCRIPTION

The 5533/5534 are dual and single high-performance low noise operational amplifiers. Compared to other operational amplifiers, such as TL083, they show better noise performance, improved output drive capability and considerably higher small-signal and power bandwidths.

This makes the devices especially suitable for application in high quality and professional audio equipment, in instrumentation and control circuits and telephone channel amplifiers. The op amps are internally compensated for gain equal to, or higher than, three. The frequency response can be optimized with an external compensation capacitor for various applications (unity gain amplifier, capacitive load, slew-rate, low overshoot, etc.) If very low noise is of prime importance, it is recommended that the 5533A/5534A version be used which has guaranteed noise specifications.

FEATURES

- **Small-signal bandwidth: 10MHz**
- **Output drive capability: 600Ω, 10V (rms) at $V_s = \pm18V$**
- **Input noise voltage: 4nV/$\sqrt{Hz}$**
- **DC voltage gain: 100000**
- **AC voltage gain: 6000 at 10kHz**
- **Power bandwidth: 200kHz**
- **Slew-rate: 13V/μs**
- **Large supply voltage range: ±3 to ±20V**

PIN CONFIGURATIONS

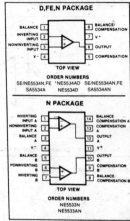

D,FE,N PACKAGE

BALANCE [1]   [8] BALANCE/COMPENSATION
INVERTING INPUT [2]   [7] V⁺
NONINVERTING INPUT [3]   [6] OUTPUT
V⁻ [4]   [5] COMPENSATION

TOP VIEW

ORDER NUMBERS
SE/NE5534N,FE   *NE5534AD   SE/NE5534AN,FE
SA5534A   NE5534D   SA5534AN

N PACKAGE

INVERTING INPUT A [1]   [14] BALANCE COMPENSATION A
NONINVERTING INPUT A [2]   [13] COMPENSATION A
BALANCE [3]   [12] OUTPUT A
V⁻ [4]   [11] V⁺
BALANCE [5]   [10] OUTPUT B
NONINVERTING B [6]   [9] COMPENSATION B
INVERTING B [7]   [8] BALANCE COMPENSATION B

TOP VIEW

ORDER NUMBERS
NE5533N
NE5533AN

*NOTE:
This device may not be symbolled in standard format.

EQUIVALENT SCHEMATIC

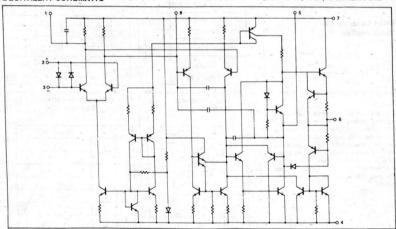

Signetics

6-59

Courtesy Signetics Corporation.

SINGLE AND DUAL LOW NOISE OP AMP NE5533/5533A/SA/SE/NE5534/5534A

ABSOLUTE MAXIMUM RATINGS

	PARAMETER	RATING	UNIT
V_S	Supply voltage	± 22	V
V_{IN}	Input voltage	± V supply	V
V_{DIFF}	Differential input voltage[1]	± 0.5	V
T_A	Operating temperature range		
	SE5534/5534A	− 55 to + 125	°C
	NE5533/5533A/5534/5534A	0 to + 70	°C
T_{STG}	Storage temperature	− 65 to + 150	°C
T_J	Junction temperature	150	°C
P_D	Power dissipation at 25°C[2]		
	5533N, 5534N, 5534FE	800	mW
	Output short circuit duration[3]	indefinite	
	Lead temperature (soldering, 10 sec)	300	°C

NOTES

1. Diodes protect the inputs against over-voltage. Therefore, unless current-limiting resistors are used, large currents will flow if the differential input voltage exceeds 0.6V. Maximum current should be limited to ±10mA.
2. For operation at elevated temperature, derate packages based on the following junction-to-ambient thermal resistances:

8-pin ceramic (FE) 140°C/W
14-pin ceramic (F) 110°C/W
8-pin plastic (N) 162°C/W
14-pin plastic (N) 150°C/W

3. Output may be shorted to ground at $V_S = ±15V$, $T_A = 25°C$. Temperature and/or supply voltages must be limited to ensure dissipation rating is not exceeded.

DC ELECTRICAL CHARACTERISTICS $T_A = 25°C$, $V_S = ±15V$ unless otherwise specified.[1,2]

PARAMETER		TEST CONDITIONS	SE5534/5534A			NE5533/5533A 5534/5534A			UNIT
			Min	Typ	Max	Min	Typ	Max	
V_{OS}	Offset voltage			0.5	2		0.5	4	mV
		Over temperature			3			5	mV
$\Delta V_{OS}/\Delta T$				5			5		$\mu V/°C$
I_{OS}	Offset current			10	200		20	300	nA
		Over temperature			500			400	nA
$\Delta I_{OS}/\Delta T$				200			200		pA/°C
I_B	Input current			400	800		500	1500	nA
		Over temperature			1500			2000	nA
$\Delta I_B/\Delta T$				5			5		nA/°C
I_{CC}	Supply current			4	6.5		4	8	mA
	Per op amp	Over temperature			9			10	mA
V_{CM}	Common mode input range		± 12	± 13		± 12	± 13		V
CMRR	Common mode rejection ratio		80	100		70	100		dB
PSRR	Power supply rejection ratio			10	50		10	100	$\mu V/V$
A_{VOL}	Large signal voltage gain	$R_L \geq 600\Omega$, $V_O = ±10V$	50	100		25	100		V/mV
		Over temperature	25			15			V/mV
V_{OUT}	Output swing	$R_L \geq 600\Omega$	± 12	± 13		± 12	± 13		V
	5534 only	Over temperature	± 10	± 12		± 10	± 12		V
		$R_L \geq 600\Omega$, $V_S = ±18V$	± 15	± 16		± 15	± 16		V
		$R_L \geq 2k\Omega$	± 13	± 13.5		± 13	± 13.5		V
		Over Temperature	± 12	± 12.5		± 12	± 12.5		V
R_{IN}	Input resistance		50	100		30	100		$k\Omega$
I_{SC}	Output short circuit current			38			38		mA

NOTES
1. For NE5533/5533A/5534/5534A, $T_{MIN} = 0°C$, $T_{MAX} = 70°C$
2. For SE5534/5534A, $T_{MIN} = − 55°C$, $T_{MAX} = + 125°C$

Signetics

Courtesy Signetics Corporation.

SINGLE AND DUAL LOW NOISE OP AMP NE5533/5533A/SA/SE/NE5534/5534A

AC ELECTRICAL CHARACTERISTICS $T_A = 25°C$, $V_S = ±15V$ unless otherwise specified.

PARAMETER		TEST CONDITIONS	SE5534/5534A			NE5533/5533A 5534/5534A			UNIT
			Min	Typ	Max	Min	Typ	Max	
R_{OUT}	Output resistance	$A_V = 30dB$ closed loop $f = 10kHz$, $R_L = 600\Omega$, $C_C = 22pF$		0.3			0.3		Ω
Transient response		Voltage follower, $V_{IN} = 50mV$ $R_L = 600\Omega$, $C_C = 22pF$, $C_L = 100pF$							
T_R	Rise time			20			20		ns
	Overshoot			20			20		%
Transient response		$V_{IN} = 50mv$, $R_L = 600\Omega$ $C_C = 47pF$, $C_L = 500pF$							
T_R	Rise time			50			50		ns
	Overshoot			35			35		%
AC	Gain	$f = 10kHz$, $C_C = 0$		6			6		V/mV
		$f = 10kHz$, $C_C = 22pF$		2.2			2.2		V/mV
	Gain bandwidth product	$C_C = 22pF$, $C_L = 100pF$		10			10		mHz
	Slew rate	$C_C = 0$		13			13		V/μS
		$C_C = 22pF$		6			6		V/μS
	Power bandwidth	$V_{OUT} = ±10V$, $C_C = 0$		200			200		kHz
		$V_{OUT} = ±10V$, $C_C = 22pF$		95			95		kHz
		$V_{OUT} = ±14V$, $R_L = 600\Omega$ $C_C = 22pF$, $V_{CC} = ±18V$		70			70		kHz

ELECTRICAL CHARACTERISTICS $T_A = 25°C$, $V_S = ±15V$ unless otherwise specified.

PARAMETER	TEST CONDITIONS	5533/5534			5533A/5534A			UNIT
		Min	Typ	Max	Min	Typ	Max	
Input noise voltage	$f_o = 30Hz$		7			5.5	7	nV/$\sqrt{Hz}$
	$f_o = 1kHz$		4			3.5	4.5	nV/$\sqrt{Hz}$
Input noise current	$f_o = 30Hz$		2.5			1.5		pA/$\sqrt{Hz}$
	$f_o = 1kHz$		0.6			0.4		pA/$\sqrt{Hz}$
Broadband noise figure	$f = 10Hz - 20kHz$, $R_S = 5k\Omega$					0.9		dB
Channel separation	$f = 1kHz$, $R_S = 5k\Omega$		110			110		dB

Signetics

SINGLE AND DUAL LOW NOISE OP AMP NE5533/5533A/SA/SE/NE5534/5534A

TYPICAL PERFORMANCE CHARACTERISTICS

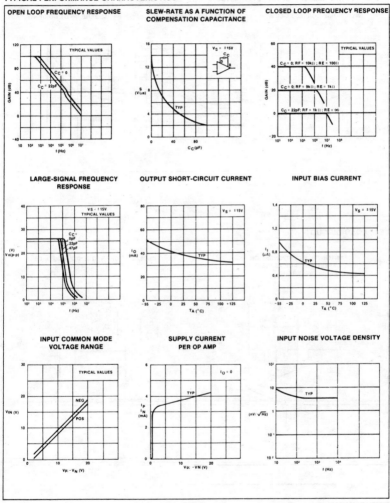

Signetics

Courtesy Signetics Corporation.

SINGLE AND DUAL LOW NOISE OP AMP NE5533/5533A/SA/SE/NE5534/5534A

TYPICAL PERFORMANCE CHARACTERISTICS (Cont'd)

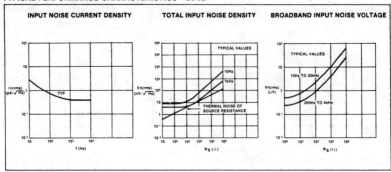

TEST LOAD CIRCUITS

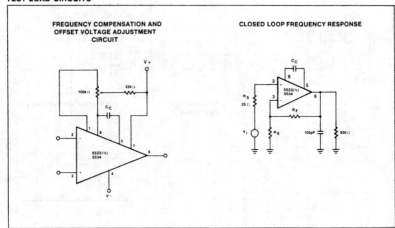

FREQUENCY COMPENSATION AND
OFFSET VOLTAGE ADJUSTMENT
CIRCUIT

CLOSED LOOP FREQUENCY RESPONSE

Signetics

Courtesy Signetics Corporation.

DUAL HIGH SLEW RATE OP AMP

SE/NE5535

DESCRIPTION
The 5535 is a new generation operational amplifier featuring high slew rates combined with improved input characteristics. The 5535 is a dual configuration. Internally compensated for unity gain, the SE5535 features a guaranteed unity gain slew rate of 10V/μs with 2mV maximum offset voltage. Industry standard pin out and internal compensation allow the user to upgrade system performance by directly replacing general purpose amplifiers, such as 747 and 1558.

FEATURES
- 15V/μs unity gain slew rate
- Internal frequency compensation
- Low input offset voltage—2mV
- Low input bias current 80nA max
- Short circuit protected
- Large common mode and differential voltage ranges
- Pin compatibility 5535
  747,1558
- Configuration Dual
- Low noise current 0.15 pA/$\sqrt{Hz}$ typ.

PIN CONFIGURATIONS

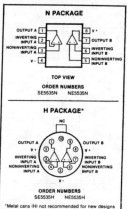

N PACKAGE

TOP VIEW

ORDER NUMBERS
SE5535N   NE5535N

H PACKAGE*

ORDER NUMBERS
SE5535H   NE5535H

*Metal cans (H) not recommended for new designs

ABSOLUTE MAXIMUM RATINGS

PARAMETER	SE5535	NE5535	UNIT
Supply voltage	±22	±18	V
Internal power dissipation[1]			
N Package	500	500	mW
H Package	800	800	mW
F Package	1000	1000	mW
Differential input voltage	±30	±30	V
Input voltage[2]	±15	±15	V
Operating temperature range	−55 to +125	0 to +70	°C
Storage temperature range	−65 to +150	−65 to +150	°C
Lead temperature (solder, 60sec)	300	300	°C
Output short circuit[3]	Indefinite	Indefinite	

NOTES
1. Rating applies for thermal resistances junction to ambient of 240°C/W and 150°C/W for N and H packages, respectively. Maximum chip temperature is 150°C.
2. For supply voltages less than ±15V, the absolute maximum input voltage is equal to the supply voltage.
3. Short circuit may be to ground or either supply. Rating applies to 125°C case temperature or 75°C ambient temperature.

EQUIVALENT SCHEMATIC   (One Amplifier)

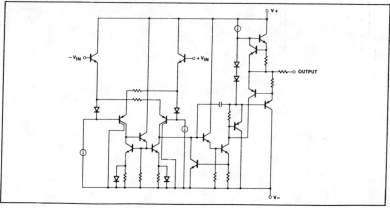

Signetics

6-65

6

DUAL HIGH SLEW RATE OP AMP

SE/NE5535

DC ELECTRICAL CHARACTERISTICS $T_A = 25°C$, $V_S = \pm15V$ unless otherwise specified.*

PARAMETER		TEST CONDITIONS	SE5535			NE5535			UNIT
			Min	Typ	Max	Min	Typ	Max	
V_{OS}	Input offset voltage	$R_S \le 10k\Omega$		0.7	4.0		2.0	6.0	mV
		$R_S \le 10k\Omega$, over temp.			5.0			7.0	mV
ΔV_{OS}	Input offset voltage drift	$R_S = 0\Omega$, over temp.		4.0			6.0		$\mu V/°C$
I_{OS}	Input offset current			5	20		15	40	nA
		Over temp.			40			80	VnA
ΔI_{OS}	Input offset current	Over temp.		25			40		pA/°C
I_B	Input current			45	80		65	150	nA
		Over temp.			200			200	nA
ΔI_B	Input current	Over temp.		50			80		pA/°C
V_{CM}	Common mode voltage range		±12	±13		±12	±13		V
CMRR	Common mode rejection ratio	$R_S \le 10k\Omega$, over temp.	70	90		70	90		dB
PSRR	Power supply rejection	$R_S \le 10k\Omega$, over temp.		30	150		30	150	$\mu V/V$
R_{IN}	Input resistance		3	10		1	6		$M\Omega$
A_{VOL}	Large signal voltage gain	$R_L \ge 2k\Omega$, $V_{OUT} = \pm10V$	50	500		50	500		V/mV
		$R_L \ge 2k\Omega$, $V_{OUT} = \pm10V$, over temp.	25			25			V/mV
V_{OUT}	Output voltage	$R_L \ge 2k\Omega$, over temp.	±10	±13		±10	±13		V
		$R_L \ge 10k\Omega$, over temp.	±12	±14		±12	±14		V
I_{CC}	Supply current	Per amplifier		1.8	2.8		1.8	2.8	mA
		Per amplifier, over temp.		2	3.3		2		mA
P_D	Power dissipation	Per amplifier		54	84		54	84	mW
		Per amplifier, over temp.		60	99		60		mW
I_{SC}	Output short circuit current		10	25	50	10	25	50	mA
R_{OUT}	Output resistance			100			100		Ω

*NOTE

Temperature range
SE types $-55°C \le T_A \le 125°C$
NE types $0°C \le T_A \le 70°C$

Signetics

Courtesy Signetics Corporation.

DUAL HIGH SLEW RATE OP AMP

SE/NE5535

AC ELECTRICAL CHARACTERISTICS $T_A = 25°C$ unless otherwise specified.

PARAMETER	TEST CONDITIONS	SE5535			NE5535			UNIT
		Min	Typ	Max	Min	Typ	Max	
Gain/bandwidth product			1			1		MHz
Transient response								
Small signal rise time			0.25			0.25		µS
Small signal overshoot			6			6		%
Settling time	To 0.1%		3			3		µS
Slew rate	$R_L \geq 10k\Omega$, unity gain, non-inverting	10	15		10	15		V/µS
Input noise voltage	$f = 1kHz, T_A = 25°C$		30			30		nV/$\sqrt{Hz}$

TYPICAL PERFORMANCE CHARACTERISTICS

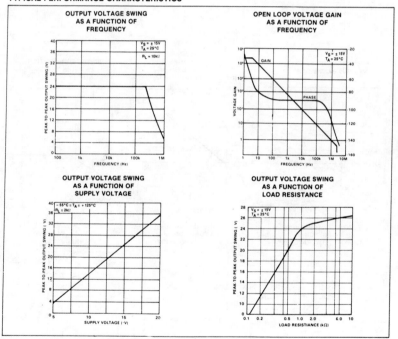

6

Courtesy Signetics Corporation.

DUAL HIGH SLEW RATE OP AMP

SE/NE5535

TYPICAL PERFORMANCE CHARACTERISTICS (Cont'd)

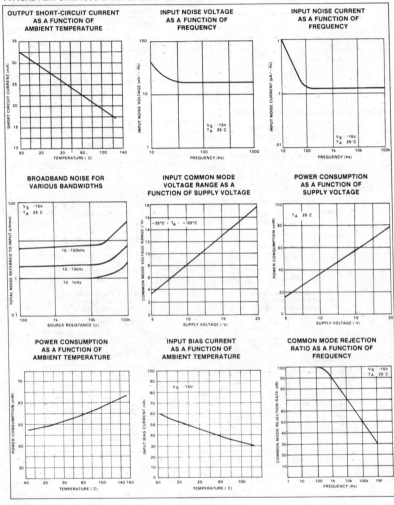

Signetics

Courtesy Signetics Corporation.

Appendix A

DUAL HIGH SLEW RATE OP AMP

VOLTAGE WAVEFORMS

TEST CIRCUITS

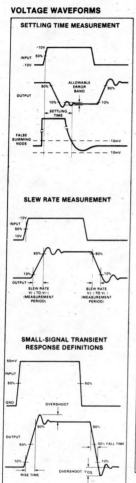

SETTLING TIME MEASUREMENT

SLEW RATE MEASUREMENT

SMALL-SIGNAL TRANSIENT
RESPONSE DEFINITIONS

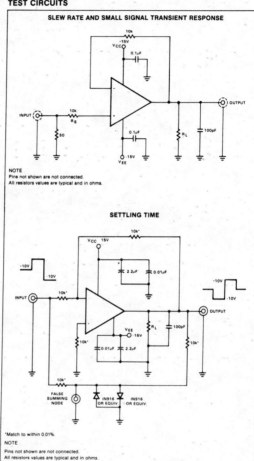

SLEW RATE AND SMALL SIGNAL TRANSIENT RESPONSE

NOTE
Pins not shown are not connected.
All resistors values are typical and in ohms.

SETTLING TIME

*Match to within 0.01%.
NOTE
Pins not shown are not connected.
All resistors values are typical and in ohms.

Signetics

Courtesy Signetics Corporation.

Op-Amp Manufacturers and Devices

Analog Devices, Inc.
804 Woburn Street
Wilmington, MA 01887

AD518, AD540, AD544, AD644,
AD711, AD712

Burr-Brown
International Airport
Industrial Park
P.O. Box 11400
Tucson, AZ 85734

OPA111, OPA404, OPA606

Elantec, Inc.
1996 Tarob Court
Milpitas, CA 95035

EL2003, EL2006

Fairchild Semiconductor
464 Ellis Street
Mountain View, CA 94040

μA709, μA739, μA740, μA741,
μA749, μA771, μA772, μA774,
μA791, μA799

Harris Semiconductor
P.O. Box 883
Melbourne, FL 32901

HA2525, HA2625, HA2645,
HA4605, HA4625, HA4741

Linear Technology Corp.
1630 McCarthy Blvd.
Milpitas, CA 95035

LT1010

Motorola Semiconductor
  Products Inc.
  Box 20924
  Phoenix, AZ 85036

MC1303, MC1436, MC1456,
MC1458, MC1741S, MC3403,
MC4741, MC34070 series,
MC34080 series

National Semiconductor Corp.
  2900 Semiconductor Drive
  Santa Clara, CA 95051

LF351, LF353, LF356, LF357,
LF411, LF412, LM301A, LM308,
LM310, LM318, LM343, LM344,
LM347, LM348, LM349, LM391,
LM833

Precision Monolithics Incorporated
  1500 Space Park Drive
  Santa Clara, CA 95050

OP-01, OP-09, OP-11, OP-16,
OP-17, OP-27, OP 37

Raytheon Semiconductor
  350 Ellis Street
  Mountain View, CA 94040

RC4136, RC4558, RC4559,
RC4739

RCA Solid State Division
  Route 202
  Sumerville, NJ 08876

CA3080, CA3140, CA3240

Signetics Corporation
  811 E. Arques Avenue
  Sunnyvale, CA 94086

NE530, NE531, NE535, NE538,
NE5532, NE5533, NE5534,
NE5535

Texas Instruments Incorporated
  Dallas, TX 75222

TL071 series, TL080 series, TL081
series

Index

MORE
FROM
SAMS

Active-Filter Cookbook   *Don Lancaster*
Need an active filter, but don't want to take the time to design it? Don Lancaster presents a catalog of predesigned filters which he encourages you to borrow and adapt to your needs. The book teaches you how to construct high-pass, low-pass, and band-pass filters having Bessel, Chebyshev, or Butterworth response. It can also be used as a reference for analysis and synthesis techniques.
ISBN: 0-672-21168-8, $15.95

Design of Op-Amp Circuits with Experiments   *Howard M. Berlin*
An experimental approach to the understanding of op amp circuits. Thirty-five experiments illustrate the design and operation of linear amplifiers, differentiators and converters, voltage and current converters, and active filters.
ISBN: 0-672-21537-3, $12.95

Design of Phase-Locked Loop Circuits with Experiments   *Howard M. Berlin*
Learn more about TTL and CMOS devices. This book contains a wide range of lab-type experiments which reinforce the textual introduction to the theory, design, and implementation of phase-locked loop circuits using these technologies.
ISBN: 0-672-21545-4, $12.95

IC Op-Amp Cookbook (3rd Edition)
Walter G. Jung
Hobbyists and design engineers will be especially pleased at this new edition of the industry reference standard on the practical use of IC op amps. This book has earned respect in the industry by its comprehensive coverage of the practical uses of IC op amps, including design approaches and hundreds of working examples. The third edition has been updated to include the latest IC devices, such as chopper stabilized, drift-trimmed BIFETS. The section on instrumentation amps reflects the most recent advances in the field.
ISBN: 0-672-22453-4, $21.95

IC Timer Cookbook (2nd Edition)
Walter C. Jung
You can learn lots of ways to use the IC timer in this second edition which includes many new IC devices. Ready to use applications are presented in practical working circuits. All circuits and component relationships are clearly defined and documented.
ISBN: 0-672-21932-8, $17.95

TTL Cookbook   *Don Lancaster*
An early Lancaster effort that is still a tech classic. This is a complete look at TTL, including what it is, how it works, how it's interconnected, how it's powered, and how it's used in many practical applications. No technician's library is complete without it.
ISBN: 0-672-21035-5, $14.95

Understanding Artificial Intelligence
Henry C. Mishkoff
This book provides an introduction and basic understanding of this new technology. The book covers definitions, history, expert systems, natural language processing, and LISP machines.
ISBN: 0-672-27021-8, $17.95

Understanding Automation Systems (2nd Edition)
Robert F. Farwell and Neil M. Schmitt
For the newcomer, here is an in-depth look at the functions that make up automation systems—open loop, closed loop, continuous and semi-continuous process, and discrete parts. This book explains programmable systems and how to use micro-computers and programmable controllers.
ISBN: 0-672-27014-5, $17.95

Understanding Automotive Electronics (2nd Edition)
William B. Ribbens and Norman P. Mansour
This book begins with automotive and electronic fundamentals—prior knowledge is not necessary. It explains how the basic electronic functions, including programmable microprocessors and microcomputers, are applied for drive train control, motion control and instrumentation. Illustrations clarify mechanical and electrical principles.
ISBN: 0-672-27017-X, $17.95

Understanding Communications Systems (2nd Edition)
Don L. Cannon and Gerald Luecke
This book explores many of the systems that are used every day—AM/FM radio, telephone, TV, data communications by computer, facsimile, and satellite. It explains how information is converted into electrical signals, transmitted to distant locations, and converted back to the original information.
ISBN: 0-672-27016-1, $17.95

Basic Electronics Technology
Alvis Evans, Jerry Mullen and Danny Smith
An overview of electronic technology based on semiconductor devices and integrated circuits. Includes information on both circuit and systems applications. The comprehensive text is divided into two major parts—analog and digital. Both sections feature general and detailed discussion, and new ideas are supported with simple math and practical, worked-out examples.
ISBN: 0-672-27022-6, $24.95

John D. Lenk's Troubleshooting & Repair of Microprocessor-Based Equipment
John D. Lenk
Here are general procedures, techniques, and tips for troubleshooting equipment containing microprocessors from one of the foremost authors on electronics and troubleshooting. In this general reference title, Lenk offers a basic approach to troubleshooting that is replete with concrete examples related to specific equipment, including VCRs and compact disc players. He highlights test equipment and pays special attention to common problems encountered when troubleshooting microprocessor-based equipment.
ISBN: 0-672-22476-3, $21.95

Sound System Engineering (2nd Edition)
Don Davis and Carolyn Davis
This reference guide is written for the professional audio engineer. Everything from audio systems and loudspeaker directivity to sample design applications and specifications is covered in detail.
ISBN: 0-672-21857-7, $39.95

MORE
FROM
SAMS

☐ **Solid-State Relay Handbook with Applications** *Anthony Bishop*
This comprehensive reference work treats SSRs on a wide range of technical levels. Particularly useful are the applications of SSRs with microprocessor-based equipment for industrial machines and the use of SSRs in interfacing with microcomputers.
ISBN: 0-672-22475-5, $19.95

☐ **Understanding IC Operational Amplifiers (3rd Edition)** *Roger Melen and Harry Garland*
Technological advances are bringing us ever closer to the ideal op amp. This book describes that ideal op amp and takes up monolithic to integrated circuit op amp design. Linear and nonlinear applications are discussed, as are CMOS, BIMOS, and BIFET op amps.
ISBN: 0-672-22484-4, $12.95

☐ **Understanding Computer Science (2nd Edition)** *Roger S. Walker*
Here is an in-depth look at how people use computers to solve problems. This book covers the fundamentals of hardware and software, programs and languages, input and output, data structures and resource management.
ISBN: 0-672-27011-0, $17.95

☐ **Understanding Digital Electronics (2nd Edition)** *Gene W. McWhorter*
Learn why digital circuits are used. Discover how AND, OR, and NOT digital circuits make decisions, store information, and convert information into electronic language. Find out how digital integrated circuits are made and how they are used in microwave ovens, gasoline pumps, video games, and cash registers.
ISBN: 0-672-27013-7, $17.95

☐ **Understanding Microprocessors (2nd Edition)** *Don L. Cannon and Gerald Luecke*
This book provides insight into basic concepts and fundamentals. It explains actual applications of 4-bit, 8-bit and 16-bit microcomputers, software, programs, programming concepts, and assembly language. The book provides an individualized learning format for the newcomer who wants to know what microprocessors are, what they do, and how they work.
ISBN: 0-672-27010-2, $17.95

☐ **Understanding Telephone Electronics (2nd Edition)** *John L. Fike and George E. Friend*
This book explains how the conventional telephone system works and how parts of the system are gradually being replaced by state-of-the-art electronics. Subjects include speech circuits, dialing, ringing, central office electronics, microcomputers, digital transmission, network transmission, modems, and new cellular phones.
ISBN: 0-672-27018-8, $17.95

Look for these Sams Books at your local bookstore.

To order direct, call 800-428-SAMS or fill out the form below.

Please send me the books whose titles and numbers I have listed below.

Name *(please print)* _____

Address _____

City _____

State/Zip _____

Signature _____
(required for credit card purchases)

Enclosed is a check or money order for $ _____
Include $2.50 postage and handling.

All states add local sales tax.

Charge my: ☐ VISA ☐ MC ☐ AE
Account No. _____ Expiration Date _____

Mail to: Howard W. Sams & Co.
Dept. DM
4300 West 62nd Street
Indianapolis, IN 46268

DC112

SAMS ™